GUINLE & Cᴵᴬ
UNICOS AGENTES
RIO DE JANEIRO, S. PAULO,
· BAHIA ·

ᴛᴇʟᴇFÓNICA URBANA. SAN SEBASTIAN

L.M. ERICSSON & Cᵒ

TRADE-MARK

STOCKHOLM

TURKIYE CUMHURIYETI
1928
P.T.T.U.M.

司公器電盛臣

PENNIES ONLY

GENERAL POST OFFICE

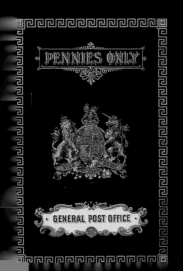

COMPAÑIA
TELEFÓNICA
DE GUANAJUATO, S.A.

COMPAÑIA ENTRERRIANA DE TELEFONOS S.A.

The Chili Telephone Cᵒ,
Limited.

THE ERICSSON
CHRONICLE

The frontispiece portrait of Lars Magnus Ericsson
is a reproduction of a copperplate engraving
by Agnes Miski Török,
based on a photograph taken in 1889.

L.M. Ericsson
1846-1926

To all the 'LMers' of the last 125 years,
who really are the company.

THE ERICSSON CHRONICLE

125 YEARS IN TELECOMMUNICATIONS

JOHN MEURLING • RICHARD JEANS

Contents

One of the leaded glass panes with paintings by Vicke Andrén from the mid 1880s that originally adorned the staircase of the SAT main building at Malmskillnadsgatan in Stockholm. Now at Telemuseum, Stockholm.
Also on pages 8, 9, 459, 467 and 473.

Introduction

In the 25 years since Ericsson's centenary history was published, there have been thousands of changes in the way telecommunications has been implemented, managed and used. But of all those thousands of changes, three stand out head and shoulders above the others.

The first was the introduction of digital switching technology. It transformed network capacity and capability, and became the platform for all the modern network services we find indispensable today. With its AXE architecture, Ericsson led and leads the world in the digital network infrastructure.

The second was mobile telephony. It brought the person-to-person – anybody, anytime, anywhere – telecoms dream closer to reality than ever before. Ericsson led and leads the world in mobile telephony.

The third, and perhaps the most remarkable of all, is the Internet Protocol, IP. The enabler of the World-Wide Web, it looks as though IP will bring to an end the traditional division between voice and data traffic, and make cheap, interactive, multi-media telecommunications available to everybody. So far, nobody has a dominant lead in IP technology, partly because so many technologies have to meet to realise it. As the millennium comes in, the prizes are in the IP area, and the current drive is towards mobile IP. We must wait and see whether Ericsson can lead the world in this area, too.

These fundamental changes in the telecoms environment have forced all the players in the industry to look inwards, as well as outwards. Telecoms is no longer just one business, it's a dozen different businesses. Or maybe it is still one business, described in a dozen different ways and from a dozen different viewpoints. 25 years ago, Ericsson didn't spend much time thinking about its company culture, and what it should do and be to fit into the telecoms world. Today, Ericsson, like every other company, has constantly to define and re-define itself, and strengthen or correct the way it feels, thinks and acts. A sense of history, and an understanding of the way the company has evolved, are the soundest basis for the conscious development of an appropriate Ericsson culture.

Now is a good point in time to sit back and reflect, while we can still remember. This book celebrates the growth of the LM Ericsson Telephone Company, from the small workshop that Lars Magnus Ericsson established in 1876 to one of the world's largest international suppliers of telecommunications equipment.

When Lars Magnus Ericsson set up his business in Stockholm in 1876,

OPPOSITE: *Stockholm 1896, Skeppsbron seen from Slussen.*

15

nothing was further from his mind than multi-media interactivity and such advanced and sophisticated concepts. His plan was to build and repair telegraph instruments for the vital telegraph services of the Swedish Government, the railways and the army.

Then, in that same year, 1876, Alexander Graham Bell in the USA invented the first workable telephone. Lars Magnus Ericsson, just a young mechanic, soon built a telephone of his own, and telephony became his company's main and continuing business. Quite simply, Lars Magnus was in at the beginning, and the history of his company is also the history of world telecommunications.

What happened is presented here in chronological order, more or less. But this isn't a detailed, fully-researched, leave-nothing-out history of record. It's a story, with background. It's an episodic narrative. It's a sort of saga with footnotes: how the company started and grew; what the conditions were in which its business developed; what the setbacks were; and how it achieved its successes. How did one do business in, say, the 1890s? How did management and the Board react to changing political and financial conditions? What happened to Ericsson in its darkest hours? Who were its competitors, and how were they met and matched – or beaten? The saga includes some off-beat material and explores a few interesting by-ways, but in general, if anything seriously holds up the story it's in a sidebar or an appendix, or left out altogether.

Over the years, the company's dependence on technology has steadily grown. In the early years, technology meant electromechanics, of increasing complexity. Then, in the 1930s, early electronics came into use, initially in radio communications and transmission. These early solutions were overtaken by the transistor, which appeared in the 1950s. It had an immense impact on telecommunications (as it did on so many other technologies) although it was many years before electromechanics was totally phased out. The book indicates how technology evolved, and was exploited in products and systems. But technology is not covered in any detail: you are referred to other documentation for the full explanations.

Nor will you find much in the way of financial detail. The finances of a giant international corporation like Ericsson are a very specialist subject. It's not simply a matter of costs and sales, or profits and losses. It's a matter of share arrangements, the frequently inexplicable movements of stock prices, currency fluctuations, the terms and amounts of borrowing (and lending), the geographical location of funds, inflation (and occasionally deflation), floating, futures, discounting, monetary nets, caps, sentiment – all the things that make the *Financial Times* or the *Wall Street Journal* or *Veckans Affärer* such jolly reading on a hot summer afternoon. Such details are included where they're crucial to the narrative – as in the Ivar Kreuger story. Where they aren't, they're omitted.

So this book, it should be pointed out, in no way replaces the comprehensive and scholarly centenary history, *Ericsson 100 years*, by Attman, Kuuse, Olsson and Jacobæus, which remains indispensable. We have set out to do quite a different job.

A number of people inside and outside Ericsson come into the story. It's natural to name managing directors, or presidents, or CEOs, and some Board members – the ultimate decision-makers – at various points. (Sometimes, we have been unsure whether a particular individual should be referred to as MD, President or CEO: the terms and their meanings seem to vary from time to time and place to place. If we have picked the wrong one, we mean no discourtesy. 'Ignorance, madam, pure ignorance,' said Dr Johnson when asked why his dictionary wrongly defined the pastern of a horse.) Every now and again, some less exalted people turn up. More people would have given the book even more life, but space and time are limited, and so is information about many of them, so the range of personalities on parade is not huge. Those who appear have to act as representatives of all the Ericsson people – the 'LMare' as we say in Sweden – who work for, or have worked for, LM Ericsson all over the world.

Today, the company is known as just 'Ericsson'. As a trade mark, the name is followed by the three inclined strokes of a stylised letter E. The full official name of the parent company is Telefonaktiebolaget LM Ericsson. This book generally uses LM Ericsson, or just LME, up to about 1982, and thereafter just Ericsson.

The title of the story is an impertinent borrowing. *The Chronicle of Erik* is the oldest existing major document written in Swedish. It covers the period from about 1230 to about 1320, and the dramatic story of Count Erik Magnusson. He and his brother Valdemar were captured by their brother Birger, and murdered, in Nyköping in 1319. Erik's son, Magnus, later became king.

A king of earlier times was also named Erik, Erik Jedvardsson. He is known for having founded a Benedictine monastery at Uppsala and for a crusade to Finland. He, too, was murdered, in 1160. Although never canonized by Rome, after his death he became known as St Erik and is the patron saint of the city of Stockholm. And appropriately, the present chronicle begins in that city, in the mid-19th century.

CHAPTER 1

The life, work and world of Lars Magnus Ericsson

History acquires a new technology

Do technologies drive history? Does history drive technologies? These are recurring questions in a technology-conscious age. Thankfully, we needn't answer them: all we need to notice is the intimate connection that exists between technology and the rest of history – mankind's other activities – from the Old Stone Age onwards.

So to put telephony, and LM Ericsson's contribution to it, into context … to see not just what happened, but why it happened … it helps to look at what was going on in the world at large at each stage in LM Ericsson's development.

The last half of the nineteenth century was the great age of the European empires. Any empire is the outcome of a variety of forces – political, military, economic, religious, personal – and the European empires of the nineteenth century were no exception. But the particular and distinguishing objectives of such dynamic empires as Germany, Belgium, France, and, most notably, Britain – although they were established by force – were chiefly economic and industrial; and their durability was largely a function of technology.

Alongside armaments, two technologies were critical: motive power for machinery; and communications. Any country, empire or not, which lags in power and communications necessarily lags in economic development, whatever its other successes.

Communications need not mean telecommunications: the Romans, the Persians, and other great empires were distinguished by the attention they paid to their system of posts. And telecommunications need not mean telephony: France first set up a 'network' of line-of-sight optical telegraph stations between Paris and Lille – 230 km – in 1793. By 1839, the UK had set up its first 21 km of electric telegraph. Even in Sweden, optical

OPPOSITE:
Stockholm in the 1880s.

telegraphy had come into use by the early 1800s – chiefly to aid shipping and for government services – and in 1853 the electric telegraph was introduced. But in Sweden, the extensive use of steam and electricity to support industrialisation lagged by half a century or so behind the UK and the USA. What world position Sweden had built up in earlier centuries had been military, not economic. In the aftermath of the Napoleonic wars, it had no great trading strength to fall back on.

It's no surprise, then, to find that Sweden in the 1850s was a poor country in comparison with many others in continental Europe and the USA. With its roots in the middle ages, the mining industry – iron, silver and copper – provided a base for smelting and foundry manufacture and exports. Later, the vast forests became important for logging, and sawmills grew up at the river mouths along the Baltic. The export of sawn timber, and such products as pitprops for the European coal mines, came to employ large numbers of workers. But the country depended primarily on agriculture.

About 50 per cent of the Swedish people lived completely rural lives, dependent on the land for their livelihood. The total population at the time was only about 3.5 million, the majority were poor, and the average life span was only about 40 years. But the birth rate was high, and the population was growing by a couple of per cent every year. The farms were becoming crowded, and migration towards the cities was beginning.

The industrialisation of Sweden

The 1850s saw the beginning of the building of railways, with which the construction of the telegraph was associated. The important conditions for industrialisation were being developed, and many of today's well-known Swedish companies were founded at around this time. These new industries drew the people from the countryside towards the cities.

The new businesses mostly began by using labour with traditional skills – the mechanics, carpenters, lathe operators and so on – from the old small workshops. It was only gradually that they were in a position to start employing unskilled labour, and to promote the migration from the land that created a new class of very poor city-dwellers, huddled into slums.

One significant feature of these changes was emigration. As early as 1845, there was a small wave of emigration, mainly to the USA, by groups of religious revivalists, persecuted by the Church and the establishment, leaving to build their new communities in a free country.

But it was poverty and famine, the result of several years of crop failures, coupled with dreams of becoming rich in the gold fields of California, that caused the first major wave of emigration in the 1860s. About 80,000 people left the country in that first period. Then for several years the economy improved, but the outflow of people continued, though at a lower yearly rate. In the 1880s, there were again severe crop failures and a new wave of people – some 400,000 – left the country. Thereafter, the numbers dropped, but a stream of emigrants continued to leave Sweden right up to the beginning of the First World War. The last major outflow came during the recession at the beginning of the 1920s.

The birth of the trade unions

For those workers who remained, conditions were, in general, appalling, and they were at the mercy of the factory owners.

In 1848, the *Communist Manifesto* by Marx and Engels was published, and a Swedish translation appeared. There were riots in Stockholm, directly related to the massive revolutionary movements in France and elsewhere in Europe, marking the first time that the working classes appeared as an independent force.

From 1853 to 1855 there were recurring bread riots in several Swedish towns, caused by food shortages and high prices indirectly related to the Crimean War.

In the Swedish political sphere, there was a growing demand for electoral reform, and in 1866 the old feudal parliament was abolished. But radical demands for universal suffrage were rejected, and the right to vote was severely restricted by requirements for minimum income and property ownership. Women did not have the right to vote. In 1868, a bricklayers' strike in Stockholm was followed by the first attempt to form a union, and during the economic boom of the following decade, there was a growing awareness of the strike as a weapon in the class struggle.

In 1879, a strike among the sawmill workers in the city of Sundsvall was put down by the military. This event led to increased effort to organise the workers, and this year is usually considered as the starting date of the Swedish trade union movement.

Industrialisation and the relocation of people provided the soil for the growth of such popular movements as workers' education, the temperance movement, and religious revivalism. Emigration also helped to broaden horizons, building strong international links with other countries.

During the '80s, there were two competing movements working for the organisation of labour. One was the liberal side, offering support to the working class, but with strong reservations about granting political power. The other was represented by the socialists, demanding political power as well as workers' rights. It was not until the beginning of the 20th century that the socialists were able to organise the workers. A general strike in 1909, in which the workers lost after a long and bitter fight, led to a large number of personal tragedies, a new wave of emigration, and the formation of the Social Democratic party. Long before that, in 1898, the first local workers' club had been formed at LM Ericsson.

Into this poor, relatively backward country was born Lars Magnus Ericsson, one of the major figures in the transformation of Sweden into an industrial country, with its high standard of living.

The Lars Magnus Ericsson start-up

The industrialisation process in Sweden, as in other countries, was started and driven by a generation of innovators and entrepreneurs, as we call them today. The innovators provided the products and ideas. The entrepreneurs built businesses out of them. Lars Magnus Ericsson was one such person – an innovator.

The sixth in a family of nine children, he was born on 5 May 1846, on a small farm called Nordtomta in the village of Vegerbols in Värmland – a county in the western part of Sweden, on the borders of Norway. The family had one horse and four cows. He lost his father when he was twelve, and at fourteen years of age began working as a smith's apprentice in Norway, rising to become a smith, and taking jobs at foundries and forges in Charlottenberg, Karlstad and Arvika.

Lars Magnus and Hilda

We're told that when Lars Magnus was walking one evening through the streets of Stockholm, he heard through a window music being played on a small household organ – an organ that was sadly out of condition.

On an impulse, he decided to offer to repair the instrument, and so met Hilda Simonsson (to whom it belonged).

His wedding present to Hilda was a new organ he had made himself – still to be seen in the parish church at Värmskog.

He also worked for a while as a miner, and as a labourer building railways. During this time, he realised that he must have further training, especially in the mechanical field, and at the age of twenty he moved to Stockholm and was taken on as apprentice with an instrument-maker, A.H. Öller. The Öller workshop manufactured telegraph instruments for Telegrafverket, the State provider of telegraph services in Sweden, the armed forces and the fire brigades. To meet competition from larger, foreign, manufacturers, Öller's firm was partly financed by the government, since it was considered important to have a Swedish workshop available for repairs, experiments and training. In the evenings, Lars Magnus studied mathematics, materials technology and technical drawing, and learned English and German.

On Öller's recommendation, Ericsson received a government grant which made it possible for him to travel, and to work and study in other industrially more developed countries in Europe. He spent the years 1872 to 1875 in Germany and Switzerland, studying electrotechnology, including periods of work with Siemens & Halske in Berlin and Hasler in Switzerland.

In 1876, soon after his return to Sweden, he left his employment at Öller's and together with a fellow worker from that firm, Carl Johan Andersson, started an engineering workshop on Drottninggatan, in central Stockholm. The firm was named LM Ericsson & Co. Its business was the manufacture and repair of telegraph instruments.

In that same year, 1876, Alexander Graham Bell filed his patent for the telephone in the USA. The potential of this new product was immediately realised, but though Bell also filed his patent in Great Britain (among other countries), remarkably enough he did not do so in Germany and Sweden. By the end of the following year, 1877, Bell telephones were offered for sale through newspaper advertisements in the Stockholm papers. They were sold in pairs, and typically bought to set up a connection between, for example, a house and a workshop, or a shop and its storeroom.

L. M. Ericsson was among the first to try out the new devices, and before long he was called on to repair them, as well. He realised the great future the telephone possessed, and he also worked out how to build a better and less costly telephone than Bell's. L. M. Ericsson's first pair of telephones left his workshop in late 1878, and in the same year, Lars Magnus married Hilda Simonsson, who soon became an active partner and helper in the workshop.

Growth was rapid. Already in 1876 the workshop had moved to Jacobsberggatan, and the following year to Lästmakargatan. In 1880 there came yet another move, to Norrlandsgatan, now called Biblioteksgatan.

Lars Magnus Ericsson at the time of the start-up.

Entrance to the first LM Ericsson workshop at Drottninggatan in Stockholm, 1876.

By 1883, LM Ericsson had to leave Biblioteksgatan and move to larger premises on Thulegatan, at that time on the northern outskirts of the city of Stockholm. (The plant, both offices and workshops, would be enlarged several times over the years, until in 1939 LM Ericsson moved its offices and main factory into a Stockholm suburb.)

In 1896, it was decided to convert the firm into a stock company under the name of Aktiebolaget LM Ericsson & Co., with a capital of SEK 1 m. There were 1,000 shares, of which L. M. Ericsson himself retained 900. The remaining 100 shares were divided up among the employees. Carl Andersson received 50 of them, and the rest were distributed as bonuses among the workers. The company was officially registered on 27 April 1896, with Lars Magnus Ericsson as Managing Director and Chairman of the Board.

Members of LM Ericsson's workforce, 1896.

Lars Magnus and Hilda Ericsson, c. 1895.

The LM Ericsson factory at Thulegatan, Stockholm.

FABRIQUES DE TÉLÉPHONES DE LA SOCIÉTÉ L. M. ERICSSON & Cᴵᴱ
A STOCKHOLM.

By 1900, just 22 years after Lars Magnus sold his first pair of telephones, LM Ericsson had become a major supplier to an international market. Sales had risen from about SEK 400,000 to SEK 4 m during the '90s, and the company had around 1,000 employees in Stockholm. In November 1900, Lars Magnus Ericsson resigned as Managing Director of the company, and in February of the following year he also resigned as Chairman of the Board. He was only 55 years old at the time, and still in his prime. As far as can be judged, he still had a lot to give the telecommunications business. But he had a strong sense of what was due from him, and once the increasing scale of the business prevented him from following and controlling every detail in the way he was used to, he decided to hand over to others.

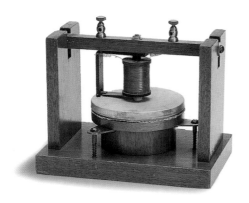

Alexander Graham Bell's first working telephone, 1876.

Bell demonstrating his invention, c. 1879.

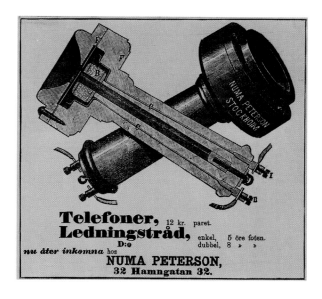

Bell telephones advertised in Stockholm newspapers, 1877, price SEK 12 a pair.

The first telephone made in Sweden – by Hakon Brunius, 1877.

Pipped at the post

Alexander Graham Bell was not alone – other men were working on early devices that were forerunners to the telephone.

An American physician, Charles Grafton Page, discovered in 1837 that causing rapid changes in the magnetism of a piece of iron will make it give out a musical note – the pitch of the note depending on the frequency of the magnetism as it changes. He called these sounds 'galvanic music'.

A German, Philipp Reis of Friedrichshof near Frankfurt-am-Main, was the first man to transmit a musical tune electrically over a distance. Reis used an 'animal' membrane stretched over a small cone inserted into the bung hole of a barrel. To the membrane was fixed a platinum wire; when sound caused the membrane to vibrate, the wire would make and break a contact in a battery circuit at the other end of which was a coil wound around a knitting needle. The knitting needle reproduced the sound as it was magnetised and de-magnetised in tune with the vibrating membrane.

In the mid 1870s, independently and un-known to each other, Alexander Graham Bell and Elisha Gray were experimenting with voice transmission, Bell in Boston and Gray in Chicago. Gray's telephone was somewhat similar to that of Reis. At the receiving end he had an electromagnet, inside which was a small rod of iron attached to a membrane.

On 14 February 1876, Gray filed a caveat with the United States Patent Office – a formal notice of his claim to the idea of a new instrument, by which he hoped to prevent others from patenting the same idea, within one year. On the same day, just a few hours earlier, Bell had applied for a patent for a similar type of instrument. Over the years there was a great deal of legal dispute, but in the end Bell was awarded the patent rights.

*Laying cable
ducts in
Storgatan,
Stockholm,
SAT, 1890s.*

Markets and marketing, customers and competitors

The early major contracts

At first, LM Ericsson's market was limited. As we've said, pairs of tele-phones were usually sold to individual customers for their own internal use. No switching, no switchboard. But by 1880, the Bell Telephone Company had set up a switchboard in Stockholm and was taking contract subscriptions – the industry pattern of public network operator and private subscriber, with rented instruments, was established. The Stockholm Bell company, of course, used its own phones, supplied from the USA.

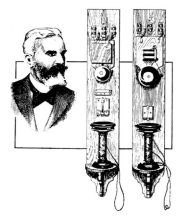

H. T. Cedergren and two early LM Ericsson telephones.

In the following year, however, 1881, in the city of Gävle north of Stockholm, a group of entrepreneurs formed a telephone company and invited tenders for equipment and network installation. LM Ericsson's bid offered equipment, installation, and running costs which he claimed were far below those of Bell, but the Gävle group expressed some doubts about the quality of LM Ericsson's equipment. Tests carried out by a third party found in LME's favour, and the first major contract had been won.

By now, the telephone was catching on all over Europe, and it was significant that in the same year LM Ericsson's second major contract came from abroad, when the city of Bergen in Norway ordered its switchboard and telephones from the company. It may not be fair to record the Bergen contract as an export order, since at that time Norway and Sweden were joined in a Union under King Oscar II in Stockholm, and operated a Stockholm-imposed foreign policy. (Both Norwegians and Swedes – most of them, anyway – were relieved when the Union was dissolved in 1905.)

Henrik Tore Cedergren, the founder of SAT.

An even more significant contract was the one between LM Ericsson and H.T. Cedergren.

Henrik Tore Cedergren was born in Stockholm in 1853, the son of a jeweller. He had a degree in engineering from the Royal Institute of Technology in Stockholm (now the Technical University, Tekniska Högskolan) and had furthered his studies during periods abroad. He joined his father's jewellery business at first, and also went into the building trade – and in this latter role he realised that building operations could be handled a lot more efficiently with the help of the telephone.

The Bell company was in a strong position but was charging its customers high rates, which meant that the telephone service was slow to grow and restricted in coverage and penetration. Cedergren saw the importance of a telephone service available to everybody, a time-saving means of communication, which would become vital to society. Since this had to mean lower rates, Cedergren's solution was to build a service to undercut Bell's prices, and in 1883 he formed Stockholms Allmänna Telefonaktiebolag, The Stockholm General Telephone Company, SAT.

*Coil-winding department at the
LME factory, c. 1890.*

In the same year, he introduced a new 'automatic exchange', for which he and Ericsson had been granted a patent – an important strategic tool – and concluded an agreement with LM Ericsson for the supply of telephone sets and switchboards, cheaper than those used by Bell. The first order was for 1,000 telephones and 22 manual switchboards (the boards with jacks and plugs at which the telephone operator set up the calls).

Cedergren was able to keep SAT's subscription fee down to SEK 100, less than half of what Bell was charging its subscribers, and the strategy worked. At the end of 1883, SAT had 785 subscribers. By the beginning of 1886, SAT had 3,164 subscribers and the Bell company 1,655.

L.M. Ericsson and H.T. Cedergren became close collaborators, though they were very different in nature. Ericsson, from a family in poor circumstances, had worked his way up. He was a skilled mechanic who understood and could handle the details of telephone manufacturing. He was cautious in business and did not readily take risks. In today's language, he was the technological innovator. Cedergren was the entrepreneur. He was a trained engineer and also a businessman. His goal in starting up

SAT was to make money, and he understood business and was prepared to take the necessary risks. His aim was to spread the telephone to every household in Stockholm, and though he never quite reached this goal, for years Stockholm had the highest penetration of telephones of any of the world's capital cities.

The customer (and competitor) on LM Ericsson's doorstep

One of the LM Ericsson Company's biggest customers – and sometimes a big competitor – grew up alongside Ericsson in Sweden. We've already referred to it as a customer of Öller's: Telegrafverket, or Televerket, as it eventually became.

Telegrafverket, the Swedish state telegraph administration, started out as Kongliga Elektriska Telegraf-Werket in 1853. It was not the first organisation to provide a telegraph service in Sweden. Before 1853, there were optical telegraph routes in Sweden, operated by the government and by the military. There were, for example, routes from Stockholm to Gävle and to Furusund and Landsort (lighthouses on the eastern and southern approaches to Stockholm), and between Malmö and Helsingborg in the southern part of the country. A new route all the way from Stockholm to Gothenburg was being planned when news of the new electric telegraph reached Sweden in 1852.

An ambitious plan, for a total of 2,000 kilometres of telegraph lines, was drawn up and approved. The first part of the new network was a link between Stockholm and Uppsala, which was opened for traffic on 1 November 1853. Telegrafverket was born.

The network was rapidly extended and soon also included a link to the Continent via a cable to Denmark.

For the repair, and some of the manufacture, of the telegraph apparatus Telegrafverket initially used local workshops – like Öller's. Öller had been among the first group of employees at Telegrafverket. He had been manager of the Uppsala telegraph station, then built new stations in Örebro and Vänersborg, and in 1855 became manager for the northern and western routes at the Stockholm telegraph station. In 1857, he was granted leave of absence to start a new business – a workshop specialising in electric apparatus. Televerket became a valuable customer.

The telegraph became increasingly important, especially to the government, to business and to the press; and both the network and the traffic expanded. In 1864, Telegrafverket started to employ women operators – an early breakthrough.

When news of Bell's newly invented telephone reached Sweden, Telegrafverket was not very interested at first. The telephone was seen

Raiding the piracy fund

There is a curious sidelight on the matter of financing. In the State's budgets of the day it was not easy to identify a source of money to invest in the telegraph network. Then somebody found the so-called 'Trade and Shipping Fund' – a dormant government fund originally set up to provide convoys to protect Swedish trade and shipping against piracy, and also used in the early 1800s to pay ransom for ships and crews taken by Barbary Coast privateers. Raiding this fund provided the initial finance for Telegrafverket.

primarily as a way of extending the telegraph system, of limited use because of its short geographical range. Telegrafverket adopted a 'wait and see' position. There were, however, three employees at Telegrafverket who had ideas about setting up a switchboard and a network. They applied for permission to do so, which was granted in 1879. In the following year this first Stockholm system was inaugurated as a collaboration with the 'International Bell Telephone Company' of New York, and it became 'Stockholms Bell Telefonaktiebolag'. Initially, it had about 100 subscribers.

A year later, 1881, Telegrafverket followed with its own first telephone network, a 'private' system with 32 extensions serving the government offices in Stockholm. And as we've seen, in 1883 SAT went into operation.

Telegrafverket's first public network was opened in the city of Härnösand in northern Sweden in 1882 (58 telephones were initially connected); and in the same year a station was opened in Uddevalla. In the following year, Telegrafverket started the process of buying up local networks in various towns. These were often owned by cooperatives or local entrepreneurs. The Bell and SAT networks in Gothenburg were acquired in 1888.

In the 1880s, the private networks began to link themselves together by building trunk lines between towns. Their main irritation to Telegrafverket stemmed from crosstalk, as the telephone lines caused disturbance to the telegraph connections (and vice versa). But, of course, Telegrafverket was also beginning to take a longer view and thinking about the future. It took its vision to the government, which cooperated up to a point, and instituted procedures for Telegrafverket to obtain exclusive rights to build telephone lines over the countryside.

Rikstelefon

Finally, in 1888, the Swedish Parliament approved a proposal from Telegrafverket to build a telephone network covering the whole country. In the cities and towns, new two-wire subscriber networks would be built, connecting to central telephone exchanges. These, in turn, would form nodes in a national long-distance network. In towns where there were existing private networks there would be head-on competition.

The new network was named 'Rikstelefon'. By the end of 1889, Rikstelefon had about 4,000 subscribers (out of a total of some 20,000 in the whole country) and the first Rikstelefon directory of 32 pages was published. In 1890, the Stockholm Bell company gave up the struggle. Its shares were acquired by SAT.

Telegrafverket's Rikstelefon was initially another important customer for LM Ericsson, but in 1891 Telegrafverket started its own workshop to handle repairs and some manufacture. By 1893, it was also making telephone sets. LM Ericsson's new customer had become a new competitor.

OPPOSITE:
Rikstelefon public phone kiosk, Stockholm, c. 1900.

The Skanstull telephone exchange, Stockholm, 1890s. The windmill still exists.

In the decades that followed, Televerket expanded its operations dramatically. Due partly to its vigorous competition with SAT, but probably more to the Government's benign influence on tariff policy, Sweden had for many years one of the highest telephone densities in the world.

In this story of LM Ericsson, Televerket will appear all the way through: as customer, as competitor, as collaborator, as reference, and as a highly professional and respected authority generally. At times, the relationship has been clouded, but notwithstanding such periodic tiffs, Televerket has been an important ingredient in the life of the LM Ericsson company.

A world company – and some early market successes

During the 1880s, LM Ericsson´s business grew in a very satisfactory way, with two of Sweden's main telephone companies, Telegrafverket and SAT, as customers.

But in the '90s, Telegrafverket started up its own manufacture of telephones and switchboards; and then, a few years later, after a rift between Ericsson and Cedergren, SAT also started making its own telephones in a new company, Aktiebolaget Telefonfabriken.

LM Ericsson's market share in its home market dropped dramatically. It became a matter of export – or die.

Fortunately, the company had already been busy in many parts of the world and could fairly readily find replacement business. By the late '90s, LM Ericsson telephones and switchboards were being shipped not only to Norway, but to the UK, Denmark, Finland, Russia, Australia, New Zealand – even China, where LME built a telephone exchange in Shanghai. The company was successful in the Cape Colony of South Africa, and when the Boer War broke out at the turn of the century, LM Ericsson supplied the British army with portable field telephones (known as 'cavalry telephones'). At the end of the century, it looked as if Russia would become LM Ericsson's largest market.

The Shanghai telephone exchange, China, 1898.

By 1901, LM Ericsson could fairly claim to be a significant world player. A look at its sales statistics for the closing years of the century shows how far Lars Magnus had brought his company in just 24 years.

TABLE 1. LM ERICSSON SALES, 1897 AND 1900

Customer/market	1897 Sales SEK '000	%	1900 Sales SEK '000	%
SAT	132	5	8	0
Telegrafverket	207	8	13	0
Other Sweden	159	6	205	5
Total Sweden	*498*	*19*	*226*	*5*
Norway	110	4	108	3
Denmark	201	7	426	10
Finland	194	7	113	3
Total Nordic countries	*1,003*	*37*	*873*	*21*
National Telephone Co.	697	26	1,859	45
Other customers in the UK	69	2	211	5
Total Great Britain	*766*	*28*	*2,070*	*50*
Germany	74	3	136	3
Netherlands	52	2	102	2
Russia	338	13	310	7
Spain	20	1	39	1
Other customers, Europe	9	0	21	1
Total Europe, excl. Nordic countries	*1,259*	*47*	*2,678*	*64*
Total Europe, incl. Nordic countries	*2,262*	*84*	*3,551*	*85*
Egypt	27	1	49	1
South Africa	108	4	46	1
China	9	0	83	2
Other customers in Asia	4	0	6	0
Australia & New Zealand	157	6	292	7
USA	45	2	76	2
Latin America	77	3	71	2
Total outside Europe	*427*	*16*	*623*	*15*
Total	**2,689**	**100**	**4,174**	**100**

* Note the drop in sales to SAT and Telegrafverket, the high proportion of sales to Europe outside the Nordic countries, and the UK's dramatic rise to dominance as a customer.

From 'LM Ericsson 100 years', vol. I.

How did LM Ericsson set about creating its international sales? How were business contacts set up in those early days? Documentation is sparse and largely gives us details of sales agreements and shipping, but we know that the international industrial expositions, exhibitions and fairs played

ELECTRICAL ENGINEERS

R E
V

13, VICTORIA STREET
LONDON S. W.

12:th April 1901.

DEAR SIR,

In reply to your letter asking whether the Cavalry Telephone sets were found satisfactory in South Africa.

I have the honour to state that they were found very satisfactory indeed. The Telephone Receivers and Transmitters were excellent, and the ›Buzzer‹ worked efficiently over any sort of line, sometimes through two total breaks in a line. Ordinary conversation was generally possible through bare 22 gauge copper wire laid on the ground — often *damp* ground — for the full length of the wire available (about 7 miles), the return circuit being made by inserting an iron spike or a Rifle Bayonet into the ground, and it was always possible to telegraph by ›Buzzer‹ under even worse conditions.

The Separators (Condensors) appear to be exactly right as they allowed signalling or conversation almost as well as when a complete circuit was used, yet they allowed the instruments to be used on Telegraph lines doing other work without interruption to the users.

Mechanically the instruments were excellent too. They were roughly used without loss to their efficiency, and the casing never broke or cracked. I suggested a slight improvement in the jack as occasionally one of the male plugs got compressed and failed to make good contact, but this gave little trouble as the remedy was so easy and obvious.

I have the honour to be, Sir, Your obedient Servant

D. BRADY CAPT. R. E.
for O. C. E. E. R. E.

AKTIEBOLAGET
L. M. ERICSSON & C:o
STOCKHOLM.

Testimonial letter from British army, reproduced in LME product catalogue.

a very important role, and such events turned up in most years in various European and American cities. Here, LM Ericsson had the opportunity to demonstrate its telephones and other equipment, and to meet interested parties. Such interested parties were typically telephone operators – and local representatives, or agents, who were interested in marketing and selling in their respective countries on commission.

In some respects the world has not changed: today, the telecommunications trade shows are still important events for showing equipment and meeting customers (and taking a close look at competitors). In fact, events today are more frequent, more expensive, and a lot more glitzy, with all the input from today's marketing communications consultants.

We can get some further insight into the selling activities of those days by tracking an agent, some of whose activities are recorded. Charles Bell was a Scot (possibly related to Alexander Graham Bell, who originally came from the same area) and successfully sold LM Ericsson products from his base in Glasgow. His major customers were in Great Britain and Russia. Charles Bell accounted for nearly all of LME's extra-Nordic sales in 1889. It was due to Bell that the Russian market could be exploited successfully – we are told how Charles Bell travelled this vast country like a pedlar, with a suitcase full of LM Ericsson telephones. One of his important early sales was the exchange equipment and telephone sets for the city of Kiev. But when LM Ericsson began to set up a local company and a local factory in Russia, the agency and sales operations had to be re-organised, and this led to a disagreement between Bell and LM Ericsson. In the end, Charles Bell completely severed his connections with LME.

That was the way of things: if an agent in a country was successful, when the time came to set up a local LM Ericsson company he lost his job. The company would handle the ordering and shipments, but would also be responsible more and more for building the networks – stringing wire lines or, later, laying cables, and installing switchboards. This, in turn, often meant that one or several Swedish installers would come in for longer or shorter periods to work with installation and testing. Many Ericsson people became widely-travelled.

The final stage in a growing market might be the setting up of local manufacture. In those days, this would be mainly for economic reasons, to save labour and shipping costs. Later, it would become more of a political issue.

Russia, and the first manufacture overseas

In Russia, LM Ericsson installed the telephone exchange in Kiev as early as 1893. It was followed by Kharkov (1896), Rostov (1897), Riga, Kazan and Tiflis (1900).

OPPOSITE: *New York 1887. The case for underground cable is becoming strong.*

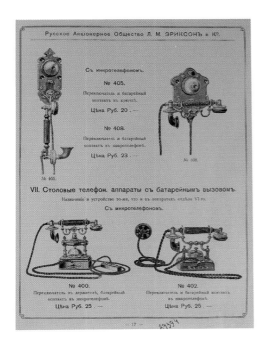

With such growth, it made economic sense to start some form of production within the country. In 1897, LM Ericsson opened a workshop in St Petersburg in which telephone equipment was assembled from components manufactured in Stockholm. In 1900, the St Petersburg operation was moved from rented premises to a new factory on Sampsonievsky Prospect and full manufacture was gradually introduced. The opening of the new factory, built at a cost of about SEK 1 m, took place in December, 1901. Lars Magnus Ericsson himself came over to preside at the ceremony and inspect the premises. He was satisfied, and to commemorate the occasion he awarded each of the workers 25 kopeks as 'vodka money'.

Page from LME catalogue for Russian market, 1890s.

St Petersburg c. 1900.

Russia nearly became even more important: the strong competition from Telegrafverket and Telefonfabriken was making life tough in Sweden, while the immense Russian market was opening its arms in welcome. Lars Magnus Ericsson's thoughts turned to a proposal to transfer the headquarters of the company to St Petersburg, and the proposal received serious Board consideration.

But then Cedergren was granted concessions to build and operate telephone networks in Moscow and Warsaw. He soon realised that his own Telefonfabriken could not competitively cope with the supply of equipment, so he turned back to LM Ericsson, and the rift between the two companies and their Managing Directors was healed. In 1901, LM Ericsson took over Telefonfabriken, paying with LME shares; the arguments for moving LM Ericsson from Stockholm to St Petersburg lost some of their strength; and the proposal was abandoned. A lot of us in Sweden are grateful that the two gentlemen were able to settle their quarrel.

The UK, the largest market

Helped by Charles Bell, LM Ericsson gained a foothold in Britain in the late 1880s, and as Table 1 (page 36) shows, this became the most important market of all during the '90s. The largest customer was the National Telephone Company, which had been formed by the merger of private telephone operating companies throughout the country. There was as yet no British supplier: the main competitor was, as always, the Bell Telephone Company, which initially imported from the US and later set up a factory in Britain. And it should be pointed out that LM Ericsson supplied only telephone instruments in the British market – the switchboards came from Bell.

The second customer was the General Post Office, the State authority responsible for postal, telegraph and telephone services. GPO policy in the early days was to protect the postal services against competition from the telephone by means of high tariffs and a generally negative attitude. (Britain was not unusual in this response, which was paralleled in a number of European countries.) The attitude is illustrated by a newspaper report of a speech made in the House of Commons by the Postmaster General, A. Morley, on 1 March 1895:

'… the Postmaster General said that the telephone could not, and never would be, an advantage which could be enjoyed by the large mass of people. He would go further and say if in a town like London or Glasgow the telephone service was so inexpensive that it could be placed in the houses of the people, it would be absolutely impossible. What was wanting in the telephone service was prompt communication, and if they had a large number of people using instruments they could not get prompt communication and yet make the telephone service effective.'

Scandinavian blood

We can't keep from the reader the following quote from a report written in 1895 by A.R. Bennett, a well-known British authority who was studying the reasons for the lagging phone penetration in the UK. The report is titled *The Telephone Systems of the Continent of Europe*.

'There would seem to be something in the Scandinavian blood which renders the possession of many telephones an essential to their owners' happiness. Wherever two or three Swedes, or Norwegians, or Danes, or Finns of Scandinavian descent, are gathered together, they almost infallibly proceed to immediately establish a church, a school, and a telephone exchange. Whatever else in life that is worth having generally comes after.'

Sweden and St Petersburg

Sweden's relationship with St Petersburg was nothing new.

After the Swedish garrison of the old fort and the small Swedish settlement which existed on the site capitulated, Peter the Great founded St Petersburg in 1703 as the new capital of the Russian empire. He brought in architects, builders, artisans and artists from many parts of Europe to build and develop the city, and St Petersburg became a rich, flourishing cosmopolitan capital.

Of the many Swedes who settled in St Petersburg in the 19th century, the Nobel family is among the best known.

Immanuel Nobel, a Swedish inventor, arrived in 1837 to seek new outlets for his inventive drive (and to evade his creditors in Stockholm). He had designed a remotely-controlled mine, which much interested the Tsar, and with support from the Russian government he built a factory. Business was good, particularly during the Crimean War, and his sons Robert, Ludvig and Alfred joined the company.

When, after the Crimean War, business declined, Immanuel went bankrupt, and eventually returned to Sweden. By 1859, Robert and Ludvig had rebuilt the company, and after Napoleon III defeated the Austrian army in the battle of Solferino, the Tsar encouraged new arms industries to make Russia less dependent on Germany. The Nobel factory in St Petersburg grew rapidly.

A day came when, en route to the south side of the Caucasus to buy walnut for rifle stocks, Robert was offered a claim among the oil wells of Baku, and was persuaded to spend his walnut money on oil instead. A well-trained engineer, he had quickly seen great opportunities for improvement in the plant for pumping and refining the oil. He grasped these opportunities firmly, building machinery, constructing the first pipeline, designing the first oil tankers, and so on. His brother Ludvig, still in St Petersburg, joined in the business, and built locomotives and tank wagons for railway distribution. After the inevitable falling-out between the brothers, Robert returned to Sweden, but the St Petersburg Nobel factory and Branobel, the oil company, stayed in the Nobel family until 1917. They were probably the two largest industries of the Russian Empire.

The third brother, Alfred, spent most of his grown life outside Russia, in Paris, Stockholm and Switzerland. He made his fortune in nitroglycerine and dynamite – and left a large portion of it to fund the annual Nobel Prize.

One early group of Swedes in St Petersburg were the prisoners of war pressed into service as labourers; but after the peace treaty of Nystad in 1721 (in which Sweden lost most of its territories across the Baltic) relations were soon back to normal, and Swedes flowed back to St Petersburg.

Silversmiths and jewellers, along with tailors, represented a large part of the Swedish community. Carl Edvard Bolin arrived in St Petersburg in 1831, and in 1839 became Jeweller to the Royal Court. When he died, his sons took over, and, among many other items, made the wedding crown for the Danish Princess Dagmar to wear at her marriage to Prince Alexander, later Tsar Alexander III. The brothers also opened branch shops in Bad Homburg, and in 1916 a shop that still exists at Stureplan, in Stockholm.

The most important jeweller alongside the Bolin brothers was, of course, Carl Fabergé. His father had moved to St Petersburg from Livland in the Baltic states. He married a Swedish woman, Charlotte Jungstedt, and became an active member of the Swedish church. Their son, also Carl, later took over the business. Most of the employees of Fabergé were Swedes.

Just one more of St Petersburg's Swedish jewellers is worth mentioning: Carl Fredric Östedt, who arrived in 1782. His business was not a success, but his daughter, Anna, married a German merchant – and they had a daughter who married a doctor and land-owner, Alexander Blank, a christened Jew. Their daughter Maria, in her turn, married a school director Ilja Uljanov. And this marriage produced a son, Vladimir Ilyich Uljanov – who as V. I. Lenin was to change the history of Russia. What if Carl Fredric Östedt had stayed at home in Uppsala?

Emigration to Russia came to an abrupt end with the 1917 revolution.

Visit to LM Ericsson headquarters by Chinese delegation, 1906.

Early breakthroughs in the Far East

LM Ericsson's telephone sales to China began in the late 1890s, with shipments to the Shanghai firm of Schiller & Co. The head of the company was a Swede, Gustaf Öberg, a former sea captain. Captain Öberg must have been an interesting character. We are told that in his earlier career he had, among other things, been a gun-runner to insurgents in French Indochina, and that the French offered a reward for his capture, dead or alive.

The telephone concession in Shanghai was held by Britain's Oriental Telephone Co. The company bought its telephone equipment from the United States, so the initial scope for LM Ericsson sales was limited. The BOT concession, however, expired in 1900. It was taken over by a new company, the Shanghai Mutual Telephone Co., with Gustaf Öberg as its head, and LME built a telephone exchange in Shanghai in that same year. Using tariff reductions and a lot of publicity, Öberg managed to attract a large number of new subscribers, and LME's telephone sales increased.

The Shanghai success led to other successes in the Far East, as the Oriental Telephone Co. selected LM Ericsson as a supplier of telephone exchanges and telephones in other concession areas. LM Ericsson's Dutch contacts also led to orders for Java, in the East Indies.

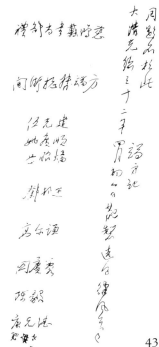

Entry from LME guest book, 1906.

43

*The exchange in the Hague,
the Netherlands, late 1903.*

Subcontractors and the ripple effect

Today, there's a lot of talk about the ripple effect – how, when you attract a big new enterprise to set up in your community, the benefits are felt not only in direct employment, but also in a secondary wave of suppliers, in infrastructure development, and so on. With LM Ericsson, the ripple effect began early.

By the late 1880s, a network of sub-contractors began to emerge. Sweden's shift into an industrialised economy had begun in earnest in the 1870s, and the rapid increase in demand for telecommunications was an expression of the needs of this emerging industrial and commercial community. The forming of the LM Ericsson company, and the resulting demand for raw materials, were the beginning of Ericsson's major contribution to the industrialisation of Sweden. A case in point was the Max Sieverts Tråd och Kabelfabrik (wire and cable factory) in Sundbyberg, established in 1888.

Prior to 1884, LM Ericsson had to import all its insulated wire (copper wire spun over with silk or cotton) and did so mainly through Max Sievert's business. In 1884, a Miss Hanna Hammarström, who was the daughter of a cotton and silk manufacturer in Stockholm, hit on the idea of using the same simple machine for insulating copper wire as was employed in making wire frames overspun with cotton yarn for ladies' hats. She, and later Mrs Hilda Ericsson, became the main suppliers of insulated wire to both LM Ericsson and SAT.

But the ladies' capacity soon became inadequate for the growing telephone business, and Lars Magnus Ericsson turned to Max Sievert with a suggestion that he should take up the manufacture of insulated wire. This was the beginning of the famous Sieverts Kabelverk. Before 1914, the production of wire and cable for the telephone industry was Sievert's main business; after that, the Swedish power companies became the largest customer group. L. M. Ericsson's idea had produced something of a chain reaction.

In later chapters, we'll see how the Sieverts cable factory eventually became part of the Ericsson Group, in 1928. In the meantime, close collaboration between Sieverts and SAT, and soon Televerket as well, produced a stream of important technological developments, adding know-how to the telephone and power distribution industries.

A footnote to history: early LM Ericsson people

Who were they, the people who worked for Lars Magnus Ericsson? We don't know them well at all, but here and there in the old documents some names and stories come through.

The early workers were trained craftsmen (as was Lars Magnus himself) with long traditions in the various workshops of the city of Stockholm. But one of the first employees was the errand boy, Gabriel Bildsten (referred to in one place as 'the Angel Gabriel'). One day, his boss sent him to Cedergren's jewellery shop to buy silver for plating contacts. In the shop, he saw Mr Cedergren fiddling with some wires on his new telephone, and started to laugh. Cedergren became annoyed. 'What are you laughing at?' he said. 'Haven't you been taught good manners?' With his eyes on Cedergren's telephone, the boy immediately answered, 'My boss does a much better job on things like that.' Cedergren was surprised, and curious, and he seized his coat and hat and followed Gabriel to the L. M. Ericsson workshop – where he soon discovered that the boy was right. The first contact had been established. If the story is true it would have taken place in late 1878.

There is some further information about LME people, only a little later, in the reminiscences of Erik Wallin, who worked there from 1885 to 1890. When he wrote his notes, in the early 1940s, Erik Wallin was in a

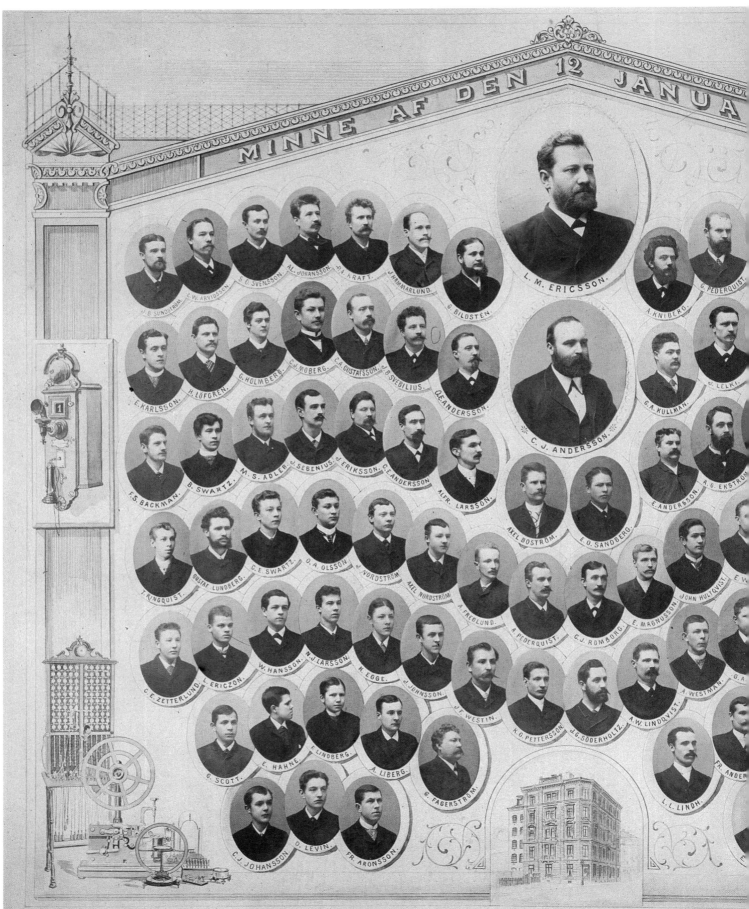

MINNE AF DEN 12 JANUA[RI]

L. M. ERICSSON.

9716

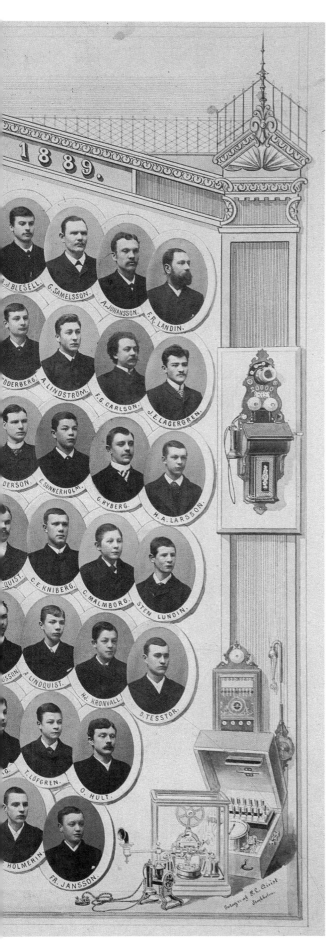

pensioners' home in the town of Södertälje. His list of old mates gives us a striking example of the lure of the USA – and indirectly of conditions in the LM Ericsson workshops, and in Sweden at the time.

AXEL KNIBERG was a foreman, whose brother Carl went to the USA. GUSTAV HOLMBERG worked the universal milling machine – he, too, left for the USA.

K. G. PETTERSSON, whom everybody called 'Bond-Pelle', got his fingers caught in a milling machine when he was making jacks. Later, he became the turret lathe operator, then went to another company in Stockholm, Radiator.

HJALMAR NORDQVIST was a filer, he came to LME from the shipyards in Karlskrona.

KARL FAHLBERG worked as a helper in the smithy, then joined the Navy, then worked in Wiklund's bicycle factory for many years. He lost two children through drowning.

ERIK WALLIN himself worked at threading screws, then at turning nuts. After that, he spent many years in Germany, before retiring to the home in Södertälje.

VICTOR HANSSON, a turner, and NILS LARSSON (who used to be called 'Lus-Lasse', and also ended up in Södertälje) worked at aligning the centrifugal lathe.

SAMUEL SVENSSON came from a smithy, worked the milling machine, went to Berlin in 1888, then went to London, and from there to the USA. He died suddenly while delivering milk in the city of Milwaukee.

There were two SILVANDER brothers. The older, John, went to the USA. The younger became a builder and died young.

L. M. Ericsson and staff, 1889.

There were three SWARTZ brothers. One of them, BENDIX, was with Gebrüder Nagler in Germany when I was there. He went to the States later, and so did his brother, CLAS. They had a workshop in Milwaukee. Mr Ekehorn, the engineer, was married to their sister.

OSCAR SVENSSON made jacks. There were two PEDERKVIST brothers. One was a foreman at SAT; one went to Russia. SVEN GUMMESSON went to Russia, as well, and worked there in a sewing-machine factory.

Then there was CARL ROMBERG. I believe he had an unhappy marriage and started to drink. His friends made a collection so he could get away to the USA.

LARS ERICSSON turned telephone bells – we called him 'Klangis'. He went to the USA. So did ADOLF ANDERSSON.

K. G. PETTERSSON HOLMGREN – we called him 'Svarta Pelle' – became a foreman at Telegrafverket.

FREDRIK BRUNSKOG once fell out of a window of the Workers' Association building. JOHN BRUNSKOG went to Russia, and had a workshop there together with OTTO FLODBERG. The last I heard he was back in Stockholm with his own workshop on Falugatan, making electric locks.

G. A. KULLMAN was foreman of the group making inductors. GOTTFRID ANDERSON could draw well – he's a foreman now at Lux (Elektrolux) on Lilla Essingen (in Stockholm). He was also very musical.

OSCAR OLSSON was in Berlin for a year while I was there too. He went to Russia later and died there.

JOHAN NORDSTRÖM'S brother went to the USA. So did SERITZ ANDERSSON.

AUGUST LINDSTRÖM first went to Berlin, then to the USA, then back to Sweden and had a workshop in Gnesta. He died some years ago. I'm told he left nearly 50,000 kronor to his widow.

'DALJERSKI', JOHAN ERICSSON, made microphones. He had a lot of children – Mr Ericsson once said to him that he ought to be careful not to have any more, or he wouldn't be able to feed the family. Daljerski answered, 'How can you think of bread, when you're feeling randy?'

OTTO FLODBERG, who had a workshop in Russia together with JOHN BRUNSKOG, later went to Copenhagen, and now he has a workshop in Lund (in the south of Sweden).

OSCAR DAHLSTEDT spent some time in Berlin, but it didn't go too well for him, so he soon came back and worked for Palmcrantz for a time. He's dead now.

DAVID KARLSSON, 'Ko-David' as we called him, spent time in Berlin. He came back with Erikson. He has been with ASEA in Västerås for many years.

ERIK NILSSON spent many years in Berlin. His first wife was German, and she's buried in Sweden. His second wife was Swedish – now she's dead, too, and buried in Berlin. He's still alive and living in Stockholm. JOHN HULTQVIST became a foreman at Luth & Rosén. He's with engineer Larsson now, somewhere on Liljeholmen. There were two fellows who assembled switchboards – they were J. SVEBELIUS and K. J. MOBERG.

Foreman Andersson's brother, JOSEF, worked for a time with a haulage contractor (Jonsson) across the street from LM Ericsson on Rådmansgatan. He went to the USA later and had his own haulier's business there. There was also a fellow called GUSTAV HUDELL. He left for the navy shipyards on Skeppsholmen (Stockholm).

ALEXANDER JOHANSSON made frames for inductors, while Långa Lasse, C. ALFRED LARSSON, spent most of his time reading the newspaper. ARVID LARSSON moved to Artillerigården, then I think he went to Separator. He also played the valve trombone in the band of the Workers' Association.

One of Kullman's helpers fell down the lift shaft and got himself killed. HERMAN ANDERSSON from Frösunda went to the USA. ROBERT JONSSON, 'Byttan' he was called, went to Herman Meyer and became master foreman. His half brother, HERMAN BERGMAN, worked in the metal foundry there. I also remember ARON BLESELL and P. A. KRAFT.

The printer, DAVID TESTOR, went to Berlin, then he came back to Telegrafverket. When he died, he was a master linesman there. GUSTEN RYDBERG went to the USA and performed there as a diver and water acrobat.

GABRIEL BILDSTEN started as the errand boy. He worked for C. J. Andersson (L. M. Ericsson's first partner in the company) later, and eventually became the stores manager. ALFRED WESTMAN was with Kullman. He was told he had to be laid off, but he explained his mother would not allow it – and was permitted to stay on. Later on he left, anyway, and went to the USA.

In the flickering light from these recollections, we see that life was hard and sometimes short, families were large, and alcohol was only too easy a way out. But we also see the typical Swedish acceptance of travel as the route to new opportunities, and the Swedish willingness to settle abroad and set up a business. We can see that an errand boy could work his way up through the company, and that the Managing Director – who had as poor a start as any of his work-force – could make and take a joke on family planning.

Above all, perhaps, you can hear the beginnings of that truly typical Ericsson conversation: 'Remember that guy who went to Shanghai to instal the telephone exchange? What was his name? Where did he end up?' 'Oh, you mean so-and-so. Well, the last I heard, he was …' Even over 125 years, some things just don't change. As late as the 1950s (as some of us remember) there were still a few old-stagers in the LM Ericsson workshops in Stockholm with nicknames like 'Shanghai Charlie', 'Cairo Gustaf', and so on – reminding us youngsters of early exploits in LME markets.

Lars Magnus himself is recorded as tall and quite stout, bearded and with a considerable presence. He was strong-willed and determined, and sometimes came across as formidable, or even pompous, but he was fundamentally kind and modest. He was calm in his manner, and never lost his temper – preferring irony and gentle sarcasm. His intelligence, capability and capacity for hard work are beyond doubt, and as a manager, he clearly had the common touch. Though he is described as averse to risk, he was obviously prepared to be radical in technology and in business, exploiting product innovation, and quite prepared to consider relocating his enterprise to Russia.

CHAPTER 2

The technology of the times

The first telephones

W hen Lars Magnus Ericsson's first pair of telephones left his shop in late 1878, the instrument bore no resemblance to the one you have on your desk (or in your pocket). It was a one-piece device described as a 'Magneto Telephone with Signal Trumpet'. It was built around an electromagnet. When you talked into it, your voice made a membrane vibrate, and the vibration induced a corresponding variation in an electric current passing through the coil of the electromagnet. The phone was connected to the other party with a single wire, the earth formed a common return for the 'loop'. When you listened at the instrument at the other end, the electromagnet there caused the membrane to vibrate and reproduce the voice. When you spoke into this phone, you held it in front of your mouth; when you listened, you held it to your ear. The 'trumpet' was a little tube, and to call the other party you inserted the tube into the phone so that a metal point touched the membrane. When you blew through the tube, the metal point vibrated against the membrane and set up a god-awful crackle at the other end. ('Blower' is still a slang English word for telephone.) And that is how it all started! In that first year, 1878, LM Ericsson sold 22 pairs of phones, at a price of 55 kroner a pair.

LM Ericsson's first telephone with signal trumpet, 1878.

OPPOSITE: *Winter in Odense, Denmark.*

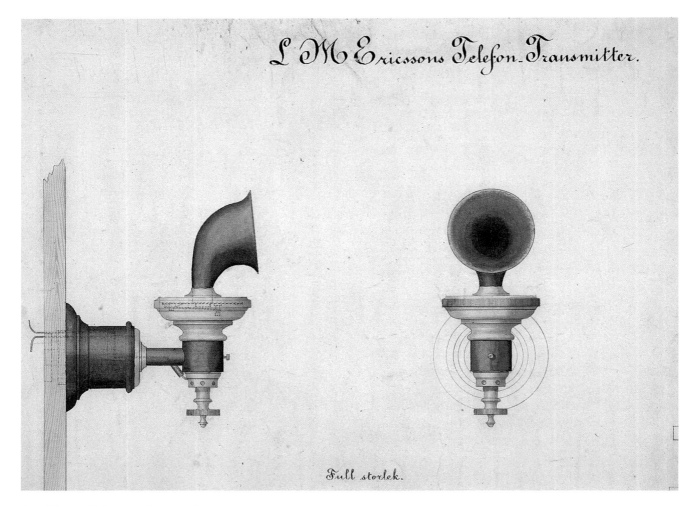

Lars Magnus Ericsson's drawing of
the helical microphone, 1880.

By the time of the Gävle order in 1881, the telephone had become a two-piece instrument with separate microphone and receiver, the predominant model being a wall type with a fixed transmitter, the receiver on a cord, and a battery and DC signalling device (or bell), which eliminated the horrible trumpeting. The transmitter of this set, called the helical microphone, was Lars Magnus Ericsson's first original contribution to telephony. The first separate microphone had been invented by Francis Blake, in the US, using varying contact resistance between a carbon and a platinum electrode. L. M. Ericsson used two series-connected contacts and a device for regulation of the contact pressure. The receiver was still of the Bell type.

Magneto and AC signalling

In 1882 came the next model, with a magneto generator and AC signalling instead of the earlier DC bell. It was a wall set with a 'writing desk', with the generator housed under the desk and above the battery, and the magneto handle on the right hand side. The illustration on page 56 shows the superb craftsmanship in the wood and metal work. This telephone was sold in large numbers and appreciated for its high quality – and was to be copied, more or less successfully, by other manufacturers.

The wall telephone was improved in several stages, the most important improvement being the introduction of the carbon microphone, originally proposed by D. E. Hughes in Great Britain and perfected by a gentleman called Hunnings in the US. LM Ericsson's carbon granule microphone was patented in 1888.

Wall telephone with helical microphone and DC signalling, 1880.

For its time, LM Ericsson's first desk telephone, in 1884, was a highly innovative piece of engineering. It was a functional design. The generator magnets served as base for the different components and the set had no case.

The next version of this desk telephone followed in 1892. It had a one-piece handset, the first such device in the world. (Handsets had been available for some time, but were used only by operators attending switchboards.) This telephone, popularly known as the 'dachshund', became an outstanding success in the market. In 1894 it was incorporated into the company's first registered trademark.

A most attractive desk telephone was introduced the following year, 1893. Popularly called the 'coffee grinder', it sold particularly well to China.

It is interesting to note that these last two telephone models, and the wall set of the previous page, were still on the active list as late as in a 1930 product catalogue. That means a product life span of some 50 years!

1884, the first desk telephone (here with two recievers).

Carbon and coal

In 1903, the company brought out the 'star' microphone. This had six sector-shaped chambers holding the granules. The star microphone was to be LM Ericsson's standard design for nearly half a century.

The characteristics of the carbon microphone depend above all on the quality of the carbon granules. For many years, important but not well-known work within LM Ericsson went into the continuous development of suitable grades of carbon granules by processing the raw material – British anthracite.

The 'coffee grinder', 1893.

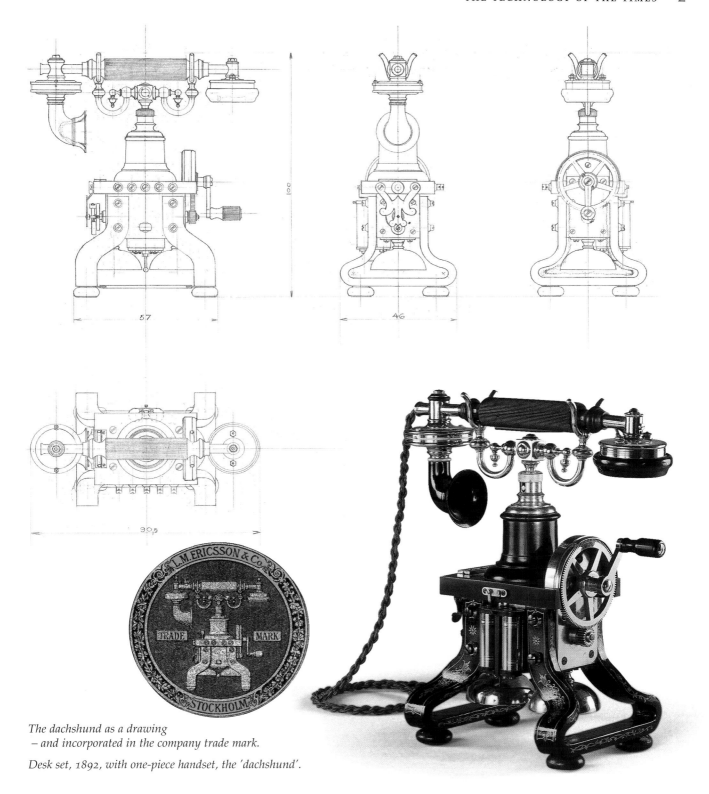

The dachshund as a drawing
– and incorporated in the company trade mark.

Desk set, 1892, with one-piece handset, the 'dachshund'.

*LME's wall
telephone with
writing desk,
1882.*

Circumstantial evidence …

Over the last century, the telephone has featured in thousands of crime or detective novels.

Often, it's just there, a natural part of the scenery to be used when required, but there must now be many hundreds of cases in which it plays an active role as an integral part of the plotting. There's room for a little monograph on the subject …

A little monograph that has been written (*Please give the Yard a call, Watson* by Mr Gar Donnelson of Lincoln, Nebraska, 1986) shows Conan Doyle and Sherlock Holmes as what we might now call 'early adopters', and makes a convincing case for an LM Ericsson presence.

As in Sweden, the first phones hit the UK in 1876. As we've seen, the spread of the

Fig 1

Fig 2

telephone was discouraged to protect postal and telegraph revenues, and by 1889 (when Holmes was 35) London had only 237 public pay stations and around 50,000 subscribers.

By 1887, in *The Man with the Twisted Lip*, Conan Doyle has a phone in Inspector Bradstreet's room probably much like the one in Fig 1 – an 1885 Western Electric magneto wall phone with a Blake transmitter and an LM Ericsson receiver.

Perhaps the same phone took the call from Athelney Jones in the 1888 *Sign of Four*. To make his call to the Yard, Athelney Jones had to cross the road from Holmes's rooms at 221 B Baker Street: it is not until *The Adventure of the Retired Colourman* in 1898 that Holmes seems to have had his own instrument. If Athelney Jones used a pay station, it is likely to have been similar to Fig 2, an LM Ericsson magneto wood wall telephone with a unique LME plug-in handpiece and a coin collection box on the top.

Still later, in 1902, Holmes asks Watson to 'give the Yard a call' from Nathan

Garrideb's flat in *The Adventure of the Three Garridebs*. Donnelson suggests the flats had a communal phone like the one in Fig 3, produced by LM Ericsson since 1900 (note the unique LM Ericsson twisted cord). There are other phones in the Sherlock Holmes canon, but there's also an unsolved mystery: whom was Athelney Jones, whom was Doctor Watson, calling?

According to Norman Lucas, an authoritative historian of the Yard, it was not until around 1903 that a telephone was installed in Scotland Yard, and 1906 that all the Met's police stations were connected (though another authority suggests that there was a phone at the Yard from 1887 onwards). Perhaps it depends on what you mean by 'the Yard' – the National Telephone Company's directory for 1902 offers us:
Police Gerard 3536 (Surveyor's Dept.) New Scotland Yard.

One does wonder what the Surveyor made of it all!

Fig 3

Switchboards and exchanges

Meanwhile, switching – or rather, switchboard – technology was developing alongside telephone technology.

LM Ericsson's first switchboard was of the crossing bars type (no relation of the much later crossbar switching system) and first left the workshop in 1880. The subscriber lines were single wires, which terminated on a set of parallel horizontal bars crossed by a set of vertical bars. The crosspoints were arranged so that connection was established when the operator inserted a single pole plug at the appropriate cross-point. A drop indicator was used to signal to the operator – to set up a call and to indicate the end of a call. The maximum capacity was about 50 subscriber lines.

The first switchboard with pairs of cords was developed for SAT. The telephone lines were still single wire, and the drop indicators remained to signal a calling subscriber, but the operator set up calls by inserting one plug of a pair in the calling subscriber's jack and the other in the called subscriber's jack. The capacity of one such switchboard was also about 50 subscriber lines.

When the number of subscribers grew, more boards had to be installed and the work of the operator became more difficult. To set up a call from a subscriber 'terminated on' (or connected to) one board to somebody who was terminated on another board, the operator had to call and alert a colleague and say which lines to connect (a junction line and the subscriber line). The telephone offices of that time were noisy places of work and setting up calls became slower as the size of the exchange grew. The practical limit was about 800 lines, with 16 operators.

A better answer to the growth problem was the subscriber multiple. The multiple had been patented in the US (but not protected in Sweden) so Lars Magnus Ericsson was able to use the principle and improve on it. Briefly, the multiple principle meant that each subscriber's jack appeared on several boards, so that each operator had access to all lines and only one operator was involved in setting up a call. The first LME multiple boards were installed in 1884. The first such switchboards were single-wire, but switchboards for two-wire subscriber lines soon appeared as well.

'Switchboards', here, means strictly manual devices, but the concept of the automatic exchange also emerged very early. In 1883, when Cedergren placed his first order with LM Ericsson for equipment for the SAT network, their collaboration had already borne fruit in the grant of a patent to them for an 'automatic telephone exchange and an automatic dialling device'. It was the first commercially successful automatic system in the world.

OPPOSITE: *Switchboard with cords and jacks for up to about 200 subscriber lines, 1880s.*

Small cord and jack switchboard, 1880s.

A competitive tool: the first automatic telephone exchange. A concentrator or remote switch, this version for 5 subscribers.

Long-distance switchboard with main local exchange in background, Finland 1890s.

'Pyramid' switchboard, wall-mounted, for 3 to 6 lines.

It is believed that Cedergren may have seen early examples of such machines at the Exposition Internationale d'Electricité in Paris in 1881, and that he was inspired by these. Ericsson worked on the design during 1882, and their patent application was submitted in February 1883. Nine days later, Cedergren made public his prospectus for the forming of SAT.

It was not, of course, an automatic switching system in the modern sense. In today's terminology it would be a concentrator, or remote switch, for up to 5 to 10 subscriber lines, connected over a single wire to a manual main exchange, or switchboard. In a typical application, it was used to connect small clusters of subscribers in remote locations. Until that time, the solution had been to install individual lines, or to set up a small exchange served by an operator – both solutions were costly, and long lines meant an additional problem: crosstalk. When the telephone lines were single wires, with the ground serving as return, crosstalk was a major problem at any distance over a couple of kilometres. The new switch became a key factor in Cedergren's business plans to offer a service that was cheaper, and of better quality, than that provided by the Stockholm Bell Telephone Company. The concentrator device was also sold to other countries, among them the UK and Switzerland.

The central battery

Until now each telephone had been powered by its own battery cells. The first technical revolution in telephony was the introduction of the central battery, CB, system, eliminating the individual batteries. This saved a lot of cost in the telephone. The subscriber just lifted his handset 'off the hook', a loop was closed to the exchange, and a 'drop' indicator or lamp alerted the operator of the call.

Again, it was in the USA that the first CB systems were introduced. In 1898, and again in 1901, engineers from LME and SAT visited the USA and studied the systems there. The two companies developed a Swedish CB system jointly: the Swedish patent is dated 1903. LM Ericsson's first such system was built in The Hague, the Netherlands in the same year.

Industrial intelligence

SAT's trials with the multiple switchboards supplied by LM Ericsson were so successful that it was decided to concentrate as many subscriber lines as possible to one exchange. The new main exchange and a large line tower were built at Malmskillnadsgatan in Stockholm.

It was also decided to travel to Great Britain and the USA to gain knowledge about the latest improvements in the telephone field, and in particular about multiple systems.

In the late summer of 1885, H. T. Cedergren, accompanied by 'the company's trusted supplier, Mr L. M. Ericsson', set off. The third member of the party was the telegraph inspector (later telegraph director) of the State Railways, Lars Meurling, whose role of a state employee on an official visit was of great usefulness to the party.

Interest in the US focused on the Bell Company, but in Stockholm, Cedergren and SAT were the main competitors of Bell, which was not at all keen to open its doors to the Swedish visitors.

In Cedergren's notes from the trip he reports on the difficulties, and makes it clear that it was not possible to act openly. It was Mr Meurling, the representative of the Swedish state, with letters of recommendation from the State Railways, who became the door opener.

From a visit to the Boston exchange, the report describes the construction of the multiple boards, and gives details of the jacks and plugs. The visitors were not allowed to see the interior wiring of the boards (by order of the Western Electric Co of Chicago) – but on 'a Sunday morning we boldly entered the exchange and were able to have a look inside the boards'.

It is a wonderful picture: three gentlemen, dressed in dark suits, probably top coats and hats, 'boldly' entering the exchange, L. Meurling chatting up the female supervisor and Messrs Cedergren and L. M. Ericsson having their peep at the forbidden fruit.

CHAPTER 3

The foundation of the modern LM Ericsson company

The end of the Indian summer

There is no real discontinuity when a century or a decade comes to an end. Life goes on, and the first years of a new century are much like the last years of the old. But 1900 is a convenient crossover point, if only as the year in which Lars Magnus (perhaps himself affected by the date) began his retirement.

The literature of the advanced countries of the western world tends to present the first decade or so of the new century as a high peak of civilisation, from which the world plunged into a hellish abyss of war and revolution. For many people in those countries, perhaps it was a period of exceptional grace and favour.

But not everywhere, and not for everybody. In many countries, the period was marked by great social unrest, and Sweden was no exception. In other countries, disorder was even more violent – Mexico, for instance, began ten years of civil war in 1910. But on a global scale, these events are insignificant, of course, compared with the war of 1914–1918, and the Russian revolutions of 1917 – events which cast their shadows over the rest of the century.

Sweden adopted its traditional position of neutrality, and in some sectors of industry the war actually increased prosperity. Over-all, it certainly increased the world demand for telecommunications equipment. But as we shall see, war and the Russian revolutions meant a significant reduction of markets for LM Ericsson, and a nearly fatal loss of large sums invested in Russia.

We shall also see the emergence of themes which curiously repeat themselves over a large part of the last century of LM Ericsson's history: the importance of local production, the growth of Latin America as a key market area, the failure for a long time to make a significant impact in the

OPPOSITE: *The telephone tower erected by SAT looms over the earlier buildings of Brunkebergstorg, in central Stockholm. When this photo was taken the wires had gone underground. The building on the left housed the headquarters of Televerket. Brunkebergstorg has been completely redeveloped and nothing remains of either structure.*

US, and a long-running division of opinion over whether LM Ericsson should act as a telephone operator.

At the time, vertical integration – equipment manufacture and telephone operation in the same company – was almost an industry norm. The Bell Company had emerged early as the largest operating company in the US, and, as Bell Telephone International, held operating concessions in a number of countries – including, as we have noted, Sweden. Autelco of Chicago was following the same strategy, as was the British Automatic Electric. Early in the century, even LM Ericsson had moved into telephone operations on a small scale, in Mexico.

The operations issue, like several others at the time, was settled by the most important event of the period to LM Ericsson: its merger in 1918 with SAT to form Allmänna Telefon AB LM Ericsson

Details of the merger will be found at the end of the chapter, but we may note here that it was a merger which boosted LM Ericsson's stature from that of a substantial supplier of telecommunications equipment to that of a telecommunications manufacturer and operator on a world scale.

It was also a merger so structured that it left LM Ericsson vulnerable later on to a disastrous raid by an unprincipled adventurer.

Axel Boström (1864–1909)

When LM Ericsson was incorporated in 1896, the first Board of directors consisted of Lars Magnus Ericsson; his original partner, now works foreman, C. J. Andersson; and the office manager, Axel Boström. Boström had joined the workforce in 1884, had attracted L. M. Ericsson's attention on account of his –beautiful handwriting, and had been invited to help with the paper work in the office. He was given increasingly advanced clerical tasks and eventually appointed as office manager. Boström became the main driver in the company's build-up of sales, with a strong focus on exports to compensate for the stagnating home market. To achieve this, he created a network of agents in many parts of the world. Lars Magnus

Ericsson was, reportedly, of a more cautious nature, but in the matter of sales he followed Boström's suggestions as a rule.

Axel Boström succeeded L. M. Ericsson as Managing Director in 1900. In 1902, the LM Ericsson company joined the Swedish Metal Trades Employers' Association, but left the following year as Axel Boström refused to join in the lock-out of workers declared by the Association. In the major strike of 1909, the LM Ericsson workers did strike, but it was declared (and accepted) as an action of solidarity with the other union members and not as directed against the company. LM Ericsson did not rejoin the Association until 1913.

Axel Boström was killed in an automobile accident in 1909.

'An early adopter': an Ericsson telephone with its distinctive handset in use in the Far East.

Markets and marketing, customers and competitors

Lars Magnus Ericsson was succeeded as managing director of the company by Axel Boström in 1900. In 1890 Boström had become the first office manager, and had been instrumental in building up the international business. He was younger and bolder than Lars Magnus and during the expansive 1890s the two complemented each other very well.

When Lars Magnus retired, Boström continued to expand the company internationally, both as a manufacturer and as an operator, and much of the commercial history of the first two decades of the twentieth century is that of adding new markets for equipment and growing existing ones.

In some countries, war conditions actually helped sales. In others, particularly those, like Russia, whose currencies were weak against the krona after 1914, exporting was difficult – and not only for LM Ericsson. (Russia, of course, soon had its own very special extra problems.)

Again, we can look at certain highlight countries.

The significant successes

The United Kingdom

By the turn of the century, about half of LM Ericsson's sales were to Great Britain. The company had opened a sales office in London in 1898, but soon demands arose for domestic manufacture of telephone equipment. By far the largest customer in Britain was the National Telephone Company, and in 1903 an opportunity arose for LME to become a partner with National Telephone in a factory for telephone manufacture in Beeston near Nottingham. The new company, British LM Ericsson Manufacturing Co. Ltd, went into business in 1904. To begin with, much of the telephone equipment was imported from Sweden, but after extensions to the factory in 1906 it became largely self-contained.

In 1911, LM Ericsson bought out National Telephone's half shareholding. This same year, National Telephone handed over its operations to the British Post Office, which now became British LME's largest customer.

British LME turned out to be a profitable part of the LM Ericsson Group. Of particular value were the significant net profits and dividends that the company produced during the war years, when many other parts of LM Ericsson were in difficulties.

Mexico

In the 1880s, a telephone operating concession in Mexico City was granted to the Compañía Telefónica Mexicana S.A., usually referred to as Mextelco or Mexicana, with a strong holding interest from Western Electric (Bell). High tariffs meant slow growth, and by 1905 the company had only some 6,000 subscribers. Happily, the Mexican constitution prohibited monopoly concessions, and an entrepreneur called José Sitzenstatter had been awarded a second concession, to provide telephone service in Mexico City and its surroundings over a period of 30 years. Sitzenstatter was originally from Hungary but had become a naturalised American. He had spent over a year in the 1880s with the Stockholm Bell company in Sweden, and spoke Swedish, but his attempts to strengthen Bell's position in Stockholm were unsuccessful. He had also got to know the LM Ericsson company, and had met Cedergren.

In 1903, Peder Hammarskjöld, the head of LM Ericsson's London office, received a surprise visit: Mr Sitzenstatter called, with a request for a tender for a new telephone exchange for Mexico City. LM Ericsson was not interested at that point; but the following year Sitzenstatter got in touch with LME in Stockholm, this time with an invitation to take over the telephone concession. H.T. Cedergren, who by now had ample experience of telephone operations in Sweden and Russia, was interested, and Klas Weman was sent down to Mexico from New York to study the situation. Weman's report was positive and it was decided to invite Sitzenstatter for negotiations. When the proposal was presented to the LM Ericsson Board, there were some reservations. Vilhelm Montelius, the chairman of the Board, pointed out that it was contrary to the articles of the company to engage in telephone operations. But Axel Boström also paid a visit to Mexico, in late 1904, and produced plans and calculations for the probable growth of the Mexican telephone business that were positive. He was supported by, among others on the Board, H. T. Cedergren.

Marcus Wallenberg (Sr), who had sent his own representative over to study conditions, was also in favour, and eventually the Board realised that a strong presence in Mexico could be a potential springboard for an approach to other markets in Latin America. So the Board proposed a change in the company's Articles of Association, stating that 'for sales of the company's products, the company has the right, alone or in conjunction with other parties, to carry out telephone installations and to engage in telephone operations'. It was approved at an Extraordinary General Meeting in December 1904.

Early in 1905 an agreement was reached with Sitzenstatter and his

The Victoria main exchange in Mexico City, 1912. Sigfrid Mohlström on left.

concession rights were transferred to LM Ericsson. LM Ericsson sought the cooperation of SAT and of Marcus Wallenberg. A consortium was formed, in which LM Ericsson held 60 per cent and SAT and Marcus Wallenberg 20 per cent each.

K. W. Gerdhem had been the engineer in charge of SAT's installations in Moscow, and he was given the task of leading the building of the Mexico City network. The network centred on a large exchange (Victoria) built on the multiple principle, and with a capacity of 15,200 subscribers. The installations were ready for service in 1907, and by the end of the year 650 subscribers had been connected. At that point, the consortium was transformed into a limited Swedish company, Mexikanska Telefon AB Ericsson, or Mexeric (in Spanish, Empresa de Teléfonos Ericsson S.A). The original share capital was SEK 3.6 m, and of this 60 per cent was owned by LME, 20 per cent by SAT and 20 per cent by K A and Marcus Wallenberg. The consortium handed over its concession and installations in Mexico to Mexeric, while the real estate was leased to Mexeric for the whole of the concession period.

There was keen competition between Mexeric and Mextelco, but Mexeric managed to attract new subscribers at a higher rate. By 1911, after only four years of operation, the two companies had the same number of subscribers (about 7,000). From 1910 onwards, Mexico suffered from more or less continuous civil strife for over a decade, but nevertheless, Mexeric's

Calle Victoria, home of Ericsson's large Victoria exchange, and headquarters of Mexeric. Picture from around 1910 – it looks like pay-day.

network continued to expand right through 1914. By this time, more than 11,000 subscribers had been connected – which led to large orders for equipment from the parent company in Stockholm. The trend was broken by the outbreak of the First World War, when shipping was severely obstructed by the blockades. At the end of hostilities, Mexeric's difficulties in getting large orders through continued, as the falling rate of the Mexican peso made financing difficult. But there was growth none the less, and by 1920 the Mexeric network had some 13,000 subscribers, while Mextelco had only some 9,000.

Mextelco did not fare so well. Its network was seized by the government following a labour dispute in 1915, and was not handed back until 1925.

Negotiating with the revolutionaries

In 1896, a certain Johan Alfred Johansson was taken on by L M Ericsson as a cabinet-maker in 1896 and within a couple of years was sent to Java to install the new exchange, and be nicknamed 'Java-Johan'. There were further assignments in the Far East, India and South Africa, then, in 1906, he was sent to Holland to install the new CB exchange there. With him on this job came his nephew, Sigfrid Mohlström. Java-Johan was later to be in charge of the installation of LM Ericsson's first automatic exchange, Norra Vasa in Stockholm.

After completion of the Rotterdam installation, Sigge Mohlström was sent to Siam, now Thailand, to lead the installation of a new exchange in Bangkok. And after a year he went on to his next job, in Paris. After a brief period at the Stockholm factory, he was off again, in 1910, to Mexico. He became responsible for the extension and maintenance of the main exchange, Victoria.

During the fighting in 1914, the Mexican general (or bandit) Pancho Villa was busy with his artillery in the streets close to the Victoria exchange. It had also become the habit of his soldiers to practise target shooting at the overhead wire and cable insulators (and to use the poles for

stringing up their prisoners). Erik Ostlund, in charge of the Ericsson operations asked Sigge to try to persuade General Villa to put a stop to the damage.

Ivar Thord-Gray was a Swedish soldier who had served with the British army in South Africa in the Matabele, Boer and Zulu wars. Later he had also fought with the Americans in the Philippines, the French in Cochinchina and the Italians in Tripoli, before landing up in Mexico as an artillery officer with Pancho Villa's revolutionary army. As luck would have it, Sigge ran into Thord-Gray in the local cantina and over a drink explained his problems and asked Gray to help. Gray arranged for Sigge Mohlström to meet with Pancho Villa at his headquarters the next day.

Sigfrid Mohlström calmly explained his problems and pointed out the severe loss to the future republic that a damaged exchange and telephone network would mean, and also that the general might be well advised to use the telephone system as a strategic tool for keeping tabs on his adversaries during the conflict.

Pancho Villa was impressed and ordered his artillery to take better aim and his soldiers to choose other objects than telephone poles and wires for their target

practice. So as to avoid misunderstandings it was further arranged that all Ericsson poles were to be painted with a blue and yellow band.

As it happens, some of Mexeric's installations were damaged in the war. They included the main exchange building, which was hit by artillery fire but without harm to staff or equipment.

Sigfrid Mohlström was to serve Ericsson in Mexico right up to 1965.

FOOTNOTE: *The above story is told as it came to us, by word of mouth. In reading 'Gringo Rebel' it becomes evident that Thord-Gray had transferred from Villa and joined Obregon's army with which he entered Mexico City in August 1914. It was probably at this time that he met Sigge Mohlström, and several other Swedes. The following month he left Mexico and travelled to join the British army in Europe.*

Pancho Villa and his army entered Mexico City some 18 months later when the revolution had taken a totally new direction, and when there was a long period of fighting in and around the city. It would have been during this time that Mohlström met with Villa and helped save the Ericsson telephone installations.

An Ericsson exchange in Austria.

Austria-Hungary

The firm of Deckert & Homolka was established in Vienna in 1874, producing telegraph equipment. When the telephone appeared, with its rapid market acceptance, equipment for telephony took over the star role.

Strong nationalistic feeling in the Hungarian part of the empire led the government to demand that telephone manufacture should be established in Hungary as well, and in 1897, Deckert & Homolka set up additional production in Budapest. The company recognised its need for additional engineering talent to follow up technical developments, and the manager of the Budapest factory, Marton Ackermann, approached LM Ericsson with a proposal for collaboration in Hungary on central battery exchange development. A collaboration agreement with Deckert and Homolka in Budapest was duly signed in October 1908.

When Deckert died in 1910, his successor, Ackermann, let it be known there was now an opportunity for LM Ericsson to take over the factories in both Vienna and Budapest, and negotiations began. LME felt it needed some involvement by a Swedish bank in the operations in Austria-Hungary, and called on Louis Frænkel of Stockholms Handelsbank. Through Frænkel and his banking contacts an agreement was reached. Frænkel died at the end of 1911, but in November 1911 and January 1912 two companies were formed, named with German regard for correct detail: 'Ericsson Ungarische Elektrizitäts Aktiengesellschaft, vormals Deckert & Homolka' in Budapest; and 'Ericsson Oesterreichische Elektrizitäts Aktiengesellschaft, vormals Deckert & Homolka' in Vienna. Karl Guttman was appointed managing director of the Vienna company, and Marton Ackermann of the company in Budapest.

Since the existing premises were small and old-fashioned, the share capital was raised and construction of new buildings and extension got under way. LM Ericsson moved into the new factory in Vienna at the end of 1914. At about the same time, the new building in Budapest was completed, but had to be handed over immediately to the military authorities for wartime use as a hospital. It remained as a hospital until 1923, and in the meantime the old building had to do. The world war brought about an increase in orders, and full employment for both factories, including lines of non-telecommunications equipment. The LM Ericsson companies in Vienna and Budapest were profitable from the beginning, paying dividends of between 7 per cent and 20 per cent over the first ten-year period. To some extent, business was made difficult by an unstable rate of exchange, and in 1919 LME in Budapest suffered a temporary setback when it was nationalised, as were other Hungarian companies, during the four-month Communist regime.

Mixed fortunes

France

In the autumn of 1908 the telephone exchange in the Rue Gutenberg in Paris burned down. The Government administration for postal, telegraph and telephone services, the French PTT, was the operator, and so responsible for specifying and ordering telephone equipment. When the Rue Gutenberg exchange was to be replaced, the PTT suspected that the French manufacturers had formed a cartel to drive up prices and so decided to invite tenders from abroad. An offer was received from Siemens & Halske in Berlin, but the PTT was not very happy about using a German firm. Through business friends of Louis Frænkel, head of Stockholm's Handelsbank and a shareholder in LME, the PTT got into contact with LM Ericsson. LME got the order and delivered equipment for the new 6,300-line telephone exchange.

Frænkel in particular now advocated that LM Ericsson should establish itself in the French market, and the French government was encouraging, provided manufacture and sales were based on a French factory. The LM Ericsson Board was positive, and in May 1911, a French limited company was formed: the Société des Téléphones Ericsson, STE. An industrial site was purchased in the Paris suburb of Colombes, and the new factory was

A telephone produced by STE in France. One of the few examples of Ericsson making a 'candle-stick' model.

completed in 1912. Production started up the following year, but operations were still in a build-up stage when war broke out in 1914. The war years proved difficult, with shortages of labour and raw materials, and were followed by the post-war depression. The company's profit record was very different from that of Austria-Hungary: in the first ten years, it showed a profit only for 1916.

Poland

Poland was a part of the Russian empire up to the First World War, and Warsaw and Moscow were the two Russian operating concessions SAT was able to acquire in 1901. SAT formed a Swedish company, Telefon AB Cedergren (actually a subsidiary of the Moscow company), to operate the Warsaw concession. After the merger in 1918, both the Warsaw and the Moscow companies became part of Allmänna Telefon AB LM Ericsson.

The concessions were.important customers, with increasing amounts of equipment supplied from the St Petersburg factory.

In 1915, the Germans seized the Warsaw network, which was handed back to the Cedergren company in 1919. The concession expired in November of that year, but since the new Polish government had not decided whether or not the telephone service should be nationalised, the Cedergren company continued the operation of the network.

The final outcome was not to be decided until 1922, and is described in the next chapter.

Some definite reverses

The USA

In 1902, LM Ericsson decided to open a sales office in New York, with Klas Weman (who had earlier worked with setting up the St Petersburg factory) as manager. Though LME had managed to sell small amounts of equipment to American independent telephone companies, the dominating supplier was Bell, which also owned most of the operating companies and had a firm grip on the market. Out of a total of 2.4 million telephones in the USA in 1902, 57 per cent were connected to the Bell System. Ten years later, the figure was 86 per cent of a total of 8.7 million. This meant that the potential market was limited, but it was still large enough to be interesting.

To provide a better service, and to position LM Ericsson more strongly as an American supplier, in 1904 it was decided to expand the US operations into a factory, in the way that had been successful in the UK. An American limited company, the LM Ericsson Telephone Manufacturing Co., was formed, in Buffalo, N.Y., with Klas Weman as manager. It went

Manufacture in the USA: manual switchboards in production in the Buffalo factory.

into operation in 1907, but the venture never became a success and Weman left in 1910. There were several infusions of new capital, and eventually production was concentrated on ignition devices for cars! The automobile industry was growing rapidly, but even so, losses continued. Finally, in 1920, the factory was closed. The shares were written off, and in 1923 the company was sold.

This was only the first unsuccessful attempt to establish an LM Ericsson enterprise in the US.

Russia

Svensk-Dansk-Ryska Telefon AB had been founded as a SAT subsidiary in 1901, to operate the Moscow concession. (The Danish component in the name of the company reflected the close relations between the royal families of Russia and Denmark. The Tsar Alexander III, 1845–94, was married to a Danish princess, Dagmar, who took an active interest in developing good relations between the two countries and in furthering the modernisation of her new homeland.)

The network grew steadily over the following years and was from the beginning an important market for the LM Ericsson factory in St Petersburg.

From 1914, the strong position of the Swedish krona against many foreign currencies posed problems for Swedish exporters. Such was the case in the company's Russian operations – it became difficult to transfer roubles, and they were allowed to remain in the bank. The company's continuing large-scale deliveries to Russian LM Ericsson meant a continuing build-up in Russia of cash belonging to Swedish LM Ericsson.

When the St Petersburg factory was extended in 1916, an agreement was made between SAT, LM Ericsson and Russian LME to collaborate in the installation of networks in Russia, and for this purpose Telefonbyggnads AB i Moskva was formed. In 1917, Telefonbyggnads AB took over the SAT installation operations – but owing to the revolution, the new company never got under way. Then, in March 1918, Russian LME and Telefonbyggnads AB i Moskva were both nationalised, without com-

The main exchange in Moscow in the Svensk-Dansk-Ryska Telefon AB network. The picture is particularly well authenticated by the handsome samovar in the foreground.

pensation. LM Ericsson subsequently made several attempts to negotiate compensation with the Soviet authorities, but with no success.

For SAT, the concession which its subsidiary company, Svensk-Dansk-Ryska Telefon AB, held in Moscow was very profitable, and SAT was anxious to have the concession extended after its expiration date of December 1919. However, the municipal administration of the city (which had been eliminated from the competition in 1901) was eager to take over the network before that date, and the Tsarist regime decided in early 1916 to start negotiations towards that objective. SAT was invited to name a redemption sum, and in August of that year presented a total sum of 34 million roubles valued at their 1 July 1916 rate.

On 16 December 1916 the central administration for posts and telegraphs requested the transfer of the network. The transfer duly took place on 1 January 1917. But the central administration also announced that it could not accept the transfer valuation and that this should be determined by a valuation commission.

This coincided with the outbreak of the Kerensky revolution, and as the value of the rouble was falling continuously, major differences of opinion arose. The valuers finally fixed the value at 24.3 million roubles, which was the book value. As the books were kept in gold roubles, the company representatives concluded that at an exchange rate of 1 rouble = 193.5 Swedish öre, the total would amount to about SEK 47 m. The company's director in Moscow, P. Å. Nilsson Åkers, was able to get the Government's support for setting the total value at SEK 50 m, payable over ten years with interest at 6 per cent – but no decision was reached: the Bolshevik revolution erupted in October 1917 and all plans had to be abandoned.

After the Bolshevik revolution, the People's Commissary for Posts and Telegraphs suggested in an official letter that the company might approve the valuation commission's redemption figure of 24.3 million roubles – paper roubles. To this the company did not reply, since it was obviously impossible to accept a payment in rapidly-devaluing paper roubles of a price that had been established in gold. Contact with Russia was cut off for several years.

In 1921, 1923 and 1925, efforts were resumed by LM Ericsson (and other Swedish companies in similar situations) to reach some sort of settlement with the Soviet authorities, but to no avail. Matters were made no easier when the Swedish government concluded a trade agreement with the Soviet government – without reference to settlements with Swedish companies with outstanding claims. In 1925, it was clear that the claims of LM Ericsson, for both the St Petersburg factory and the former SAT network in Moscow, had to be written off. The factory in what had now become Petrograd, was renamed Krasnaia Zaria (Red Dawn), and is still there, among the largest industries in St Petersburg.

Technology and products in the early 20th century

Telephones and dials

In 1891 Televerket began its own manufacture of telephone equipment. It was the start of a long period of alternating competition and cooperation between LME and Televerket. In 1893 Televerket brought out a wall set, in wood, and in 1894 a desk set with a metal casing.

At the turn of the century telephone exchanges abroad were increasingly built on the central battery principle. The first exchange of this type, delivered by LME, was in the Hague in 1903 and the CB telephones were designed on the pattern of the magneto sets. By 1909 a new, steel-cased, model was introduced, which became the standard telephone for many years in Sweden as well.

During these years, the dial, that familiar feature of the telephone and apparently permanent addition to the language, made its appearance.

LM Ericsson's first dial for telephones was designed in 1915. LM Ericsson's dials always enjoyed a good reputation: for years, LME supplied dials to Televerket. Dials were initially supplied as components – the first complete dial telephone supplied by LME in 1921 was a 1909 central battery model with a dial added. From then on, production rationalisation and increased durability generated new designs every ten years or so. (From around 1975, dials were rapidly replaced by pushbuttons, key-sets – but we still 'dial' to make our calls.)

LM Ericsson's and Telegrafverket's desk set, 1910, now in steel casing.

Public telephone service in a Mexico City exchange.

But though your phone might have an LME dial from 1915 onwards, you would not be using it in an LME network. Dial phones are only useful in an automatic network (a network without operators to set up and route calls at the exchanges), and in 1915, LME was still several years away from introducing its first automatic switchboard, or automatic switching system.

Manual switchboards

As ever-larger capacity was required in telephone exchanges, new ways were found to extend the number of lines they could handle. Call distribution was one such development, first used by Televerket in a manual application. LME also built exchanges with call distribution in Moscow and Warsaw (1903) and Rotterdam (1907). A further refinement came when the call distribution function was made automatic, replacing the distribution operators. LME's first such exchange was installed in Rotterdam in 1914. Some of these systems lived for a long time. The last manual exchange with automatic call distribution was opened in 1939 at Odense in Denmark using 500-point selectors for the distribution function.

With call distribution, exchanges could be increased to 30,000 lines, but in some countries even larger exchanges were required. Through miniaturisation, LME managed to design a system for up to 60,000 subscriber lines. This system was installed in Moscow, Warsaw, Copenhagen and Stockholm, but in none of these locations was it extended to full capacity. This was fortunate – for the operators would have needed extremely long arms.

LM Ericsson's manufacture of switchboards became an impressive operation. At the time, LM Ericsson's factory in Stockholm included Sweden's largest carpentry workshop.

Automatic switching

LME held a leading position in manual switchboards, but played a wait-and-see game when it came to automatic switching.

The first patents for automatic telephone switching were granted as far back as 1879, in the US. And in 1883, as we know, Ericsson and Cedergren had introduced the small semi-automatic concentrator. It was of great importance at the time, but it was made for single-wire subscriber networks and its usefulness was limited to a short period. Ericsson was in no hurry to take the concept forward.

Outside Sweden, other people were demonstrating a great deal more enthusiasm, and the most important of these was Almon Strowger.

Strowger and direct-drive step-by-step

Almon B. Strowger was an undertaker in the US who became irritated by the way the telephone operator in his home town was handling his calls. He decided to do something about it by rendering operators superfluous, and hit on a method for which he was granted a patent of principle in 1891. This was the Strowger step-by-step switch, which moved through a cylindrical bank of contacts by vertical and rotary stepping movements to set up the called number. To exploit Strowger's invention, the Strowger Automatic Telephone Company was founded in 1891. In 1906 its name was changed to the Automatic Electric Co. (Autelco).

In December 1905, Strowger was granted the epoch-making US patent number 638249, covering the step-by-step driven decadic switch with vertical and rotary movements in a contact bank with a capacity of 10 x 10 lines. This was the invention that has ensured Strowger a place in the history books.

The following year, the invention of the telephone dial enabled subscribers to set up their own calls – the Strowger switches are directly driven by the pulses from the dial.

In 1901, automatic telephone switching came to Europe, when the Strowger company built an experimental exchange in Berlin for the Reichspost. Siemens & Halske set up a licence agreement with Autelco, and in 1909 the first automatic exchanges manufactured by Siemens were put into service in Germany.

Machine drive and registers

The Strowger system was protected by powerful patents and many inventors made equally powerful efforts to find alternatives. One such alternative was the principle of machine drive, in which the movement of the switches, or selectors, was brought about by connection to a common rack shaft. The switches were no longer controlled directly by impulses from the dial; instead, the numbers dialled were received by registers that in their turn controlled the setting of the switches. One of the important features of these systems was that the stepping mechanisms receiving the pulses from the subscriber dial were located in the registers, which meant less switch wear and lower maintenance.

The registers acted as translating devices, and so eliminated the fixed relationship between the dialled number and the setting of the switches. The step-by-step systems were decadic, which meant a fixed relationship between the numbering scheme and the number of switching stages, whereas in register-controlled systems the numbers dialled could be freely translated to control the optimum number of switching stages.

The first machine-driven system to be developed was the Rotary System, proposed by F.R. McBerty of the Western Electric Co. in 1908. However, this and other designs had no success in the US since the large operating companies belonging to American Telephone and Telegraph Co. (AT&T) were not yet interested enough in automatic switching. The development project was entrusted to Western Electric's Belgian subsidiary.

Televerket and the search for the right automatic system

In Sweden, LME had decided that the company did not have the resources to develop a system of its own, not least because it would involve circumventing a number of strong patents. Instead, in 1911 the company started to negotiate for a licence agreement with Siemens & Halske. The conditions proposed, however, proved to be altogether unacceptable and the negotiations broke down.

Things were different for Televerket. Televerket's network, especially in

Stockholm, was suffering from wear and was running out of capacity. It considered a variety of solutions, including both semi-automatic and fully automatic switching, but after a visit to the US in 1910 by Axel Hultman and Herman Olsson, two Televerket engineers, the Televerket Board decided that the future required full automation. It started a search for a suitable system, preferably Swedish, for the Stockholm network.

There were several possibilities to consider, and three significant new Swedish front runners, all with their roots in Televerket, emerged.

The first was an invention by Axel Hultman, a multiple with bare wires instead of the soldered contacts of the individual contact bank multiples, which meant an important cost saving. Hultman's aim was a switch capacity of 10,000 lines that would dramatically reduce the number of switching stages. LM Ericsson and Hultman agreed in 1913 that LME would take part in the development of an automatic switching system alongside any investigation of products licensed from abroad.

The second was a system designed by Herman Olsson, with registers and small rotary-type 30-line switches. The registers controlled the switches over independent special circuits, using what was later termed the by-pass principle.

The third belonged to Gotthilf Betulander, who together with his assistant, Nils Palmgren, had taken leave of absence from Televerket and founded a development company, AB Autotelefon Betulander. The two of them had already designed a register-controlled relay system for small exchanges, and were now developing this system for larger applications. It was based on a new principle, using groups of relays interconnected through link circuits instead of large switches in a 'link system'. To set the switches, common markers were used, which made it the first application of the common control principle. (A marker is a device that is brought in momentarily to operate the switches.)

The Swedish systems on trial

In 1915 Televerket ordered trial exchanges of the three prototypes, all register-controlled, to be installed. Hultman's system was manufactured by LM Ericsson; Herman Olsson's system was made at Televerket's factory; and Betulander's system was made at his experimental workshop with components from Televerket. The results of the trial were interesting.

Herman Olsson's system turned out to be too expensive and further development was abandoned. The three Swedish runners were down to two.

The trial demonstrated that the Hultman/LME 10,000-line switch would be too cumbersome, and a hunt began for a smaller switch. At LME, Kurt Kåell made an extensive study in 1918 of different switch sizes and exchange configurations and found the optimal size to be a 600-line switch. As a result, a 500-line switch was developed on a new principle – a rotary movement followed by a radial movement into the bare-wire multiple. The multiple was arranged with vertical fan-shaped 'mats' of bare wires and the result was a flat, horizontal 500-line switch. LME acquired from Hultman the rights to his invention of the bare-wire multiple.

Betulander feared that his system, like Olsson's, would become too costly, and began to look for methods of reducing the number of coils in his groups of relays. Late in 1918, he became aware of a switch invented in 1913 by the American, J.N. Reynolds. This switch had a number of contact springsets, of which one at a time was actuated by 'fingers' affixed to rotating bars. This unexploited invention gave Betulander the missing link to the solution of his problem. He and Palmgren developed the Reynolds principle into a workable switch that they patented late in 1919. It became known as the crossbar switch, and by replacing the relay groups in their system they were able in 1919 to demonstrate the first link-connected crossbar system in the world. The Betulander company had made an agreement that LME should manufacture the crossbar system, and LME had acquired the shares of AB Autotelefon Betulander. Betulander returned to Televerket, and Nils Palmgren joined LM Ericsson.

The hot-shoe shuffle

In 1918, Herman Olsson, nick-named Moscow-Olle from previous exploits in network construction, visited the USA and had a meeting with Mr McQuarry, a manager at Western Electric's laboratories in New York. When ushered into McQuarry's office he found him with his shoes off – his feet were hurting. As he made his excuses, McQuarry explained the cause of his suffering as something to do with faulty insteps. As it turned out, Moscow-Olle had suffered from the same ailment a few years earlier, but had found a remedy which he would be very happy to demonstrate – Olle took off his shoes, pulled up his trousers and performed a wild war dance all over the large blue carpet. This sort of exercise, on a regular basis, was what would do the trick. Mr McQuarry was very grateful indeed.

So grateful that, when in their exchange of views Olle was explaining what they had been doing in Sweden with link-connected relays, resulting in a 100-line selector made up of 100 relays, McQuarry countered with the information that here in the US they could do the same job with 20 relays. And he tripped over to his wall cabinet and brought out a patent drawing of Reynolds's crossbar switch. He explained that this thing had been lying here for several years, and that they had the theoretical solution, but had not come up with a practical design. Olle was allowed to study the documentation in detail – then he went back to Stockholm and told his colleagues about it, in detail (we assume the patent drawings were publicly available).

Televerket's choice

To complete the story, we may go forward a little in time.

By 1921, after the period of trials, Televerket was ready to decide which automatic system to use for large automatic exchanges, initially for the cities of Stockholm and Gothenburg. There were four systems on offer:

- Siemens & Halske's pulse-driven step-by-step system;

- Western Electric's machine-driven register-controlled Rotary system;

- LM Ericsson's Hultman-invented machine-driven register-controlled 500-switch system;

- LM Ericsson's Betulander-invented machine-driven link-connected crossbar system, also with register control.

Televerket's choice was obviously much influenced by its desire to use a Swedish system, and the final choice was between the systems offered by LM Ericsson.

With the Betulander system, the engineers were afraid that occasional relay faults might cause total stoppages. They also realised that there were

A line maintenance team in action in Stockholm.

Over 60 years of service!

The Norra Vasa 500-point exchange was equipped for 5,000 subscribers when cut into service in 1923. It was soon expanded to 10,000 lines and over the years underwent several technical upgrades, including the introduction of crossbar registers in 1943. Norra Vasa remained in operation until 1985, when the subscribers were moved to a new, computer-controlled, digital AXE exchange. Below: the famous Ericsson 500-point selector.

as yet no reliable methods for calculating traffic capacity in link systems – necessary to determine the numbers of switches an exchange would need.

The choice for the large exchanges therefore was the 500-point system. This choice became decisive for the future development of LM Ericsson, whose resources were now entirely channelled into the completion of the system. LME's interest in crossbar cooled off. It was the 500-point switch system – familiarly known as the pancake selector – that would become the basic element of LME's switching systems for many years, and with which it was now to enter the international markets for automatic switching systems.

The first automatic exchange, Norra Vasa in Stockholm, was ready in 1923 and opened for traffic in January 1924. In the same year, other exchanges went into service in Rotterdam in the Netherlands, and in the Norwegian towns of Hamar and Kristiansund.

And crossbar? Extraordinarily, as the pancake selector finally came to the end of its long life, crossbar emerged again as Ericsson's mainstay for another quarter of a century. The Televerket trials effectively determined Ericson's technological direction in switching for the next fifty years. But that's a story to pick up in a much later chapter.

The merger: 1918

For both LM Ericsson and SAT, the period between 1900 and 1918 had been characterised by a vigorous build-up of foreign operations, and by increasing interdependence.

SAT depended on LM Ericsson for equipment to build and operate telephone networks. LM Ericsson depended on SAT for a large part of its sales. In Mexico, SAT was directly involved as a minority owner in Mexeric, the LM Ericsson operating company.

Together, SAT and LME made important contributions to the over-all development of manual telecommunications in the early twentieth century. And indeed, both LME and SAT considered manual service more reliable than automatic, and wished to exploit manual technology as long as possible.

But by 1918, several of LME's competitors were able to offer automatic systems to capture new market shares, especially in large cities, and they were forcing LM Ericsson to seek markets in smaller towns.

The company needed to make higher investments in the development of new products generally, and automatic telephony in particular. For that, it needed more capital, and in Stockholm, SAT had an asset of considerable value in its subsidiary, AB Stockholmstelefon. AB Stockholmstelefon had a widespread telephone network in the Swedish capital, and more subscribers than its competitor, Telegrafverket's Riks-telefon.

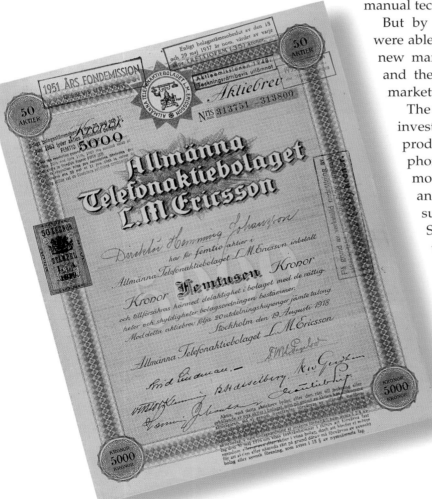

A share certificate in the merged Allmänna Telefon AB LM Ericsson.

There were strong arguments for a merger of the two companies: LM Ericsson; and Stockholms Allmänna Telefon AB, which by 1918 had developed into a holding company, with several subsidiaries – AB Stockholmstelefon in Sweden, Svensk-Dansk-Ryska Telefon AB in Moscow, Telefon AB Cedergren in Warsaw, and others.

So in July 1918, two transactions took place: LM Ericsson merged with SAT, in a new company called Allmänna Telefon AB LM Ericsson; and, with Government approval, Televerket bought AB Stockholmstelefon's network operations.

The share capital of the new company totalled SEK 61.5 m, valuing LM Ericsson at SEK 27.2 m and SAT at SEK 34.3 m. Later the same year, the share capital was increased to SEK 73.8 m through new share issues. Hemming Johansson, from LME, and Gottlieb Piltz from the SAT side, were appointed joint Managing Directors. In the following year, K.F. Wincrantz, formerly Managing Director of Allmänna Industri AB H.T. Cedergren and AB Stockholmstelefon, was made a permanent member of the Board. In 1922, he replaced Piltz as one of the Managing Directors.

Hemming Johansson (1869–1955)

Hemming Johansson, a graduate engineer, joined SAT in 1893 and was made head of AB Telefonfabriken in 1896. In 1898 he transferred to LM Ericsson,and succeeded Axel Boström as managing director in 1909. After the merger Hemming Johansson and Gottlieb Piltz became Joint Managing Directors of Allmänna Telefonaktiebolaget LM Ericsson.

Hemming Johansson was a member of the board of AB LM Ericsson & Co. from 1903 to 1918, and of Allmänna Telefonaktiebolaget LM Ericsson from 1918 to 1952, over 30 years.

Hemming Johansson was the author of an LM Ericsson history, covering the years 1876 to 1918, published in 1953.

Gottlieb M. T. Piltz (1874–1937)

Gottlieb Piltz was managing director of Stockholms Allmänna Telefon AB 1910–1918. He was a joint managing director (with Hemming Johansson) of Allmänna Telefon AB LM Ericsson 1918–1922, when he was appointed technical director. Member of the Board of the company 1918–1925.

Gottlieb Piltz headed the company's entry into the Italian market in 1925, and thereafter was technical director of the Italian company until 1937.

CHAPTER 4

1918–1932

Advancing on four fronts

Telephony takes off

After the war the world economy enjoyed a brief boom, but as early as 1920 a serious depression was beginning, from which recovery was slow and painful. Many of the traditional industries were forced to undergo long-drawn-out and painful structural change. This period also marked the shift of the world's economic activities towards the USA, with industries that could increase productivity through 'mass production'; and to oil- and coal-rich economies.

The engineering industry in Sweden, which depended to a large degree on foreign markets, was naturally deeply affected. Customer demand from abroad was uncertain, while worker demands were becoming ever stronger. In 1920, statutory working hours in Sweden were reduced to eight hours a day – without, initially, a matching cut in wages. To managements, whose ideas on cutting costs went no further than cutting wages, this was bad news. When, in 1922, in the depth of the depression, the employers managed to reduce wages, the situation for the workers became increasingly difficult at a time when unemployment was high. These problems lingered on throughout the 1920s and 1930s.

But one man's wage cut is another's price drop. As always, the effects of recession were unevenly distributed. Worldwide, the '20s were a play-time for the better off. The flappers, the bright young things, chattering at cocktail parties and charlestoning away in nightclubs and on the roofs of taxis, became a symbol of hectic (and expensive) enjoyment. In households that had a telephone, it moved out of the study of the master of the house, and typically settled in the hall, where every member of the household had access.

As telephones moved nearer to becoming commodities (and very few people at the time would have claimed them as necessities) telephone

OPPOSITE: *Cable duct laying in Mexico City.*

operations became substantial businesses – substantial enough to attract the attention of international entrepreneurs and financiers. A telephone 'concession' – a licence to offer telephone service in a particular area – became a valuable security in its own right, and could be used as collateral for a loan, or even, in some circumstances, traded.

At LM Ericsson, a four-fold advance

At that point, it was not at all obvious how or whether LM Ericsson should develop next. It was an open question whether the company could hold its own in the strongly competitive market emerging internationally. Did it have the financial resources to invest in the development of modern products, and in growing the concessions business? Or would it have to settle back and become a national company, dependent for a large part of its sales on its home market, and probably ending as an acquisition of one of the strong international groups?

For the new LM Ericsson company, the decade of the 1920s was a time for repairing the losses of the war, as we have already seen in the cases of Russia and Poland – and of protecting and building business.

It was a busy time, and LM Ericsson involved itself in a wide range of activities. With hindsight, we can group those activities under four objectives (which is not to say that it looked like that at the time).

The first objective was to gain new concessions, and expand the existing ones. Wars and revolutions aside, concessions were a proven source of income, and strong validation for any claims of internationalism.

The second was the acquisition of companies – to broaden the product base rapidly, and expand the inventory of expertise.

Next came involvement in cartels and restrictive agreements. The objective here, of course, was to preserve existing business for as long as possible. However we see them now, these things were a part of commercial life – and not to be included could easily lead to commercial suicide. And it has to be said, in fairness, that cartels did provide a sort of stability in some areas, and allowed the taking of longer-term views and decisions.

Finally, and whether the company took this decision, or whether (as quite often in LME's life) the market took it, we can see the beginning of a technology strategy with a growing focus on telephone exchanges.

But underlying, and often driving, these choices – if they were choices – there was one overriding factor for LM Ericsson to take account of: its own size and weight against some of the toughest competition it would ever encounter.

K. F. Wincrantz (1874–1932)

Karl Fredrik Wincrantz was managing director of
AB Stockholmstelefon, 1910–1918, and of Allmänna
Industri AB H T Cedergren, 1918–1921. In 1922 he
became, together with Hemming Johansson, a joint
managing director of Allmänna Telefon AB LM Ericsson,
and from 1925 to 1930 sole managing director.

The competition

In the period following the First World War, two US corporations domin-
ated the international telephone industry. They were the American
Telephone and Telegraph Company (AT&T, also referred to as the Bell
System) and the Automatic Electric Company of Chicago (Autelco).

AT&T and the others

AT&T goes back to Alexander Graham Bell. His company grew rapidly.
Way back in the last century, it had concessions in many countries; owned
a large portion of the US telephone operating companies; and by the 1920s
had established telephone factories not only in the US, but in several
European countries. The manufacturing arm of AT&T was the Western
Electric Company, which manufactured the Rotary system in Chicago
and, among other places, Antwerp in Belgium. Oddly enough, the US Bell
operating companies did not use Western Electric's Rotary system. Instead,
they had standardised on Strowger, manufactured initially by Autelco.

Autelco too had a subsidiary, the International Automatic Telephone
Company, manufacturing in Liverpool (the Automatic Telephone
Manufacturing Company) and selling Strowger equipment to the non-US
markets.

The third major player in the game was Siemens & Halske AG of
Germany, a leading manufacturer not only in telephone equipment but

Colonel Sosthenes Behn
(1882–1957)

With his brother Hernand, the founder of International Telephone & Telegraph, ITT – over many years Ericsson's most bitter competitor (and for a while, owner).

across a wide product range – power generation, electric motors, locomotives, and other heavy electrical products. Until the war, Siemens owned the British Siemens Brothers & Co. Ltd, which was taken over by British interests after the war. In Germany, Siemens had acquired the Strowger patent and had developed the system further. The Siemens step-by-step equipment was more compact than the Autelco-designed Strowger.

There were a number of other companies making telephone switching systems, but they were basically limited to providing their respective home markets and their dependencies.

And during the 1920s, LM Ericsson was itself becoming one of the international suppliers.

But a new challenger was on the way.

Sosthenes Behn and ITT

From the 1920s well into the 1980s, one of LME's most dedicated competitors would be ITT, the International Telephone & Telegraph Corporation. It's worth tracing the origins of ITT, and the career of its founder, Sosthenes Behn.

Sosthenes Behn was born in the Virgin Islands when they were still Danish, of a Danish father and French mother. He was sent to school first on the island of Corsica, and then to Paris. When the US acquired the Virgin Islands in 1917, for $ 30 m, the Behn family, including Sosthenes and his younger brother Hernand, became American citizens, and soon became high-level achievers.

They started as sugar brokers in Puerto Rico. As settlement for a bad debt, they happened to become the owners of a small telephone company. Aware of what was happening in the US as the telephone swept the country, Sosthenes saw the possibilities, and bought more telephone companies, in Puerto Rico and then in Cuba.

During the First World War he rose to become a Colonel in the US Signal Corps, and this was the title he preferred for the rest of his life.

After the war, he and his brother founded their own small company, which they called International Telephone and Telegraph. They chose the name deliberately to confuse, with an eye to the mighty AT&T which operated most of the telephone systems in the United States. ITT's objective was to build telephone operations in different countries: looking at the way telephone development was lagging in most parts of the world outside the USA, Behn saw the scope as enormous.

His first major opportunity came in 1923 in Spain. The country had been taken over by the dictator, Primo de Rivera, who decided to invite private companies to run the chaotic telephone service. The two main

Building pole lines in Latin America.

competitors for the concession were ITT and LM Ericsson. Behn set himself up in a grand hotel in Madrid, spent lavishly and, with his fluent
Spanish and grand style, made a strong impact. LME spent a lot of effort
in preparing the technical documentation, with plenty of references to
successful operations in many other countries. But the colonel won the day.

ITT set up the Compañía Telefónica de España and signed up American
engineers to plan and build the networks. The equipment and plant were
purchased from the USA (Western Electric-AT&T; and Autelco).

Part of the deal required ITT to buy up the existing privately-owned
telephone companies, including a small concession in Valencia which had
been acquired by LM Ericsson as a preparation for the bidding for the
main Spanish concession. There was at least one personal meeting between Colonel Behn and Mr Wincrantz, the MD of LME at that time.
Wincrantz got a fair price for the network, but the tone of the conversations is not reported as friendly.

We shall hear much more of Mr Wincrantz and his relationship with Sosthenes Behn.

In 1925, an even greater opportunity for Behn arose when, after an anti-trust action, by consent decree, the Western Electric Co. was forced to sell off its international holdings. The Behn brothers, helped by the Morgan Bank, offered $ 30 m for International Western Electric and won the deal. This meant that overnight ITT became the owner of telephone equipment factories in many parts of the world. The new network of manufacturing companies was named International Standard Electric. ITT also took over the Bell Telephone operating companies outside the US.

Security for the participants in the deal, Western Electric with AT&T, and ITT with International Standard Electric, was ensured by a secret cartel agreement. By the terms of this agreement, AT&T promised not to compete with ITT abroad, in return for using it as AT&T's export agents – and ITT undertook not to compete with AT&T in the USA.

Among many other well-known companies that were now in the ITT fold were Standard Telephones and Cables, STC, in Britain, and the Bell Telephone Manufacturing Company, BTM, in Antwerp. LM Ericsson's competition had acquired a new and tougher face.

In 1928, Behn and his company headquarters transferred to a new 33-storey skyscraper at 67 Broad Street in New York. Above the entrance there is still a mosaic showing an angel with a flash of lightning between outstretched hands, and two hemispheres representing the world.

Behn moved into an apartment on the top floor and soon established a reputation as a royal and elegant host. His appearance was commanding, he had great charm, and he carefully developed his image. Above all he was a clever businessman, with an eye for a successful strategy.

And there is no doubt that by 1928, one of the strategies he was nursing was the acquisition of LM Ericsson.

In 1930, Colonel Behn was able to secure a key piece for his European business. Together with AEG, he formed a holding company, Standard Elektricitäts Gesellschaft. AEG soon sold out. Then he acquired the Lorenz company from Philips. This brought him into a head-on collision with his biggest rival, Siemens and Halske, who fought back by going into a partnership with LM Ericsson. This union did not last long, however, since Behn contacted Ivar Kreuger, head of a financial empire and by this time officially in control of LME, and started discussions about a new deal. It is not quite clear if it was Behn who contacted Kreuger, or the other way round.

Behn. Wincrantz. Kreuger. We shall soon come back to the story of these three men.

Against the background of this steadily intensifying international competition, LM Ericsson was pursuing its various objectives.

The battle for concessions

Latin America

An important part of the company's strategy during the 1920s was to develop the telephone operating concessions and to gain new ones.

Mexico

In Mexico, the original concession for Mexico City was expanded when, in 1926, LM Ericsson was granted a 50-year concession to operate the country's long-distance traffic. A further strengthening followed in 1928, when a renewal of the Mexico City concession was granted.

Apart from several periods of political unrest during the 1910s, Mexeric's main difficulty in Mexico was competition from the US-owned Mexican Telephone & Telegraph Company, Mexicana. In 1925, Mexicana was acquired by ITT as a result of the AT&T break-up.

A merger of Mexicana and Mexeric had already been discussed, and when LME's managing director, K.F. Wincrantz, met Colonel Behn in Paris late in 1929, he proposed the sale of the Mexeric installations to ITT. The price was SEK 20 m and an undertaking to stop the legal proceedings for patent infringement that Western Electric had brought against LME earlier that year. Colonel Behn was not interested. He thought ITT's position in Mexico was strong enough. (By now, the Colonel's only interest in LME was to acquire a majority shareholding in LME itself.)

All over the world, the battle for concessions meant a dramatic expansion of the networks. A typical member of a duct-laying team in Mexico.

Argentina

In Argentina, about 85 per cent of the concessions were controlled by British capital. Siemens controlled two smaller companies, and there were also a number of small rural concession companies. In 1920, LME became a partner in one of these, Compañía Entrerriana de Teléfonos S.A., CET. The following year, LM Ericsson also formed a sales company in Buenos Aires, the Compañía Sudamericana de Teléfonos LM Ericsson, CSE.

Network construction, Argentina.

Business in Argentina expanded fairly rapidly, but was hampered by the need for substantial new capital during the build-up period. LME now approached the Herlitzka group, which, in 1927, had formed the telephone company in Mendoza, Compañía Argentina de Teléfonos S.A., CAT, and purchased its equipment from CSE. The equal pooling of resources, in 1929, allowed rapid expansion.

In that same year, the largest telephone company in Argentina, the Compañía Unión Telefónica del Río de la Plata had been taken over by ITT. To strengthen their opposition to this fierce new rival, LME-Herlitzka and Siemens came to a series of 'arrangements' – gentlemen's agreements – regarding demarcation lines and favoured equipment suppliers.

Europe

Generally speaking, LME was cautiously interested in acquiring new concessions in Europe during this period. Telephone operations provided certain captive markets, but at the same time substantial capital investments had to be made, especially during the initial growth period, and there were obvious political risks, especially in the setting of tariffs.

Poland

The years of occupation had caused considerable losses in Poland, and the company's debt had increased.

For Allmänna Telefon AB LM Ericsson the question was how to get paid for the Warsaw telephone network, and, at the same time, hold on to its Polish operating concessions. In 1922, the negotiations resulted in an agreement by which the Polish government and the Cedergren company together formed a Polish telephone company, to which the Warsaw network was sold. The company was named Polska Aksynja Spółka Telefoniczna, PAST, and PAST was granted a 25-year concession. The sale involved a loss to the Cedergren company, since the selling price did not cover its debts, and its share capital of SEK 4.5 m was lost completely. The accumulated loss on the sale was added to the balance of Svensk-Dansk-Ryska Telefon AB's liabilities in 1923.

From 1922, PAST took over not only the Warsaw network but also the operations in Lwów, Łódź, Lublin, Białystok, Sosnowiec and Borysław. At the end of the year, just under 39,000 subscribers were connected, 30,000 of them in Warsaw.

When PAST was formed, it was assumed that the company would be paying no dividends until 1927, but in fact it proved possible to pay a dividend of 3 per cent as early as 1924. By the terms of the concession, the tele-

phone tariffs were set, from 1927 onwards, in such a way that annual dividends of at least 8 per cent were guaranteed.

Although the losses in Poland due to the upheavals of the First World War were considerable, LM Ericsson was able through PAST to continue with a major role in the development and operation of the Polish telephone system. PAST was to provide LME with a good income over a long period.

In 1924, the LM Ericsson Polska Akcynja Spółka Elektryczna (PASE) was formed to complement the PAST operating company. PASE was initially primarily a sales company, but in 1928 a new factory was built in Warsaw to take on contracts for the Polish Army. The PASE factory increasingly performed assembly work on telephone exchange equipment. To meet rises in customs tariffs, in 1932, a stronger manufacturing base in Poland was established when PASE formed a new company, in Katowice, to produce telephone and railway equipment. The company was named Wytwórnia Telefonów i Syknalów Kolejowych Spółka Akcyjna, or Telesyg for short.

Finland

In Finland, LME had a subsidiary company, A/B LM Ericsson i Finland, formed in 1918, selling and installing telephone equipment for the various operating companies. Finland had a large number of small concession companies operating local services under relatively short-term licences from the government. A larger private company, Södra Finlands Interurbana Telefon AB, to which LME was also a supplier, operated the long-distance services.

But the Government was playing an increasingly important role in the long-distance service, and by 1930 it had a network of the same size as that of Södra Finland. The result was, of course, head-on duplication. A Government commission recommended that one of two alternatives be implemented: either a single long-distance state-owned network, or some form of privately-owned long-distance operation. Anticipating the decision, LME, like Siemens and ITT, began to build up its influence in a possible private long-distance company. Through a nominee, LME purchased a substantial portion of the shares of Södra Finlands Interurbana Telefon AB, and majority share-holdings in several local telephone companies – Tammisaari (Ekenäs), Porvoo (Borgå), Loviisa, Hamina (Fredrikshamn) and Hyvinkää (Hyvinge). The number of subscribers in these various networks was small, and LME never became a major operator in Finland, but the equipment sales were sizeable.

The interior of the Ericsson factory at Getafe, Spain. Light assembly of this kind offered many work opportunities for women. Late 1920s.

Spain

When Behn won his Spanish concession, LM Ericsson's hopes in Spain withered. It had formed Compañía Española de Teléfonos Ericsson, CEE, in 1922, and a factory had been built in Getafe, on the outskirts of Madrid. CEE now had to content itself with supplying the San Sebastian area, where it had obtained a foothold with the supply of exchange equipment in 1924. CEE was later to take up the manufacture of other equipment, such as railway signalling.

Italy

In Italy, the Mussolini Government decided in 1923 to modernise the country's telephone system. Italy was divided into five zones, and within each zone the telephone operating concession was offered to private interests, which had to be Italian. The long-distance service would be handled by the Government.

Together with British and Swedish banks, and some Italian interests, LME formed a syndicate which in 1924 was transformed into an Italian

Network construction staff at SIELTE make a dramatic composition.

Stringing cable in Sicily as part of the modernisation of the networks in Southern Italy.

company, Societá Esercizi Telefonici, SET. In 1925, SET obtained the concession to operate the network in the fifth zone, the southern part of the country, including Sicily. The largest cities in this zone were Naples, Palermo, Messina and Catania.

Early in 1925, LME became a partner in a small telephone factory in Rome, Fabbrica Apparechi Telefonici e Materiale Elettrico, FATME, which was equipped to manufacture LM Ericsson telephone equipment. The former LME agency in Genoa was transformed into a contracting and sales company, Società Sistema Ericsson, SIELTE, and an installation company was formed, Compagnia Installazioni Reti Telefoniche, CIRT. SET, FATME and CIRT were taken into a new holding company in 1927, and in 1930 SIELTE was brought in as well. The holding company was named Società Elettro Telefonica Meridionale, SETEMER, in which LME officially held 40 per cent of the shares.

The modernisation and extension of the networks in Southern Italy required large supplies of equipment from both FATME and the Stockholm factory. By 1931, the number of subscribers had grown from 25,000 to 62,000.

Turkey: cable duct production at SATS.

Turkey and the Balkan States

Turkey

In 1925, it became possible for foreign interests to obtain minority holdings in telephone operations in Turkey. LME and the local authorities formed a company to run the Smyrna network, and in 1926 the Société Anonyme Turque de Téléphones de Smyrna et ses Environs, SATS, began to build exchanges and a network, which went into operation in 1928. The company's name was later changed to Izmir ve Civari Telefon Türk A.S. It was a small network, with only some 2,000 subscribers.

Romania

In Romania, LME became a partner in the country's largest electrical company, Energia, in 1927, and later also acquired a majority shareholding in Banca Danubiana, one of the Kreuger Group's finance companies. LME also set up a sales and service company. Under Wincrantz's direction, every effort was made to ensure a good position in the forthcoming contest for the concession. The competitors were, as expected, Siemens & Halske, Autelco and, above all, ITT.

In the autumn of 1929, LME, represented by Hemming Johansson, had a meeting in Berlin with Behn and others from ITT. The tone was conciliatory, now, since LME was eager to arrive at a settlement on the forthcoming concessions in both Romania and Yugoslavia, and both parties wanted to avoid competition. At the next meeting, in Paris in December 1929, LME, this time represented by Wincrantz, let it be known that it was prepared to give up its Mexican interests in return for a free hand in the Balkan states. Nothing was decided, but it is recorded that Behn and Wincrantz again parted on somewhat cool terms. A further meeting was discussed, but it never took place.

As in Spain a couple of years earlier, the financial resources available to ITT decided the issue. In a final, desperate move, the other three companies joined forces and submitted a joint application for the concession, but the somewhat loosely allied threesome could not manage to keep in step in the final quick march of the competition.

By the summer of 1930 it was clear that ITT had won the coveted prize.

Greece

In Greece, LME initially won the bidding for the concession. But the German government stepped in to support Siemens and offered to finance the network as part of paying war damages. So the winner was Siemens; but as a very minor consolation, LME was awarded the contract for building the Athens outside plant network.

A reasonably successful strategy

LM Ericsson did respond to an invitation to tender for Yugoslavia, but the bidding never took place, and no concessions were awarded at that time.

Negotiations for concessions also took place in several countries in South America, but without results.

There is little doubt, in looking back today, that the strategy LME followed, in large part based on winning and operating telephone concessions, was important, and indeed necessary, though the volume of business, as we shall see, was not impressive by today's standards. By 1931, the numbers of subscribers in the LME concessions were as shown in Table 2.

In the same year, sales of equipment (telephone exchanges, cable, telephone sets, etc.) to the LME concession companies amounted to more than SEK 12 m (also in Table 2).

This total of just over SEK 12 m represented about 40 per cent of total sales from the parent company, i. e. the Stockholm factory. This means that during those years, the parent company had well over a third of its market under its own control.

TABLE 2. SUBSCRIBERS IN AND SALES TO LM ERICSSON'S CONCESSION NETWORKS, 1931

	Subs	Sales SEK
Mexico	46,270	4,718,000
Argentina	33,555	1,443,000
Italy	61,707	2,831,000
Poland	92,209	3,028,000
Turkey	1,925	14,000
Finland	3,652	-
Total	**39,318**	**12,034,000**

Compiled from tables in
'LM Ericsson 100 years', vol. I.

Looked at in this way, it's obvious that the concessions business was important, indeed crucial, to the development of LM Ericsson. It is difficult to imagine that the company would have survived as an international business of any standing without it.

Company acquisitions – for a broader product base ...

LM Ericsson also moved to build or acquire subsidiaries to gain control over the production of a wider range of products.

An early radio set from SRA.

Svenska Radio Aktiebolaget, SRA, was formed in 1919 by three Swedish companies: ASEA, AGA and LME. In 1921, the British Marconi company came in as a part-owner; and in 1927, LME bought out the other two Swedish owners. SRA's main business was the manufacture and sales of radio transmitters and radio sets for the home. The Radiola set became a prized feature of many Swedish homes. SRA also became the supplier of radio equipment to the Swedish armed forces; SRA produced marine radio equipment; and it was at SRA that the first transmission systems for telephone networks were developed (though this business was transferred to the parent company).

Max Sievert Fabriks AB was the leading Swedish manufacturer of power and telephone cable and, as we've seen in an early chapter, it became closely associated with LM Ericsson. This association became even closer as network construction activities expanded in so many countries. The Sievert company was also a competitor to LM Ericsson's Älvsjö cable works, formerly owned by Allmänna Industri AB H.T. Cedergren. In 1928, LM Ericsson and Sieverts came to an agreement, and the Sievert cable company became a fully-owned subsidiary of LM Ericsson, though it continued to operate independently of the parent company. Apart from LM Ericsson, its main customers were Televerket and the power supply companies in Sweden.

In 1929, LME acquired AB Alpha, a company in Sundbyberg making bakelite products, special tools and testing equipment, and small capacitors.

Yet another acquisition took place in 1931, when LME acquired Svenska Elektromekaniska Industri AB in Helsingborg. LME's interest in Elektromekano was its copper wire production, but the company also made electric motors and generators.

… and for market presence

The Baltic countries did not represent a large market, but the region was part of LME's sphere of interest. When plans were announced for the introduction of automatic service in Tallinn (Reval), the capital of Estonia, it was decided to strengthen the company's presence in that market. LME had supplied the existing manual equipment in the beginning of the century and had an on-going relationship with the authorities. In 1928, a majority shareholding was acquired in the country's only important telephone factory, Tartu Telefoni Vabrik A.S. in Dorpat (the city's name was later changed to Tartu). The factory was to produce telephones for the Reval and other PTT networks until 1940, when it came under Soviet control.

In Norway, also in 1928, with fierce competition from ITT, LM Ericsson acquired a majority shareholding in A/S Elektrisk Bureau in Oslo. Albert Kvaal became the company's Managing Director. Among other things, Elektrisk Bureau manufactured radio equipment, electric stoves and radiators. In 1931, a cable factory in Drammen, A/S Norsk Kabelfabrikk, came into the LM Ericsson fold in an acquisition through Elektrisk Bureau.

In 1920, LM Ericsson had taken a two-thirds interest in N.V. Nederlandsche Telefoonfabrieken, at Rijen in the Netherlands, intending to manufacture telephone equipment for that country and the Dutch

Ericsson's first cable truck, Stockholm.

colonies. Later, the name of the company was changed to Nederlandsche Ericsson Telefoonfabrieken. Production build-up was slow during the '20s, and most of the equipment sold in the Netherlands through the firm of Koopman & Co. was still manufactured in Stockholm.

Through its Austrian company, LM Ericsson had had some involvement in a factory in Czechoslovakia since the beginning of the 1920s. The operations were not profitable and a new approach was taken. In January 1929, Ericsson Elektrizitäts Kommandit-Gesellschaft Scholta & Co. became a partner in B.K. Prachalové a Spol., a family company with a factory in Kolin. LME remained a minority share-holder, with three-sevenths of the share capital. The Kolin factory manufactured telephone and radio equipment and electrical components for cars.

In Table 3, the role of LM Ericsson's foreign and Swedish subsidiaries during the late 1920s is summed up.

During the five-year period covered by the table, sales from the foreign subsidiaries more than doubled. As a percentage of the Group's total sales the proportion remained fairly stable, at about 33 per cent, since sales by the Swedish companies grew at the same pace. The relatively flat development of sales from the parent company reflects the fact that the Stockholm factory had reached the limits of available space and that foreign factories were called in to supplement production.

An early cab rank.

TABLE 3. MANUFACTURING IN THE LM ERICSSON GROUP

	1927 SEK m	1931 SEK m
Parent Company	25.7	31.5
Swedish Subsidiaries	-	28.0
Total Sweden	***25.7***	***59.5***
Ericsson Telephones Ltd, UK	5.8	10.5
STE, Colombes, France	1.1	6.0
Ericsson Oesterreichische El. AG, Vienna	1.5	1.6
Ericsson Ungarische El. AG, Budapest	1.2	0.7
FATME, Rome	2.2	2.3
Nederlandsche Ericsson, Rijen	0.4	0.8
Prachalové & Co, Kolin, Czechoslovakia		0.8
Cía Española Ericsson, Getafe, Spain	0.2	0.6
PASE, Warsaw	0.5	1.5
Tartu Televoni Vabrik, Estonia	-	0.6
A/S Elektrisk Bureau, Oslo	-	3.7
Total, foreign subsidiaries	***12.9***	***29.1***
Total	**38.6**	**88.6**

Compiled on data from 'LM Ericsson 100 years', vol. I.

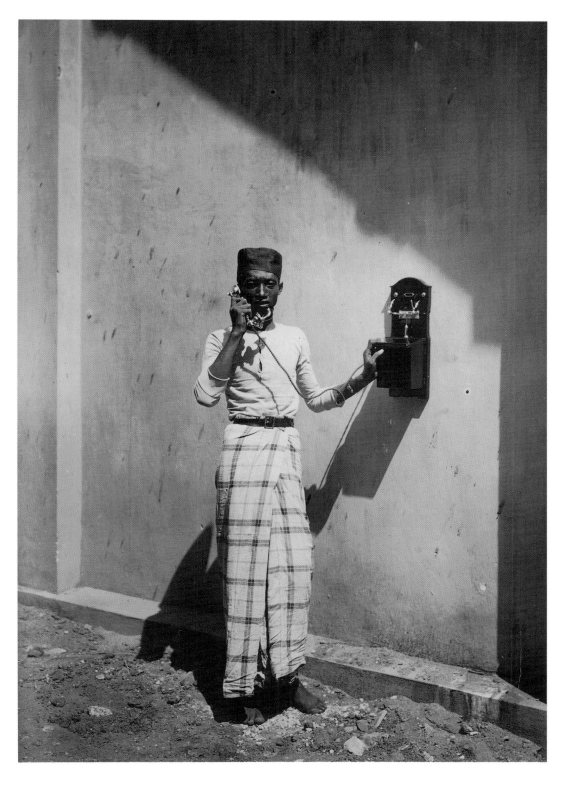

Subscriber access in Java, now Indonesia.

Market agreements and cartels to protect market shares

Like every period since, the 1920s were a period of constant conflict, as the major companies competed for a share of the market. As a natural consequence, there were continual attempts to set up cartels and 'market agreements'. The most ambitious plan was to form a worldwide cartel within the telephone industry, a concept that came up in the days of the post-war depression. There was a meeting in Amsterdam in November 1921, with leading representatives of Autelco, Western Electric, Siemens & Halske and LM Ericsson.

The idea was to allocate market quotas, at the same time permitting the use of each other's patents (for modest fees) so that the parties might manufacture each others' equipment. No final agreement was reached at this meeting, but it was decided that each party would prepare and submit details of production capacity and patent situation in preparation for a subsequent get-together. That meeting never came about and no general cartel agreement was ever reached.

However, in many markets, especially in Europe, different forms of cartels and market share agreements were set up. In Great Britain, for example, the manufacturers formed The Telephone Apparatus Association, TAA, in 1924, as a cartel to handle the supply of manual exchanges and telephones to the Post Office. This agreement gave British LM Ericsson 20 per cent of the market – a disproportionately large share, since there were a total of eight manufacturers at the time. In 1928, a similar agreement was reached for the supply of automatic exchanges by the Automatic Telephone Association, ATA. In this case, there were five companies in the cartel, but the LM Ericsson company, which was lagging in bringing out its first automatic exchange equipment, was not allocated a full share initially. But, since the Post Office had standardised on the Strowger switching system, with 'Director' equipment for the larger cities, the British Ericsson company obtained the patent rights and, after some years of preparation, became one of the five suppliers to the Post Office with a full market share of 20 per cent.

The five British suppliers, later known as 'the Ring', were the UK's General Electric Co. (GEC, formerly associated with GE of the US), Automatic Electric (ATE, formerly associated with Autelco of the US), Siemens Brothers (formerly part of Siemens & Halske), ITT's Standard Telephone and Cable (STC, formerly part of International Western Electric) and Ericsson Telephones Ltd (ETL).

By 1925, ITT's forceful operations were seen as a problem by most of the telecoms manufacturers, and from then on, the actions of LME and the other companies were more and more defensive, with repeated attempts to form combinations against ITT. During the following years, LME held several discussions with Autelco, in particular, with a view to collaboration in Britain and Mexico.

In 1929, there was an attempt to stop ITT in France. In 1927, the Compagnie Générale d'Electricité, CGE, had become a majority shareholder in LM Ericsson's French company, STE, which had increased its production capacity to supply exchanges in the Paris area. But now this promising business was threatened by ITT through its French company, Le Matériel Téléphonique, LMT. The French authorities had decided to standardise on a modified version of the Rotary system, developed by ITT. A. F. Adams of the Autelco group suggested that the interested parties on the French market should get together and jointly offer Autelco's Strowger system, or, as an alternative, the modified Rotary system that Autelco had the rights to under its agreement with Western Electric. The plan was that the automatic exchange equipment would be manufactured partly at LME's French company and partly in Germany.

There were several meetings in the spring of 1929, and a draft contract was drawn up, but there were too many obstacles, and by July negotiations had broken down.

The Bangrak telephone exchange and staff, Bangkok, Thailand, in 1930. The exchange was first installed in 1909.

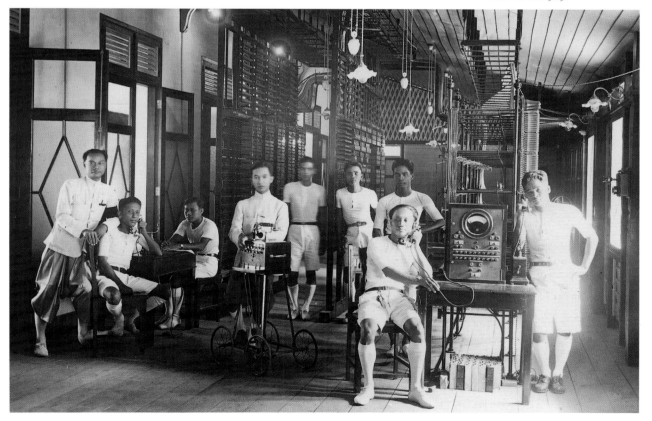

Gambling on success

As shown by Table 3 (page 104), during the 1920s the largest foreign manufacturing unit of the LM Ericsson Group was the British factory in Beeston, outside Nottingham, which from 1926 was named the British LM Ericsson Manufacturing Co. Ltd, ETL. ETL supplied the Post Office in Great Britain, Ireland, and certain British colonies, including South Africa.

The Racecourse Betting Act of 1928 opened up a business opportunity of a new sort – the automatic totalisator for race courses. Automatic Totalisators Ltd held the key patent and set up a factory, for which ETL supplied a large portion of the parts. The customer was the Racecourse Betting Control Board, which supervised all betting. In 1930, ETL bought out its customer and continued to manufacture totalisators at the Beeston factory, adding trotting and dog tracks to its market in the following year. That same year a special company was formed, Electric Totalisators Limited, which, together with dog track owners, operated installations purchased from Automatic Totalisators Ltd.

The focus on exchange technology

The business facts behind the technology strategy

LM Ericsson's manufacturing business situation in the beginning of the post-war period is illustrated by Table 4, summarising the sales from the Swedish factory in 1920.

**TABLE 4. TOTAL SALES FROM
THE SWEDISH LME FACTORY, 1920**

Customer/Country	SEK x 1000
Telegrafverket	1,301
Other customers in Sweden	2,354
Total Sweden	**3,655**
Norway	703
Denmark	1,553
Finland	699
Nordic countries	**6,610**
Great Britain	153
Germany	18
Russia	731
Poland	453
The Netherlands	2,368
France	73
Austria and Hungary	147
Spain	527
Other customers in Europe	438
Europe (incl. Nordic countries)	**11,518**
Egypt	40
South Africa	551
Africa	**591**
China	189
Dutch East Indies	338
Other customers in Asia	89
Asia	**616**
Australia and New Zealand	**381**
Mexico	236
Argentina	708
Other customers in America	151
America	**1,095**
Total	**14,201**

The sales figures for Poland, Mexico and Argentina include equipment supplied to the Ericsson concession networks. The low numbers for Great Britain and France reflect the local production in LME-owned factories in these countries. The main part of the sales to Russia were channelled through a sales subsidiary in Stockholm, Svenska Telefon AB Ström, and corresponded to minor expansions of the former SAT networks.

**TABLE 5. DISTRIBUTION OF SALES BY
MARKET, 1931** (from whole LME group,
excluding internal sales)

Market	per cent of sales
Sweden	**34.8**
Norway	3.7
The Netherlands	3.6
France	6.0
Great Britain	8.9
Italy	10.0
Poland	4.5
Other Europe	12.3
Mexico	5.1
South & Central America	9.2
Asia	1.1
Other	0.8
Total sales outside Sweden	**65.2**

Data selected from 'LM Ericsson 100 years', vol. I.

Even at this time, while the world was recovering from the First World War, exports accounted for 75 per cent of the Swedish operations. The international character of the company was well established.

The pattern was maintained throughout the 1920s, though while at the beginning of the 1920s sales were very wide-spread, during the decade there was a strong move to concentrate on fewer, larger markets. Table 5 (page 109), which includes sales from subsidiary LME companies, illustrates the market structure in 1931 in percentages.

Notwithstanding the substantial market losses due to the First World War, and the post-war recession, the export market, including sales from subsidiary factories, still accounted at this time for two-thirds of the company's business

The subsidiary factories in France, Great Britain and Italy represented a significant part of LME's total sales. The second group of markets were the countries where LME had its operating concessions, with Mexico, Poland and Argentina (plus, from 1925, Italy) being the most important. Key markets for the Stockholm factory were the Scandinavian countries, especially Norway, and the Netherlands. Outside Europe, there were substantial markets in the British and Dutch colonies.

Defying Mount Etna: the telephone network in Sicily.

The importance of telephone exchanges

The installed base in 1920 totalled 187 telephone exchanges, most of them in cities. The largest exchange in the world was in Moscow, now lost as a market, but there were many other cities where LME had installed large exchanges – in the Nordic capitals, Warsaw, The Hague, Rotterdam, Mexico City, Kansas City and so on.

As a base for continued and expanding business, the installed base of telephone exchanges was however of limited value since all of them were manual, and many would soon be reaching their capacity limit. It was beginning to be clear that LM Ericsson must be able to offer the market automatic telephone exchanges in order to be competitive and to grow.

Though the beginnings of the decade were problematic, a look at the sales numbers shows that it became a period of growth. Table 6, which lists sales from the telephone factory, plus the Älvsjö cable works, illustrates this fact.

The second-largest product group was telephone instruments, sold to the operating companies and also in growing numbers to private customers, together with switchboards installed in offices, factories and other organisations. But telephone exchanges accounted for about 50 per cent of LME's equipment sales. And, from 1924 onwards, a large proportion of the sales to Televerket (which with other Swedish customers made up about a third of LME's sales) were of automatic exchanges of the new 500-point type, called the AGF system. As we have seen, the first AGF exchanges were installed in the larger Swedish cities, such as Stockholm and Gothenburg, and other early contracts were for Rotterdam and to Norway.

And it's significant that for the first time we find LM Ericsson distinguishing between the public market (public exchanges, cable and line material, telephone sets, etc.) and the private market (office, or private, switchboards, telephones, wire and cable). In both market sectors, LME offered installation and testing as well as equipment.

It could be said that by choosing the 500-point selector in 1921, Televerket had taken the technology strategy decision for LM Ericsson!

It's worth pointing out, however, that Televerket continued to experiment with its own automatic system, based on the crossbar switch. A first crossbar exchange was installed in the city of Sundsvall in 1926, and a second in Limhamn, Malmö, in 1930. Technically, the exchanges were successful, but it was to be some time still before the new technology could be proven commercially.

Meanwhile, the Swedish AGF exchanges proved important as reference installations in marketing to customers outside Sweden.

But vital as all this technological development was, LM Ericsson was about to encounter a major, unexpected and sinister distraction …

TABLE 6. SALES BY YEAR FROM LM ERICSSON'S SWEDISH FACTORIES, 1920–1931

Year	SEK m
1920	14.8
1921	19.3
1922	12.2
1923	12.2
1924	12.1
1925	14.3
1926	17.7
1927	22.8
1928	29.1
1929	29.7
1930	30.2
1931	29.6

The figures shown do not, of course, represent the Ericsson company's total sales, since the factories in countries outside Sweden are not included, nor is income from concessions shown.

From 'LM Ericsson 100 years', vol. I.

CHAPTER 5

The Kreuger crisis

The rise and fall of K. F. Wincrantz

Shares, votes, collateral

The story of Ivar Kreuger is one of the most dramatic episodes in the entire history of Swedish industry and of LM Ericsson. A story of competing ambitions between powerful men, it ended in tragedy for Kreuger, and came close to doing the same for LM Ericsson. Yet it was an industrial power game, played out among the dry complexities of share dealings and state financing.

In this brief account, some of the complexities will inevitably be coarsened – the full story is dazing in its difficulty. Here, we shall be concentrating on the story as it affected LM Ericsson.

The ingredients are the management and capital structure of the merged companies in Allmänna Telefonaktiebolaget LM Ericsson, the demand for capital for the expanding company, and the ambitions of Karl Fredrik Wincrantz, Colonel Sosthenes Behn and Ivar Kreuger.

We may start with the structure of the company formed by the merger of 1918, where all that needs to be noted is that there were two Joint Presidents, Hemming Johansson and Gottlieb Piltz. Other Board Members were supplied by the two companies, including Wincrantz, who had been MD of Allmänna Industri AB H. T. Cedergren, and who became a permanent member of the Board in 1919. In 1922, Wincrantz replaced Piltz as one of the Joint Presidents. He also set about acquiring a dominant ownership position in the new company by establishing an influence over strategic shareholdings, and by 1925, he had succeeded.

The shareholdings in the new company were inevitably complex, and since it was a public company there were, of course, a large number of different shareholders, some private, some institutional.

At the Annual General Meeting in 1919, of the total of 738,000 A shares (shares carrying one vote each) 286,603 were represented at the meeting.

OPPOSITE:
Secure line: an emergency telephone installed and under guard after an earthquake in Naples, Italy, 1930.

They included these large blocks, amounting to 221,918 votes between them:

SAT in liquidation (*SAT i likvidation*)	63,520
SAT Pension Fund	18,000
The Cedergren Education Fund (*Telefondirektören H. T.Cedergrens uppfostringsfond*)	101,592
Mrs Ida Cedergren	38,806

SAT, though liquidated for the merger, remained in being as a subsidiary company of LME – 'SAT i likvidation'. It had its own bond debts and assets, but most important, it held a large block of shares in the parent company, which it had received in exchange for a holding it had of shares in the old, pre-merger LM Ericsson. With issues, and some purchases of parent company stock, this block amounted to 79,728 by 1920. As SAT's main representative on the Board, Wincrantz effectively controlled these votes.

As he did also the SAT Pension Fund holdings. Originally 500 shares in SAT, purchases and issues meant that this block amounted to 21,600 shares in the new company by 1920.

The Cedergren Education Fund is obviously significant. When H.T. Cedergren died in 1909, it was found that a will drawn up by him and his wife, Mrs Ida Cedergren, left significant funds to provide scholarships for poor but gifted children in Stockholm to acquire a good education. The funds were largely invested in SAT shares, which were exchanged in 1918 for shares in the new company, and Mrs Cedergren was a Board member of the Education Fund. She also had a substantial personal holding.

In 1915, the Fund and Mrs Cedergren had used their SAT shares as security for loans, to invest in a new SAT issue; and after the merger, they used the same collateral to borrow for investments in the new issue from the new company.

There was nothing foolish or unusual about these transactions, but, through no fault of the Fund or Mrs Cedergren, they were to have dire consequences.

As we've seen elsewhere, the revolutions and subsequent nationalisation in Russia came as a cataclysm for LME. In 1920, LME postponed its dividend – which stayed at a low level for the following years. Then, in 1922, the company was forced to write down the value of its shares by half.

This left the Education Fund and Mrs Cedergren dangerously exposed. Though there was little or no income on their shares, interest had still to be paid on the money they had borrowed to buy them. And as the value of their collateral collapsed, the banks pressed for repayment of the loans or for the provision of further security.

Wincrantz 'in control'

With who knows what motives, Wincrantz came to the rescue. On 13 February 1925, he set up a company, AB Ängsvik (Board Member: K.F. Wincrantz; Deputy Board Member: Mrs Ellen Lindström), 'for the administration of property'. A week later, this company bought from Mrs Cedergren and the Fund the shares which were being used as security for loans from Svenska Handelsbanken and Sundvalls Enskilda Bank – 154,630 shares altogether, at SEK 34 each.

Wincrantz took over liabilities for the loans (which he immediately reduced by SEK 0.5 m), paid the interest due, and paid SEK 50,000 each to Mrs Cedergren and the Fund. He also undertook to pay the Fund any dividend on one third of the shares which exceeded 7 per cent of SEK 34 per share.

So with his control of the SAT votes and the Cedergen holdings, Wincrantz became overnight the dominant voting force at LME, and his company, AB Ängsvik, became a major shareholder.

Through a Mr Callmander, who had power of attorney for AB Ängsvik, a new LM Ericsson Board of Directors was appointed with Carl Ramström as chairman and including Professor H. Pleijel, Gösta Klemming, K.F. Wincrantz and Hemming Johansson. K.F. Wincrantz became sole managing director and Hemming Johansson was demoted to technical director.

A year later the company's name was changed. Allmänna Telefonaktiebolaget LM Ericsson was causing some confusion, especially in Spanish-speaking countries, where the word 'Allmänna', meaning 'general', was misunderstood to mean 'Alemania', meaning Germany. There was, also, a risk of confusion with ASEA, Allmänna Svenska Elektriska Aktiebolaget. In 1926 it was accordingly decided to change the name to just 'Telefon-aktiebolaget LM Ericsson'.

It seemed as though Wincrantz was on track to achieve his over-all goal of total control of LME. In fact, he had taken the first steps towards his own downfall. Ängsvik was capitalised at SEK 1 m, set up by deposits in two different banks of SEK 0.5 m each. The name of one of the depositors is not recorded on the receipt, but it was presumably Wincrantz or someone working for him.

The name of the other depositor *is* recorded. It was Ivar Kreuger.

Some variations on the LM Ericsson trademark theme, at the time of Kreuger's coup. *Ericsson Review* still appears regularly.

The shadow of Ivar Kreuger

Who was Ivar Kreuger?

In the '20s, any man in the street would have answered the question straight away: 'The Swedish Match King.'

Ivar Kreuger was born in Kalmar in 1880. He was trained as a civil engineer, spent some time in South Africa and then moved to the United States where he worked as an estate agent, property developer and building contractor. After a spell in Latin America, he came back to Sweden in 1907, still only 27 years old, and founded Kreuger & Toll in 1908. K&T became a successful building contractor, introducing new construction methods using re-inforced concrete.

In 1913, at 33, he set up the United Swedish Match Company, and in 1917 Kreuger & Toll became a holding company. By the time of his involvement with LM Ericsson, deals, acquisitions and mergers had put him in control of something like 75 per cent of the world's match trade, but his interests were widespread, and his activities were those of a global financier rather than an entrepreneur. A major plank of his business approach was to lend money to governments in exchange for monopoly concessions for making and selling matches.

Kreuger worked largely through his own holding company, Kreuger & Toll. He was famous, but not surprisingly he was also close and secretive in his dealings.

It is clear, for instance, that AB Ängsvik was owned equally by Wincrantz and Kreuger from 1925, though Kreuger was not registered as a shareholder before 1930. Before that time, the LME Board was unaware of his involvement. Ängsvik never paid a dividend, but after 1928, as soon as the interest on LME shares exceeded the interest needed to service the bank loans, Wincrantz and Kreuger each drew equal annual 'commissions.'

However, in 1925, Kreuger's time was yet to come. Ängsvik, and his control over the SAT voting blocks, gave Wincrantz effectively absolute power. Under Wincrantz, the company expanded for more than five years.

And like all expanding companies, LME needed cash – which may explain why Wincrantz became involved with Kreuger in the first place. Wincrantz pushed for the introduction of new issues of B shares (carrying only 0.001 votes each) which could be placed abroad. Overall, by issues in 1928 and 1930, LME was committed to the sale of 800,000 new B shares.

But while Wincrantz had been building his power, Kreuger had been building something even more important: ownership.

And in 1930, Kreuger struck.

Ivar Kreuger shows his hand

He had been acquiring LME shares for five years. He began with his partnership in Ängsvik. Then Kreuger & Toll bought shares on the open market, on a scale which by as early as 1926, affected the price. By November 1929, Kreuger & Toll held 117,119 A shares.

It also acquired large holdings of B shares. It subscribed for 61,540 of the 1928 issue and received another 100,000 from Kreuger. By the end of 1929, it held 165,905 B shares. And shareholdings were also being built up through another company, brokers AB M. Billing.

At this distance, it's not easy to keep track of the comings and goings. Kreuger worked secretly, but there must have been many

Meetings accepted, meetings refused,
Meetings unended or endless
At one place or another …

Nevertheless, at the beginning of 1930, most members of the Board of LME were still quite unaware of Kreuger's involvement in Ängsvik and LM Ericsson.

They were not to remain in ignorance for long. The AGM of June 1930 approved the new issue of B shares – but, far more important, when it was over, Kreuger had shown his hand, and the Board was packed with his supporters. And at the Board meeting in July, the showdown came between Wincrantz and Kreuger. Before the end of October, Wincrantz had lost his shares, his power base, and his Presidency. Johan Grönberg became Managing Director.

Kreuger went for the shares first. By the end of August 1930, Wincrantz had agreed to sell Kreuger his half-shareholding in Ängsvik and his personal 6,683 A shares. Nobody knows why Wincrantz agreed. He and Mrs Lindström resigned from Ängsvik in September.

Next, Kreuger & Toll went for the LME A shares held by 'SAT i likvidation' – and got them! The new 'Kreuger' Board in power at LME since the June AGM decided that it was not legal for 'SAT i likvidation' to hold shares. The transaction was complex, but the outcome was clear-cut: in October 1930, it was agreed that Kreuger & Toll should receive 509,150 new B shares and 118,517 old A and B shares in return for $ 11 m in German bonds acquired 'in connection with the German match monopoly'.

On 4 October, Wincrantz resigned from the Board, and Kreuger owned LM Ericsson.

By the end of 1930, Kreuger and his companies held 573,271 A shares out of the total of 806,651; and 823,257 B shares of the total of 1,209,975.

But the extraordinary story was not over …

Kreuger 'in control'

As soon as he was in control of LM Ericsson, Kreuger embarked on a flurry of financial activities, largely carried out through Kreuger & Toll. He was able to siphon off money from LME as and when he chose, and he set off on – or rather, accelerated his progress on – the desperate course of borrowing money to act as security for further borrowings, or to service borrowings already in place. The effects on the finances of a company which was already fairly extended were severe.

And soon he was doing more than borrow money. He was setting up a deal with Sosthenes Behn.

As we've seen, Behn developed an early interest in acquiring LM Ericsson. From 1925 onwards, he was exploring various avenues, with and without talking to Wincrantz, without success. Concluding that Wincrantz

OPPOSITE:
Ivar Kreuger – a rare picture.

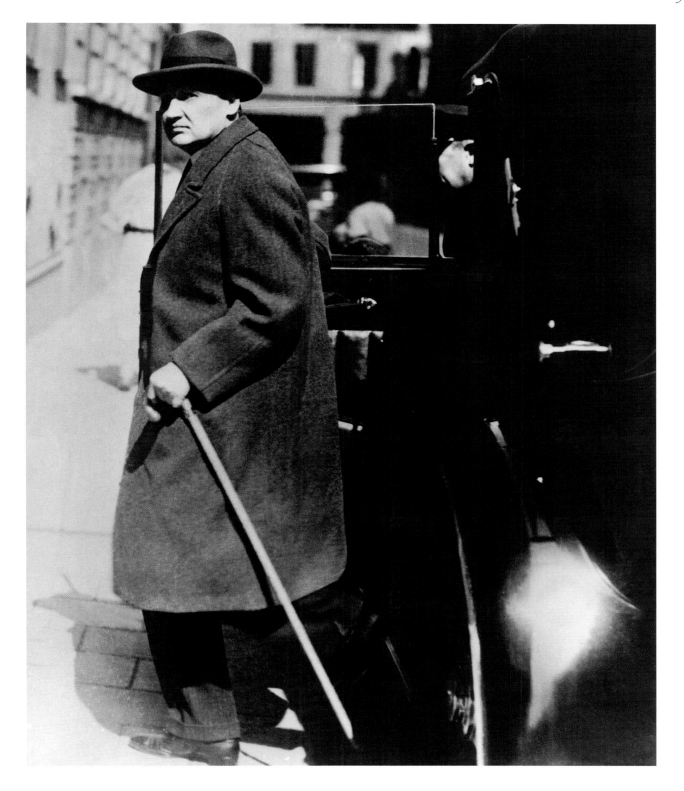

was opposed to such a deal, he had tried a discreet approach to Stockholms Enskilda Bank – again, without success. In 1929, it was even suggested that a deal might be made through Kreuger, who already had a substantial holding in LM Ericsson, but it came to nothing. Undoubtedly, however, Behn and Kreuger were in touch with each other, and in September 1930 Kreuger made sure Behn knew that he had bought Wincrantz's shares.

For Kreuger – and no doubt for Behn – there was considerable attraction in the idea of carving up the telecoms world with monopoly concessions.

Kreuger sells LM Ericsson

Kreuger had no sentimental attachment to LM Ericsson. By the spring of 1931, if not before, he was actively discussing with Oscar Rydbeck – a trusted intimate, Vice-Chairman and Managing Director of Skandinaviska Kredit AB (by this time becoming known as Skandinaviska Banken) and a Board member of both LM Ericsson and Swedish Match – the sale of the company to ITT. On 28 April 1931, he talked to Behn, while in the same month Kreuger & Toll was informing its shareholders that it had acquired control of LM Ericsson and was proposing to keep its 410,000 A shares as 'a permanent investment'.

In fact, Kreuger & Toll's liquidity was already a considerable worry to Kreuger and Rydbeck, with dividends due to be paid on 1 July.

In the middle of May 1931, Kreuger began negotiations with ITT in earnest, and by 12 June, Kreuger had in principle sold LM Ericsson to ITT.

The Kreuger spin

That is not at all how he described the situation.

While the agreements were being worked out, Kreuger was manipulating the press, the public and the Board of LM Ericsson with all the wizardry of a modern political spin doctor.

Briefly, the deal was this: Kreuger would hand over to ITT 410,000 A shares in LM Ericsson, plus 600,000 B shares. The transfer of the A shares was to be immediate; the B shares were to be delivered in October 1931 (200,000) and March 1932 (the remaining 400,000).

In return, ITT was to deliver $ 11 m dollars in cash for the 410,000 LM Ericsson A shares; and 600,000 shares in ITT (out of 6,400,206 – a very minority shareholding!).

What it boiled down to was that Kreuger had sold LM Ericsson for $ 11 m. Or, you could say, he had borrowed 11 million dollars from ITT, handing over 410,000 LME A shares as security.

I. T. & T. WILL ENTER ERICSSON COMPANY

Arranges to Get Dominant Interest in the Swedish Telephone Concern.

RIVALS REDUCED TO TWO

Reports Indicate That Holdings Are to Be Acquired From Kreuger & Toll.

The International Telephone and Telegraph Corporation will soon complete arrangements to acquire a dominant interest in the L. M. Ericsson Telephone Company of Sweden, one of the two principal foreign rivals of the International organization. This will leave only the German Siemens & Halske Company as a competitor for foreign telephone business, outside of the General Telephone and Electric Corporation, which is sponsored by the Transamerica Corporation in this country.

While reports indicated that the substantial interest in the Ericsson company is to be acquired from Kreuger & Toll, which last year

AGREEMENT NEAR IN ERICSSON DEAL

Announcement by I. T. and T. and Ivar Kreuger Expected in Forty-eight Hours.

CONTRACTS ARE INVOLVED

Negotiations Include Production of Equipment as Well as Stock Acquisition.

Although reported as a passenger sailing on the Bremen for Europe on Saturday, Ivar Kreuger, head of Kreuger & Toll, is still in New York engaged in conversations with International Telephone and Telegraph executives and bankers with respect to the acquisition of an important interest by the International in the L. M. Ericsson Telephone Company of Sweden.

These conversations are understood to have reached the stage where an announcement is imminent, and some statement is expected within the next forty-eight hours. Bankers and International executives alike refused yesterday to com-

KREUGER BECOMES WORLD PHONE FIGURE

I. T. & T. Alliance With Ericsson Company Widens Activities of Match Monopoly's Head.

LARGE CHANGES EXPECTED

Standardization of Equipment, Hook-Ups and Division of Patent Rights Probable.

The alliance between the International Telephone and Telegraph Corporation and the L. M. Ericsson Telephone Company extends to the operation of telephone companies in many foreign countries and to the manufacture of telephone, cable and other communications equipment for the use of private and public telephone systems throughout the world.

The transaction has made Kreuger & Toll, which concern controls the

Headlines in the New York Times, 1931. A master spin doctor at work.
© *The New York Times Co.*

But when Kreuger described the deal, he made no mention of the LM Ericsson A shares. Instead, he concentrated on the ITT shares he was acquiring, and his seat on the ITT Board, to present himself as acquiring a position of commanding influence within ITT in return for the sale of some LM Ericsson B shares! As late as October 1931, the Managing Director of LM Ericsson appears to have been unaware of the true facts.

The deal unravels

The deal had two serious flaws.

The first concerned the Swedish law restricting non-Swedish ownership of real estate. A limited company was released from restrictions if a provision was included in its articles showing that less than 20 per cent of the voting rights of the company might be acquired by foreign citizens or foreign companies. At the merger in 1918, such a provision had indeed been included in the new company's articles. Legally, ITT could own no more than 157,000 A shares.

The agreement between Kreuger and ITT shows that both parties were well aware of this fact. ITT agreed that the shares should continue registered to Kreuger & Toll for the time being, and Kreuger & Toll agreed always to vote as instructed by ITT. There seems to have been a view that ITT might get away with a Swedish nominee owner – a Swedish bank, for example. Nominee share ownership was not illegal at the time. Presumably, the situation might, eventually, have had to be tested at law.

It never came to that, because, as it happened, the second flaw was more serious. Kreuger had dramatically exaggerated LM Ericsson's assets.

As 1931 drew to a close, the time came for LM Ericsson's final accounts to be examined by ITT, so that its cash requirements to operate in 1932 could be estimated for the audit. It emerged that LM Ericsson had substantial debts, and not much cash. Its bank debts alone had risen by 100 per cent over 12 months, and some of the cash its accounts represented it as having was in fact on loan to Kreuger & Toll. Kreuger and Toll figured substantially among its debtors. The ITT examiner left Stockholm distinctly underwhelmed.

Since the event, this area of the deal has attracted many comments. George Soloveylchic, for example, in his book *Ivar Kreuger* (London, 1932), said, 'How it is possible that the management of ITT, which included some of America's foremost bankers, did not discover this until then, is inconceivable'.

LM Ericsson's bankers were also worried. By 2 January 1932, Oscar Rydbeck was telephoning Kreuger in New York to explain that Skandinaviska Kredit AB was unable to extend LM Ericsson's credit. By the beginning of February, Kreuger was admitting that he could not finance LM Ericsson's outstanding commitments, and Rydbeck was making it clear to ITT that it would have to intervene in the financing of LM Ericsson.

It was clear to ITT that the deal would have to be cancelled. On Friday, 19 February, ITT told Kreuger so. On Saturday, 20 February, Kreuger had a 'breakdown'. A flurry of cables begged Rydbeck to come to New York with a member of the Wallenberg banking family. On Sunday, 21 February, the President of one of ITT's banks notified Lee, Higginson & Co., Kreuger & Toll's bank, of the problem. Lee Higginson professed itself unworried, and said it would help Kreuger to repay ITT's $ 11 m.

The desperate days …

But the word was out. Kreuger had other heavy repayments to make and loans to service, unrelated to LM Ericsson, and his credit had gone bad. Kreuger & Toll warned a Swedish Under-Secretary of State at the Ministry of Finance that, without help, it would go under. The Governor of the Bank of Sweden refused to act. Eventually, the Prime Minister intervened, and some credit was raised for Kreuger – enough to keep him going through the last week of February 1932.

But on Friday, 26 February, Kreuger received from ITT the written annulment of its agreement. It issued orders for the return of the 410,000 A shares and the 200,000 B shares it had received, and asked for the immediate repayment of the $ 11 m, plus interest at 6 per cent from 22 June 1931.

Kreuger had no hope of repaying the $ 11 m. He returned the orders, to avoid a tacit acceptance of the cancellation of the agreements. On Sunday, 28 February, he talked on the telephone to Oscar Rydbeck. He said he had not been well for a fortnight, but made an appointment to see Rydbeck on 4 March.

The banks tried hard to prevent Kreuger from cancelling his agreement with ITT, but on 3 March they gave him a free hand to reach a deal. Instead of meeting Rydbeck on 4 March, Kreuger sent ITT a letter accepting that the deals were off, and agreeing to pay back the $ 11 m with interest before 1 September. ITT was to keep the A and B shares as collateral until then. He asked ITT to continue its examination and audit of LM Ericsson's position, with a view to a possible new deal at some time in the future. Persuaded by the loyal Lee, Higginson & Co., ITT agreed.

That same night, Ivar Kreuger left New York on the *Ile de France* for Paris, to meet Rydbeck. His situation was unenviable. ITT had lost all confidence in him. So had any financial institution (except Lee, Higginson) which knew about his affairs. Throughout his last horrible week he was under pressure on other financial matters – not related to LM Ericsson, but if anything on an even larger scale.

The 'most satisfactory solution'

The *Ile de France* docked on 11 March. Kreuger took the train to Paris with some colleagues from Lee, Higginson & Co., and Johan Grönberg, the MD of LM Ericsson. He had a meeting in the evening, and the next morning, he shot himself. In a farewell letter, he wrote, 'I have made such a mess of things that I believe this to be the most satisfactory solution for everybody concerned.'

Johan Grönberg (1887–1974)

Johan Grönberg had headed the Kreuger match monopoly in Rumania before being brought in as Managing Director of Telefon AB LM Ericsson in 1930. After the Kreuger crash in 1932, he worked in the French LM Ericsson company, STE, until 1939, and thereafter was MD of LM Ericsson Kassaregister AB. He retired in 1958.

Dr Marcus Wallenberg Jr (1899–1982)

Executive Vice President 1927–1946 and President of Stockholms Enskilda Bank 1946–1958. Vice Chairman 1958–1969 and Chairman of the Board of Stockholms Enskilda Bank 1969–1971.

Chairman 1972–1976 and Honorary Chairman of the Board of Skandinaviska Enskilda Banken 1976–1982.

Vice Chairman 1933–1953 and Chairman of the Board of Telefon AB LM Ericsson 1953–1977.

The master negotiator who patiently unravelled the web of the master spin doctor. Ericsson owes its independence largely to Wallenberg's dealings – first with Sosthenes Behn, and then with Harold Geneen.

Mopping up

Kreuger's death left both LM Ericsson and ITT in a situation of unbelievable complexity. The unravelling process was interminable – in fact, it was not until 1960 that the situation could be regarded as normalised. But the essentials, if not the finer details, of the story can be quite briefly told.

The dilemma was almost farcical. ITT held 410,000 voting shares in LM Ericsson, when legally, as a foreign company, it could hold no more than 20 per cent of the voting rights. LM Ericsson, or strictly, Kreuger & Toll, could have recovered them by paying $ 11 m which it could not raise. Kreuger & Toll couldn't help: in fact, it filed for bankruptcy on 24 May 1932. The world economy was in a deep slump, and LM Ericsson was in enough trouble without the complexities of the ITT situation to distract it.

The first action was for Kreuger & Toll, acting on a proposal by the Government, to set up an investigating committee, the Nothin Commission. The committee included representatives of Kreuger & Toll, and of the creditors – among whom we may notice the names of Jacob Wallenberg and Martin Fehr.

On 19 April, the three major banks involved allowed LM Ericsson a breathing space until the end of July.

Winning an early battle

Of LM Ericsson's many major problems, one was paramount: an agreement had to be reached with ITT.

Eminent legal opinion was that ITT had a right to retain its LM Ericsson shares, as collateral for the $ 11 m, even though it could not exercise the full voting power they gave.

Jacob Wallenberg and Martin Fehr suggested a way out. They proposed that ITT should buy its shares at a price considerably above their current price. Only the proportion of shares which ITT could legally own would be registered to ITT. The rest would be registered to a Swedish buyer.

Instead of paying for them, ITT would deduct the cost from the $ 11 m it was owed. ITT would be reimbursed for the A shares bought on behalf of the Swedish buyer by the equivalent in B shares. Any balance would be ITT's claim on the bankrupt Kreuger & Toll.

Between April, when Wallenberg and Fehr made their proposals, and 9 December 1932, there were a series of discussions and agreements. The outcome was:

- ITT would renounce its entire claim for $ 11 m against Kreuger & Toll;

- ITT would receive 154,600 A shares and 455,400 B shares in LME (about 19 per cent of the voting rights);

- the banks (notably Svenska Handelsbanken and Stockholms Enskilda Bank) would receive the remaining 255,400 A shares;

There were two important provisos.

ITT wanted the legal restriction to 20 per cent ownership by foreign companies raised to 35 per cent, and stipulated that it should then be able to swap its B shares for A shares up to the new legal amount.

If the legal restriction could not be raised, ITT stipulated that it should be able to swap its 255,400 B shares for A shares, to be sold to Swedish nominees (through whom it would exercise voting control).

The Board of LM Ericsson agreed that it would prefer to change its Articles of Association to permit foreign nationals to own up to 35 per cent of the company, and applied for the change to be ratified. The request was approved by the King in Council on 26 June 1933.

18 years of guerilla warfare

LM Ericsson had won a major battle, but the war with ITT was still being waged. Behn had hoped to carve up the world such that ITT would give up Scandinavia and LM Ericsson would give up Britain and France and, ideally, Mexico and Argentina. By now, Marcus Wallenberg Jr was handling negotiations, and he told Behn bluntly that if that was to be the deal, all bets were off. In the end, Wallenberg not only solved the problem of the ownership of LM Ericsson but guaranteed that it could operate as a vigorous and effectively independent Swedish company. Even ITT could hardly resist his appointment as Vice Chairman of LM Ericsson in 1933.

LM Ericsson's other problems, and its recovery from the disastrous

financial position in which Kreuger had left it, are covered elsewhere. For many years (until 1941), shareholders received no regular dividend – and ITT retained its shareholding for far longer. Indeed, Behn was dead when LM Ericsson finally regained its independence, and Wallenberg found himself negotiating with the even more formidable Harold Geneen.

Working with Behn had been a struggle, in spite of the agreement that LM Ericsson should operate as a vigorous Swedish company. But LM Ericsson could play tough, too, and for the period 1946–49 actually voted Behn off the Board. Wallenberg recalled a dinner meeting scheduled in London during the Second World War which deteriorated so rapidly that it never got past the cocktail stage.

Victory: 1960

Freedom finally came, after a number of abortive attempts, in 1960 when Geneen agreed to sell. It seems likely that ITT needed the money, and certainly its holding in LM Ericsson had not brought it any vast return. Heading off any suggestion that the shares might be sold to, say, Philips or Siemens, Wallenberg declared that LM Ericsson would give them no Board places, but to the end Geneen said (at least) that he was considering selling the shares in America. Perhaps the final price Geneen negotiated, $ 22.7 m, or SEK 109 million, was higher than Wallenberg had hoped, but, as he himself pointed out, LM Ericsson's shares had risen considerably and the company was doing well. In the end, the deal was done on 16 February 1960.

As a press release issued at the time put it, 'Through negotiations conducted for the Swedish side by Dr Marcus Wallenberg, the whole of ITT's shareholding has been acquired, the B shares included in the holding being placed on foreign markets, and the additional A shares in firm hands in Sweden. Since the B shares only carry one-thousandth of a vote, the transaction means in practice that LM Ericsson has once more become a Swedish company and that an epoch in the history of LM Ericsson has been brought to a close.'

Ivar Kreuger remains an enigma. The man and his dealings continue to fascinate. There are those who believe that Ivar Kreuger was the victim of circumstance and of ruthless manipulators, others who claim that he became his own worst enemy in his struggle for power. In the 1990s, books continue to be published, the authors representing both sides. We shall probably never know the true, full story of the man who was Ivar Kreuger.

CHAPTER 6

Reconstruction

Recession and depression

The Wall Street crash in 1929 led to an economic depression which affected the whole world throughout the 1930s. One result was a pronounced decline in the growth rate of the telephone networks. In 1920, there were some 20 million telephones connected to the world's public networks. By 1930, this number had grown to about 35 million. But from 1930 to 1940, only some 7 million new subscribers had been connected, giving a total of just under 43 million. Indeed, during the initial years of the period, 1930 to 1933, the total number actually declined by 2.8 million phones, most of this in the US.

Another effect was that the privately-owned networks lost ground in the face of a general move towards nationalisation and the strengthening of the government-owned telephone systems. The exception was the US, where the networks remained in private ownership, but even there, many of the small operators were bought up by the Bell System and the other large operators.

In Sweden, the engineering industry suffered an acute export crisis, and the role of the domestic market became larger than during the previous decade. For LM Ericsson, the export markets declined, including sales to the LME operating companies, whose financial position was undermined in many cases. It became imperative to develop the home market.

Lay-offs and wage reductions

Typically, LM Ericsson's product range called for a high labour content in relation to raw materials. Labour became a natural target in the effort to reduce costs.

OPPOSITE: *Frosty morning – Swedish winter road, 1930s.*

In May 1932, the salaries of office staff were reduced. Eight per cent was deducted from salaries of up to SEK 4,800 per year, 10 per cent from salaries between SEK 4,800 and SEK 7,200, and 15 per cent from those above that range. There was no reduction of salaries below SEK 2,400. All bonuses were abolished also, which meant that employees in the top salary group suffered substantial cuts – over 20 per cent, in many cases.

Within the Group there were apparently slight variations in the reductions. An internal memorandum from the management of the Elektromekano company in Helsingborg reads:

Elektromekano, 30 May, 1932

To all employees.

Due to the general depression, which is now affecting us as well, the Board has decided that, from July 1 (or as soon as individual agreements allow) the following reductions of monthly and weekly wages will be introduced:

5 per cent on salaries up to 7,200 kronor per year
10 per cent on the part of all salaries above 7,200 kronor per year

No reductions will be effected if the resulting annual wage should fall below 2,400 kronor. The Board is convinced that all of the company's employees and workers, male and female, understand the necessity of this measure and the need to make sacrifices.

The pay reductions concerned all employees, both the workers in the factories (on hourly pay) and salaried staff in the offices. But some employees fared even worse since they were laid off.

Personnel statistics for the years 1931, 1934 and 1937 (Table 7) show the effects of the lay-offs. The numbers refer to the main factory in Stockholm.

Hans Theobald Holm (1877–1964)

After the death of Ivar Kreuger in 1932, the reconstruction of the company was put in the hands of Hans Th. Holm, MD 1933–1942. Mr Holm was described as the 'doctor of reconstruction' in Swedish industry at the time; and he came to LM Ericsson from similar jobs in his home country, Norway, and with other companies, among them Bofors, in Sweden. Along with the financial reconstruction of the company, the '30s involved abandoning the earlier strategy of building telephone concessions, and developing a new and more modern organisation. It was during this period that company headquarters and the main factory moved from central Stockholm to the new facilities in the Midsommarkransen suburb.

TABLE 7. NUMBERS EMPLOYED: Stockholm main factory

A: Workers

Year	Aged 18 and above		Below 18		Total
	Men	Women	Men	Women	
1931	1,500	753	184	27	2,464
1934	710	352	55	-	1,117
1937	1,359	839	200	70	2,468

B: Salaried staff

Year	Men	Women	Total	Total staff (A+B)
1931	416	112	528	2,992
1934	435	128	563	1,680
1937	671	222	893	3,361

Data selected from table in 'LM Ericsson 100 years', vol II.

Proportionally, lay-offs between 1931 and 1934 affected more workers than office staff. Similarly, the return to more normal conditions appears to have been more rapid on the office side. It is also interesting to note that the proportion of woman workers was increasing after the bad years – a reflection, in part, of the fact that female labour cost less than male.

The task of recovery

It was against this less than encouraging background that the company faced the huge task of recovery from the Kreuger catastrophe.

LM Ericsson's problems as a result of the Kreuger crash were many, and extremely complex. To begin with, it was necessary to reach an agreement with ITT. Next, ways had to be found to solve the immediate liquidity problems, and also to reach agreements with the banks providing credit, both in Sweden and abroad. There were also unresolved problems regarding the French and Argentinian subsidiaries, and there were outstanding debts related to the acquisition of Sieverts Kabelverk and to payments for Hultman's patent.

Furthermore, since Kreuger had transferred a large portion of LME's liquid assets to Kreuger & Toll, there were large claims against that company's estate in bankruptcy. It was also necessary to find a way of re-solving the Finnish telephone operations commitment, which required long-term loans.

The company did hold some strong cards, such as Ericsson Telephones Ltd in Britain, and the telephone operating companies in Mexico, Italy and Poland, but it was genuinely questionable whether LM Ericsson could survive as an independent company.

'Mobile phone service'
LEFT: *Jakarta, 1920s.*
OPPOSITE: *Italy 1930s.*

LM Ericsson in competition with its biggest shareholder

In the previous chapter we saw a settlement reached on ITT's share-holding in LM Ericsson, and how Marcus Wallenberg deflected Colonel Behn's plans regarding Mexico and Argentina. Wallenberg was also particularly insistent on defending LME's interests in France. In all, the outcome of these negotiations was the major settlement of December 1932, in which it was established that LME would remain an independent Swedish company. Behn's proposals for dividing the market, heavily to ITT's advantage, were rejected.

After the settlement, ITT owned a total of 34 per cent of the voting rights of LM Ericsson (277,151 A-shares and 332,849 B-shares).

From June 1933, ITT had three representatives on the board of LM Ericsson. One of the three was Sosthenes Behn. It was a unique situation: the company's most aggressive competitor owned the largest sharehold-ing. It was, however, a shareholding on which no dividends were paid for a long time; and even though ITT had more than one third of the voting rights in LM Ericsson, it would never exercise any influence over the Company. The involvement was, however, to pave the way for certain other types of agreements between ITT and LME in various parts of the

world. But, notwithstanding certain deals, from an LM Ericsson perspective ITT would be the company's most formidable competitor in all its markets through the following 55 years or so.

Rebuilding the foundations: SEB, SHB – and SEK

In May 1933, the new Board took over, with Waldemar Borgquist as Chairman. Hans Theobald Holm replaced Johan Grönberg as Managing Director. In addition, a special finance committee was set up, chaired by Marcus Wallenberg Jr.

It set to work to restructure LM Ericsson's debts.

Among the early successes were agreements with Sievert to extend the payment period for the acquisition of the cable company, and with Hultman for a delay in the payment of licence fees.

The situations in Argentina and France were more difficult to resolve. In both areas, Kreuger himself had been involved, incurring debts with shaky collateral.

France

In France, Kreuger had used shares in Swedish Match – now of rather questionable value – to underwrite a debt owed by Société des Téléphones Ericsson (STE) to Compagnie Générale d'Electricité (CGE). To stabilise the relationship, STE received a long-term loan agreement with repayment by instalments until 1939. A further guarantee was provided by orders to STE from the French PTT. LME itself had a claim against STE, which CGE insisted should be met by being converted into STE shares. And furthermore, immediately before it went into liquidation, Kreuger and Toll met its own liability to LM Ericsson in France by handing over its shares in STE. K&T also transferred to LME its own claims against STE; plus the Kreuger Group's claims on Grammont (one of the three companies which controlled the telephone market in France, to which Kreuger had lent some FFr 55 m against the security of Grammont shares). At the same time, LME wrote off a SEK 21.6 m claim against Kreuger & Toll.

Argentina

In Argentina, Mauro Herlitzka was on the warpath. LM Ericsson owed him 6 million Argentinian pesos, and now he was threatening to seize CSTT and sell it to ITT. LM Ericsson's negotiator, W. Borgquist, persuaded him instead to accept a repayment of 1 million pesos in December 1932, 1 million in January 1934, and 8 bills of exchange, each for 0.5 million pesos, payable between 1935 and 1938. As security, LM Ericsson offered its shares in Cía Entrerriana de Teléfonos (CET) and some CET bonds.

Gradually, in this laborious, piecemeal way, LME pledged its medium-term future to reduce its indebtedness. But there remained its obligations to the Swedish and foreign banks, and an involvement in Finland.

Finland

In 1932, the Finnish Parliament decided that the State should take over responsibility for all long-distance telephone operations. Until this time, there were two separate networks with two different owners – the Board of Posts and Telegraphs on the one hand, and Södra Finlands Interurbana Telefon AB on the other.

LM Ericsson owned 43 per cent of the shares of Södra Finlands Interurbana Telefon, and also a majority in several small local telephone operations.

After long negotiations, an agreement was reached between the Finnish State and LM Ericsson/Stockholms Enskilda Bank. The bank's important

Spanning the wide-open spaces: Argentina.

*Genoa, 1930s. It's hard to
separate the few phone wires
from the clothes-lines.*

role in this settlement was to provide the Finnish State with financing for both the buy-out of the LME interests and expansions in the Finnish long-distance network. During the discussions LME had also tried to get a sup-ply agreement clause included in the contract – a clause which would make LME the preferred supplier of equipment for modernising and extending the Finnish networks. The Finns refused, however, and the only result was a compromise wording to the effect that both parties wished to 'maintain the spirit of collaboration and excellent relations which had pre-vailed during negotiations'!

The banks

Marcus Wallenberg undertook the negotiations with the foreign banks. His first achievement was to get the repayment terms extended – for which LM Ericsson had to pay, of course, which meant increased indebt-edness to the Swedish banks. At the end of 1935, this stood at SEK 41.4 m, over and above the SEK 10.5 m in debts to foreign banks. In 1936, LME revised its credit terms with the Swedish banks yet again, with Stockholms Enskilda Bank (SEB) and Svenska Handelsbanken (SHB) as its largest sources of credit – which guaranteed them the bulk of LM Ericsson's banking business. This particular agreement lasted until 1940.

But by 1937, there was spring in the air. The world recession was be-coming less severe. The dividends from Kreuger & Toll's bankruptcy began to flow, and years of successful (if dividend-free) trading were making their contribution. The claims against the Kreuger & Toll Group turned out to be less insecure than was feared immediately after the crash. Out of LME's total claim of SEK 65 m in 1931, SEK 51.4 m was paid back in instalments, which meant that the Company's eventual loss was less than SEK 15 m.

At the end of 1939, LM Ericsson's debt was down to just SEK 12 m, owed to the Swedish banks, and it was time for normal business to resume. From 1941, LM Ericsson began to pay shareholder dividends on a regular basis.

It has been suggested that the banks, and Stockholms Enskilda Bank in particular (which before the crisis hardly figured as an LME bank), saw in the affair a virtually risk-free opportunity to acquire substantial holdings in a major Swedish enterprise. (With ITT, SEB and SHB controlled the voting majority in LME – and SEB actually represented ITT at General Meetings until 1945.) Well, maybe … but that's one of the things that banks are for. It is doubtful whether LM Ericsson would have survived at all without its banks and its bankers, particularly Marcus Wallenberg Jr, to steer it through the turbulence created by Kreuger. Banks and bankers worked very hard, and the labourer is worthy of his hire.

CHAPTER 7

1932–1940

Trading through thick and thin

W hile the sweeping-up operations were taking place, LM Ericsson had somehow to stay afloat. In fact, it had to put every ounce of energy into its markets, its trading approach and its technologies. The world was in recession for everybody, but LM Ericsson had its own particular, personal, black cloud: the muddle Kreuger had left. LM Ericsson had to try that much harder than everyone else – and did.

Hanging on in the key markets

Mexico and Argentina

The problems arising from the competition with ITT in these countries were of a very special character. In Mexico, LME was somewhat stronger than ITT; while in Argentina, the acquisition of the Unión Telefónica gave ITT the upper hand. In Mexico, the two companies operated in parallel in several cities, including Mexico City. The competition was ruinous, and there was no interconnection between the networks. In Argentina, the two competitors had their respective concessionary areas, but, again, there was no interconnection.

After protracted negotiations between the parties, an agreement in two parts was reached in November 1933. The first part concerned the exchange of telephone interests in Argentina and Mexico. In Argentina, LME would hand over a number of interests which operated in competition with Unión Telefónica in the Buenos Aires area, and would receive in

OPPOSITE: Stockholm 1931. Cable splicing by Televerket.

139

Surveying for long-distance lines. Peru, 1934.

return the San Juan network, plus a cash payment. The agreement would reduce the number of LME subscribers in Argentina from some 33,000 to about 21,500. As payment for the Argentinian interests, ITT would transfer to LME about 46.6 per cent of the ordinary shares of its Mexican operator, Mextelco.

The result of this agreement was that LME would end up with a significant minority shareholding in ITT's subsidiary Mextelco.

However, implementation of the agreement had to be deferred. There was criticism from both the Mexican and the Argentinian Ericsson companies, who called for modifications, and even within ITT there were calls for postponement and further negotiations. When the Mexican Government suggested its own conditions for the physical consolidation proposed for the Mexeric and Mextelco networks, negotiations slowed to a crawl.

Then, late in 1935, a new Mexican Government introduced new tariff conditions which would make a privately-operated telephone service economically impossible. New discussions between LME and ITT took place in May and June of 1936, and a supplementary agreement was signed on 12 June 1936.

During the latter part of 1936, the exchange of interests in Argentina took place. LME's Argentinian holding company received a block of shares in Mextelco which were subsequently (1938) transferred to LME.

In Mexico, on 18 June 1936, the Minister of Communications instructed Mexeric and Mextelco to arrange for interconnection of the two competing networks – so that Mexeric subscribers could call Mextelco subscribers and vice versa. Such interconnection was gradually implemented throughout the country, except in Mexico City, where the work was delayed because of World War II. It was to take until 1948 to complete.

But even after 1936, the situation in Mexico continued to cause problems. The negotiations that each of the companies was holding with the government proved abortive, and late in December 1937, ITT cancelled the agreements of 1933 and 1936, and returned to cutthroat competition. This proved as unsatisfactory as ever, and eventually ITT asked for new negotiations. These began in Berlin in 1938, and got as far as an agreement that a joint company should be formed. At first, the sticking point was management, but late in 1939 Colonel Behn abandoned his demand for management authority, and in January 1940 a status quo agreement to this effect was signed. For a time, the competition stopped.

In Argentina, a geographical settlement with ITT and Siemens to eliminate competition confined LME's operations to certain provinces in the eastern and western parts of the country, including such cities as Mendoza, San Juan, Tucumán and Salta. The number of subscribers served

Mexico 1930: inaugural call to New York. Bernhard Wahlqvist at attention.

fell and the company had to give up its plans to break into the densely populated areas surrounding Buenos Aires. But with its dramatically improved situation in Mexico, where it now held 47 per cent of the shares of the ITT company, Mextelco, LM Ericsson could feel reasonably satisfied.

There was yet another hitch, however, when ITT, apparently instructed by the State Department, went back on its agreement and demanded a majority of the votes in the consolidated company proposed – a demand which was, of course, not accepted by LME.

In all these long-drawn-out discussions, the chief players were Colonel Behn and Marcus Wallenberg Jr. In 1941 the beginning of a solution emerged, when Gunnar Beckman, the managing director of Mexeric, managed to secure from the Mexican Government tariff increases which would provide greatly improved conditions. Both companies were now able to operate with a profit (and with identical tariffs) and LME began to receive some dividends on its 47 per cent shareholding in Mextelco.

A Grand Opening

In the '20s and '30s, the opening of a new telephone exchange was always a great event. In a small town or village, the telephone was something new and wonderful. And the operator and LM Ericsson would make the most of such an event, to make sure that it was celebrated with due pomp and dignity.

One story comes from somewhere in Latin America. The cables and lines had been installed, the new automatic equipment had been set up and tested, the first couple of hundred subscribers had been signed on. For the grand opening there was a band, refreshments and a somewhat lengthy speech by the mayor. Then the parish padre and his entourage performed the rites: first, the long-distance board and the operators were given blessings, then the main frame and the diesel engine and batteries – and finally the automatic switch room.

The acolyte swung his censer, and the priest spoke his blessings and sprinkled holy water generously over the equipment. Which, maybe, he should not have done. It became a sparkling ceremony, but it took a while to mop up the water and replace the blown fuses.

Everybody agreed, however, that it was a fine, worthy and enjoyable event.

LM Ericsson and the stamp collectors – Latin America

Alongside these dramatic developments in Mexico and Argentina, LM Ericsson had also been busy in most of the other countries in Latin America.

In the 1930s, there were local LM Ericsson companies in some countries; in others, business was based on networks of representatives or agents; and in some, both arrangements operated simultaneously. Technical support was provided by engineers from LME in Stockholm, resident or visiting. In most countries, the existing telephone networks had originally been set up by the local authorities, the 'municipios', and many of these were later bought up by one or more of the dominating operators, often US-, Canadian- or British-owned.

The agents in the different regions were referred to as 'stamp collectors'. Their objectives were to sign up as many European and American manufacturers as possible – the stamp collection – with exclusive sales rights for their region, and offer the wares to the various customers. LME telephone products would be just one line out of a variety of merchandise: refrigerators, electric motors, power plants, steel, etc. They were unwilling to buy stock, and to a large extent they were unwilling to do much work: for any major sales, they expected LME and its resident engineer to make up technical projects and offers, instal the equipment and generally look after the customer. The agent would appear at contract-signing time.

In 1935, Göte Fernstedt arrived in Colombia as the resident LME representative. At the time, there was a cartel agreement with Autelco of Chicago, which was unfortunately based on earlier sales of manual equipment, and so excluded LME from many of the the most promising regions. Only Antióquia, Caldas and Tolima remained. The only major city left to LME was Medellín in Antióquia.

By 1935, LME had been successful in getting contracts for automatic exchanges in Caldas, Manizales and Armenia. A small exchange had also been contracted (1932) for the town of Honda on the Magdalena river. The next objective was Medellín, for which city the first contract for 500-point selector exchanges was signed in 1937. For LME this was a significant coup.

Göte Fernstedt's goal was to open up the market further. In Bogotá, the capital, Autelco had taken over an old concession from the Marconi company, with CB telephones and manual exchanges manufactured by Peel-Connor in the UK. The network was run down and badly overloaded, causing a brisk black market trade in telephone numbers, with a rise in commercial and decline in residential subscriptions. The need for extension and automation was obvious.

By around 1940, Autelco was getting a bit nervous about the cartel it had entered into with LME: the US government was becoming increas-

Tactics for a quick sale

During his time in Colombia, Göte Fernstedt also managed to fit in a couple of other visits. In early 1938 he and his wife, Maggie, were returning to Colombia by ship. They made a stopover in Curaçao to follow up a proposal which had been submitted. Göte met the Governor, Peet Kastel, and explained that his wife was expecting and that he had but a short time. Mr Kastel immediately understood the need for a quick decision and the order for the Punda exchange in Willemstad was signed.

ingly critical of such arrangements. Since the war had started, and LME had great difficulties in getting shipments from Sweden, Autelco decided it was a good moment to sell its concession to the local authority. To Fernstedt, this was good news, but the risk was that the sale would be accompanied by a materials-delivery agreement in Autelco's favour. Fernstedt set to work to demonstrate the advantages of open-tender competition.

In 1942, Autelco sold Empresa de Teléfonos de Bogotá, ETB, to the local authority, the 'município'. There was no delivery agreement for Autelco. In 1943, the LME technical office, which by now had moved from Medellín to Bogotá, was upgraded to company status as Compañía Ericsson Limitada, and the cartel agreement with Autelco was cancelled. The road to Bogotá was open.

In the end, the first Bogotá order was not obtained until 1946, when Göte Fernstedt had transferred back to Sweden. But at the same time there was a breakthrough in Ecuador, with orders for Quito, Guayaquil and Cuenca.

LM Ericsson was tightening its grip on the most valuable market open to it during the 1930s, Latin America, and laying the foundations for a very strong presence in the years to come.

There remained Brazil, where the Companhía Telefônica Brasileira, CTB, had been the dominating telephone operating company since 1923. CTB had operations in all the major cities in the states of Río de Janeiro, Guanabara, São Paulo, Minas Gerais and Espírito Santo, and it bought its telephone equipment from Autelco and STC (ITT) in Britain. LM Ericsson was thus cut off from the most important markets in Brazil, but was active in selling outside the CTB areas. A sales company, Sociedade Ericsson do Brasil Ltda (EDB) had been set up in 1923 in Rio de Janeiro.

An important task for Ericsson do Brasil at the time was to keep a watch on the market and in particular on CTB, while actual sales were insignificant. Then, in 1934, EDB hired as a salesman Wolf Kantif, with responsibility mainly for the north-eastern areas of the country, outside the CTB concessions. Wolf managed to persuade local interests to form telephone companies, which then bought equipment from LME in Sweden. In 1935 Kantif signed contracts for LME's automatic exchanges in the towns of Fortaleza, João Pessoa, Campina Grande, Parnaíba and Natal in northeastern Brazil, and the following year in Manaus on the Amazon. A few years later some towns further south were added, such as Goiânia in 1940. LM Ericsson had managed to build a secure foothold in Brazil.

OPPOSITE: *Mexico c. 1923: Line construction staff posing for the camera.*

Focus on profit, at home and abroad

In the '30s, as we've discussed, LM Ericsson was forced to concentrate more and more on its home market. The results of this strategy are illustrated in Table 8.

TABLE 8. SALES FROM THE PARENT COMPANY

	1931	1932	1933	1934	1935	1936	1937	1938	1939
A: In per cent									
Sweden	26	44	59	58	58	64	64	65	62
Exports	74	56	41	42	42	36	36	35	38
B: Total									
million SEK	29.6	16.7	17.2	18.3	19.5	24.4	34.8	42.2	45.3

From tables in 'LM Ericsson 100 years', vol. II.

The sales numbers for the foreign factories are not shown, but even so, the importance of the markets outside Sweden is obvious, and export remained vital.

The largest export market was Poland, followed by the Scandinavian countries, and then by Holland and Italy. Towards the end of the decade, the Latin American markets saw some recovery in Mexico, Argentina and Brazil.

The LME manufacturing companies outside Sweden accounted for about one third of the Group's total sales in the years immediately before the crisis. This proportion increased in 1932 and thereafter, to reach some 50 per cent in 1934. It was not until 1939 that this percentage declined towards the 1930 level.

The flight from concessions

The strategy of building telephone concessions, which had been so marked during the 1920s, was abandoned during the 1930s. Governments were increasingly inclined to regard telecoms as their business, and not to confine themselves to setting tariffs. As for LME, the capital so necessary to establish and grow new concessions was impossible to come by in the aftermath of Kreuger and in the world economic recession.

Similarly, the company's policy of establishing new manufacturing companies in foreign countries was distinctly cautious. The exceptions were the setting up of a Danish company, Dansk Signalindustri A/S in 1935; and the move of the Polish factory to a new location, in Radom.

In 1937, the Hungarian company was sold to Standard Electric and in 1939 an agreement was signed for the sale of the Austrian manufacturing company to Austrian interests.

During the 1930s, the British company, Ericsson Telephones Ltd, in Beeston, continued as the most important production unit abroad – indeed, around 1935, Ericsson Telephones' sales were of the same order as those of the main factory in Sweden. Elektrisk Bureau in Norway was second in size.

The most important competitors were ITT and Siemens & Halske. During the 1930s, these concerns also abandoned their strategies of acquiring new concessions. They followed similarly cautious investment policies, and concentrated on making their operations profitable. As we have seen earlier, all three parties were active in trying to eliminate competition through cartels and market agreements.

In 1937, LM Ericsson sold its concession in Smyrna (Izmir) to the Turkish government.

In 1939, there now remained under LM Ericsson's control telephone-operating companies in Mexico (94,000 subscribers), Argentina (28,000), Italy (80,000) and Poland (140,000 subscribers). The Polish operation, PAST, was not only the largest but also by far the most profitable. Both the Polish and the Italian operations required only minor investments during the 1930s and were, on the whole, not subject to damaging competition.

The cartel solution

LME's sales to its own telephone operating companies were, in principle, protected from competition. In other important markets, the company tried to protect its sales by setting up agreements with its competitors.

As we've seen earlier, in Great Britain, where the Post Office made Strowger technology a national standard for switching systems, the market was divided between five manufacturers, 'the Ring'. LM Ericsson's membership of the Ring meant that LME could rely on supplying one-fifth of the switching material purchased every year.

In Denmark and Norway, ITT and LME reached an understanding not to compete in the field of automatic telephone exchanges, and that the companies would market their respective systems only in areas where they had already provided manual systems. LME thus became barred from both the Copenhagen and the Oslo districts. The Norwegian company, Elektrisk Bureau, had a stronger position and was able to expand strongly during the 1930s.

The Italian market was regulated by a quota agreement. LME was sole supplier of telephone exchanges to the operating concession in Zone V, Southern Italy and Sicily, but also had 25 per cent of the market in Zones I–III. Similar quotas were set for manual and trunk exchanges, private exchanges and telephone sets.

The 1935 agreement in Colombia with Autelco (represented by the Associated Telephone & Telegraph Company, ATT) was mentioned earlier. The market outside the ATT concession areas was divided between the companies – ATT's task was to 'deter' Siemens Brothers and Siemens & Halske from entering the market, while LME was 'to use its best endeavours' to keep ITT out. Should the competitors manage to enter, the quotas would be reduced accordingly.

In Portugal, LME reached an agreement assuring the company of 33 per cent of the telephone apparatus market, but no automatic exchange equipment.

Today, the word 'cartel' has ugly overtones of big business carving up markets for their own benefit, without any particular care for customers and consumers. True, there are still plenty of cartels in operation, but they tend to keep their arrangements rather quiet. We seem to prefer the philosophy of competition. But in the 1930s, cartels were still regarded as a natural way of doing business: by assuring income to their members, they took some of the risk out of capital-intensive enterprises, and allowed an orderly approach to investment. In technology, cartels smooth the way for the faster adoption of standards. We must remember that if one of the alternatives to a cartel is competition, the other is monopoly. The world has still not yet learned the trick – if there is one – of balancing the interests of suppliers and consumers.

Generally speaking, through all these market agreements LME was in a relatively good position, and could look forward to growing production, sales, and profitability. Still, from LME's point of view, the 1930s was a period of more rigidity and protectionism than the 1920s. The many international cartels were to a large extent the consequence of the earlier period of cutthroat competition and the depression, and, of course, they all came to an end with the outbreak of the Second World War.

The technology of the times

During the 1930s the company's core business – to use a modern term – was clearly telecommunications equipment. Development of the 500-point system went on continuously, aimed at adding new features, adaptations to new market requirements and improved designs to enable more cost effective production.

The following overview discusses other main lines of product development during the period.

Transmission equipment

Loading coils

Transmission equipment is designed to make efficient use of different transmission media. An early example is the deployment of loading coils to enable telephone conversation over longer distances. Such devices were inserted at regular intervals into each pair of wires to reduce attenuation for the voice frequency band.

Michael Pupin, a professor at Columbia University, New York, invented the loading coil, and was granted a patent in 1899.

LME started to manufacture loading coils in 1928. They were based on a toroidal core, pressed out of fine-grained iron powder, around which wire was wound. Toroidal cores were still manufactured in the 1950s, but then new ferrite material with greatly improved characteristics came into use, and dimensions could be reduced to 20 per cent of the original size. A coil unit weighing 7.5 kg in 1930 had been reduced in weight to 175 grams in 1975.

From 1933, LME supplied Televerket and the Swedish Railways with

Submarine telephone cable being laid in Stockholm.

their entire intake of loading coils. In the 1930s, the yearly output averaged 25,000 coils; in 1969 it reached a record, with 500,000 coils. Since then, new cable technology has reduced the need.

In the '60s, LME also started manufacture of loading coils in Mexico, Spain, Australia and Brazil.

Amplifiers, carrier systems – and more market agreements

Coil loading allowed the transmission of speech over distances up to about 100 kilometres. With the invention of the electron tube, and its use in amplifiers for telephony repeaters, very much longer distances could be spanned, and more conversations could be carried.

The human voice was, by early agreement, defined as having a range between 300 Hz and 3400 Hz, which became the standard requirement for transmission equipment. The carrier principle – frequency division multiplex – modulates different speech channels with different carrier frequencies, allowing several telephone circuits (conversations) to share the same pair of wires (one pair for each direction).

From the US, where it began in the 1910s, the development of carrier systems moved to Germany. The first commercial systems came into operation in the 1920s over open-wire lines. LME started to develop carrier systems in the '20s, and its first system started up in 1922 in Finland. It was an open-wire, single-channel system, later extended to two channels.

1924 saw a remarkable achievement, with the supply to Televerket of carrier equipment for the Örebro-Sundsvall route (550 km). This was followed in 1926 by equipment for the Stockholm-Umeå route (850 km). The originator of these systems was Mauritz Vos.

Vos was at the time technical manager at LME's Svenska Radiobolaget (SRA). In 1931 the SRA telephone engineering department was, together with Vos, transferred to the parent company. Vos remained in charge of transmission systems development until his retirement in 1950, and thereafter acted as a consultant for several years.

These early systems did, however, have certain weaknesses. The imperfections of the early electron tubes caused interference between channels and crosstalk, which limited the number of channels the systems could carry. In 1934, H.S. Black and H. Nyquist at Bell Labs in the USA developed the negative feedback principle, which laid the foundation for rapid improvements in carrier systems for both open wire and cable.

LME provided a 16-channel system for submarine cable to Finland in 1938 and a 12-channel system to Televerket for the Gothenburg-Helsingborg-Malmö line in 1940. This latter system was later extended to 24 and 29 channels respectively.

1940 also saw an 8-channel system brought out, which became widely used in the Swedish network. This system was mainly used on existing loaded cables. Methods were developed for the re-balancing of such cables originally designed for low frequencies. The 8-channel system played an important part in the extension of the Swedish long-distance network during the war, when copper and lead for making new cables were scarce. The pioneers in this work were Stig Jansson of Televerket and Ragnar Stålemark of LM Ericsson.

During this period, transmission technology made significant advances and took on increased importance. In 1932–34, agreements were reached between manufacturers covering loading coils, amplifiers and carrier systems for overhead lines. These agreements assured LME of a monopoly on the Swedish market, but of limited quotas only (around 5 to 10 per cent) elsewhere, except in the Baltic states, Finland, Poland and the Soviet Union. The chief competitors were ITT and the German companies Siemens, AEG and Felten & Guillaume.

LME also introduced carrier systems for underground cables, and was able to market these products outside the quota system, but in 1938 a new comprehensive quota arrangement was agreed. LME received a high proportion of the Swedish market and its own operating companies, plus between 7 and 12 per cent of other markets, but since large markets were excluded (British Empire, France, China, Japan, USA, Canada and Italy) the agreement had some limitations.

In general, only LME was allowed to manufacture transmission equipment in Sweden, though an agreement was reached at the same time allowing Standard Radiofabrik (ITT) to start making radio valves.

Private telephone exchanges

Private telephone exchanges, often called PBX, serve company offices, organisations and so on. A PBX is used for internal connections and, usually, connections to and from the public network.

PBX stands for Private Branch Exchange. The designation 'branch' means that it is a private system with interconnection to the public network. If a PBX is operated manually ('operator-served'), it is a PMBX; if it is automatic, a PABX. These old definitions are today becoming obsolete, but to tell the story means bringing them to life for a few chapters.

The first private exchanges were manual. They were built up around one or more manual switchboards of the same sort as those in public exchanges. The change from magneto to central battery operation occurred at the same time as in the public systems, beginning at the turn of the century. At the time, up until, say, the mid 1920s, there were still relatively few private switchboards: the private sector – business enter-

A manual private exchange.
Carlton Hotel, Stockholm.
Photo from the 1950s.

prises and government departments – was comparatively small and was, after all, well used to working with mail, messengers and telegraph.

With the advent of automatic switching, first introduced in public networks, it was natural to build automatic private exchanges as well. Initially, these were used for internal calls only, which meant that those extensions which were permitted to make and receive outside calls had a second telephone, served by an operator. By the 1920s, development had caught up and automatic branch exchanges could transfer calls to the public network, while incoming calls had to be handled by an operator.

LM Ericsson built its first automatic private exchange system in the early 1920s, based on small, 25-line stepping switches. A series of branch exchanges serving from 20 up to a few hundred extension lines were on sale by the end of the decade.

Until this time, automatic branch exchanges offered no additional features, but around 1930 Siemens & Halske introduced a series of PABXs, the 'Neha-Zentralen', with several new facilities, of which the most important were enquiry and transfer. The solutions were protected by a German patent. The functions of enquiry, transfer and alternation between external and internal lines were performed with the aid of an earth button on the extension telephone.

These new facilities were practical and desirable, and soon became popular with customers. LM Ericsson and Televerket worked together to find a method that could not be blocked by the German patent. The solution was to use the dial of the extension set for signalling instead of the earth button. This solution also had the advantage that standard telephone sets could be used in private branch installations as well.

The new services, and others, were implemented in a new series of PBX systems introduced in the early 1930s and based on the 500-point selector. The series included standard exchanges for 90, 400 and 900 extensions, and larger installations could be supplied. There was a big demand for these exchanges from Televerket, and the larger versions were also particularly successful abroad. Extensions and new sales coninued through the 1950s.

In the mid-'30s, the company brought out a switching element known as the XY switch. The XY switch was a compact, flat, step-by-step device with 10 positions in each direction. It was used for a series of private exchanges for up to 270 extensions. The XY switch also found limited applications in small public exchanges.

In 1946, the manufacturing rights for the XY switch were licensed to the Stromberg-Carlson company of the USA (of Swedish descent, to judge by the names). Stromberg-Carlson developed a telephone exchange system for the US independent rural market, and the first such exchange was cut into service in August 1947 for the Kittanning Telephone Company, in Worthington, Pennsylvania.

The exchange was equipped with 80 subscriber lines serving 250 subscribers – clearly, the company used a lot of multi-party subscriber connections.

Centrex

The small private branch exchanges were comparatively costly, and since the mechanical gear required fairly frequent inspection and overhaul, maintenance costs were relatively high. In the late '30s, LME started the development of a centralised automatic branch exchange (CABX), the concept being one of combining equipment for several private branch exchanges in the local telephone exchange building. The extensions and operator lines were connected directly to the local exchange.

The first (and only) customer was the Rotterdam Telephone Administration, which ordered an installation corresponding to 3 x 460 extensions and 500 exchange lines. Shipment and installation were interrupted by the outbreak of the Second World War, and the installation finally went into service in 1946. Two further contracts followed.

The CABX in Rotterdam was an elegant solution, but ahead of its time.

During the 1950s, the Bell System in the USA introduced its Centrex system, which from a functional point of view was essentially the same as CABX. In the USA and Canada, the Centrex service has become very widely used, and it is only in the last decade of the 20th century that other solutions for providing customer premises telecommunications and data services have started to dominate the market.

Announcing machines

At the beginning of the 1930s, LM Ericsson introduced a first version of an announcing machine, a simple device to deliver brief recorded messages. The machine was photoelectric and based on the sound-film technology developed a few years earlier. The sound was recorded on a disc with the aid of a special recording apparatus.

Different types of recording machines were developed – some for short messages to reduce the work of operators, others for more complicated announcements, such as the time of day.

Time-announcing machines had several (usually 5) discs holding separate hour, minute and ten-seconds recordings. They were first installed in Stockholm and Warsaw, and over the next twenty years were introduced in some 70 different telephone administrations. The service became popular with the public and, for administrations with subscriber call metering, an important additional source of income.

In the 1950s a new generation of announcing machines based on magnetic recording came out. The age of photoelectric recording was over, and LM Ericsson discontinued the business.

Business on the home market

LM Ericsson never had the luxury of a protected home market for its key products. An exception, as we've seen, was transmission equipment, but for other telecommunications products Sweden, from LME's point of view, was a minor (but obviously important) market.

Telephones and exchanges

During the difficult years of the early 1930s, sales of telephone sets to Televerket dropped as Televerket increased its own production capacity.

A time announcement machine, popularly known as 'Miss Clock'.   *And Miss Clock herself, Ebba Beckman, in 1967.*

Televerket's policy was to protect the employment of its own staff, and outsource for reserve capacity only.

In the field of automatic telephone exchanges, the situation was also becoming disturbing. As we know, Televerket had built two crossbar exchanges, in Sundsvall and Limhamn, outside Malmö, on a trial basis and carried out extensive testing. At the beginning of the '30s, Televerket had completed development and began producing a series of crossbar equipment for rural and private branch exchanges. LME's XY switch, mentioned above, never found a market in Sweden. In addition, LME's sales of the 500-point system dropped, but picked up to some extent towards the end of the 1930s. And by that time, LME was also producing some crossbar exchanges to Televerket's specifications.

In loading coils and amplifiers, LME was able to keep its lead – thanks mainly to the cartel agreements mentioned earlier.

LME had a home market for private automatic exchanges, sold to large companies, institutions, government offices etc, but these were strictly private systems which did not connect to the public network. Private branch exchanges, with the exception of the larger installations, were provided primarily from Televerket's own factories.

Other 'private' installations

From its early days, LM Ericsson had extensive installation operations in Sweden. Much of this work was under contract to Televerket, but the company also carried out a range of installation and service undertakings on the 'private market'.

To look after the installation work, a new company, LM Ericssons Anläggnings AB, was formed in Stockholm in 1929, with local offices in Gothenburg, Malmö and Sundsvall. In 1931 this company took over from LM Ericsson the sales of private market products, and responsibility for the sales exhibition at Södra Kungstornet in Stockholm. The name of the company was changed to LM Ericssons Försäljningsaktiebolag (FÖB).

In 1934, FÖB's responsibilities were extended to certain markets outside Sweden, and in the following year a company called Production Control Ltd was established in Great Britain. Production Control's business was the marketing of the centralograph and time-control products described in the next chapter.

Cooperation with ASEA

Power equipment and communications equipment were often combined in a single contract. As a result, the installation business saw competition between LME and ASEA. In 1933, a cartel agreement between the two companies was reached, 'arranging' dividing lines and allocating to LME all communications and signalling contracts; the production of communications equipment, power capacitors, wall sockets, etc.; and the sole right to produce electricity meters, measuring instruments, railway signalling equipment, electric bulbs and electron tubes for telegraphy, telephony and radio. ASEA agreed to discontinue its collaboration with German and French electricity meter manufacturers.

A further field of collaboration defined in the 1933 agreement was the cable sector. LME, with both the Sievert company and the Älvsjö cable works, had great strengths in cable. ASEA owned the Liljeholmen cable works. LME and ASEA set up a collaboration agreement that allocated the markets. Both companies were also members of the European Power Cable cartel.

Final adjustment of 500-point selectors.

In 1931, Svenska Elektromekaniska Industri AB, Elektromekano, had been added to the LME group to secure the supply of copper wire. Elektromekano also made electric motors and generators, and so competed with ASEA. In 1933, LM Ericsson sold all its shares in Elektromekano to ASEA, although the company formally remained under LM Ericsson Group management all through the 1930s.

As far back as 1914, LME had received a contract to manufacture electricity meters for the firm Zander & Ingeström. LME designed a meter built on the Siemens-Schuckert German patent and started deliveries in 1916. This was a decidedly interesting business at the time in view of Sweden's intensive electrification programme, but the competition from German manufacturers was intense. LME tried to get the government to set up increased customs protection, but failed. Still, the meter business in LME continued through the 1920s, with mixed success. The business improved with the purchase of Sieverts, since electricity meters were often sold in connection with power cable installation and wiring, and in the '30s, the company increased its efforts to develop improved (and more competitive) meters. These improvements, along with a change in tariff policy, and the agreements with ASEA, eventually bore fruit. In 1936, LME entered into a cartel agreement with Siemens and AEG, and at the same time became linked to an international price-fixing cartel formed in Paris in 1934. LME was allocated 50 per cent of the Swedish market. Prices had been forced down but were now successively raised within the cartel up to the outbreak of war.

Cash registers and electron tubes

Another example of the company's strategy of diversification during the 1930s was Svenska Kassaregisteraktiebolaget (KRB), which was formed in 1936 to exploit the market for cash registers. KRB brought out its new product in 1938, but it was many years before its sales made any significant contribution.

Aktiebolaget Svenska Elektronrör (Swedish Electron Tube Co) was set up in late 1938. The threat of the coming war made it imperative to secure domestic manufacture of electron tubes, both for the expanding broadcast radio market and for transmission systems for long-distance telephony. Production did not start until the end of 1940.

The true Ericsson touch

To strike a more cheerful note in the story of the depressing 1930s, the following episode may help. Sven Ture Åberg joined LME in 1927 as a graduate engineer and became something of a network-construction expert, travelling widely, especially in Latin America, and then eventually based in Argentina. On the point of leaving for a holiday in Sweden, he was reached by notice of his dismissal (hard times!). But immediately before this telegram, an earlier communication had instructed him to visit Chile, Peru and Equador on his trip home, and he saw no reason to change these plans.

After visiting Chile and Peru, and there discussing several business opportunities,

he arrived in Quito, where the installation of a manual exchange was in progress. The customer there – the 'municipio' – had requested that the canalisation pipes be caulked with bitumen, but then the cables had become stuck in this glue. Sven Ture successfully designed a little wagon which could be pulled through the pipes to force the cables loose. He later obtained a patent for his wagon. By now, things in Stockholm were looking a little bit brighter and Sven Ture was rehired.

In Ecuador, he also visited Guayaquil and Cuenca, in the mountains, to investigate market potential. To get to Cuenca, he had to travel by mule. From Ecuador he eventually returned to Stockholm.

In 1934, he travelled to Persia and successfully managed to set up an LME business. At the same time, he became interested in oriental rugs, an interest which soon developed into a serious and beautiful collection. But it was Latin America that was his main interest and, at the end of the '30s, the USA. He and his family moved to New York and he opened an LM Ericsson sales office. Then came World War II, and the main task was to serve the Latin American markets, while the US market had to wait. Some twenty years after he was fired, Sven Ture Åberg became MD of LM Ericsson.

Other products

Other products manufactured by LM Ericsson in the '30s were time-recording and time-control equipment; fire alarm systems; and various types of signalling products. These, and other products taken up at the same time, demonstrate LME's strategy: to use a wider portfolio of products to compensate for the weak export market and competition from Televerket at home.

The 1933 cartel agreement described for the Swedish market for electrical supplies was a reaction to the depression of the 1930s. The number of such arrangements, in many different business sectors, increased significantly during the period. The Government view was not entirely negative – it considered that cartels could work well and be of benefit as long as they were not abused. This view would change considerably after World War II.

Explosive demand for a hot product

After the Kreuger crash, the company made great efforts to keep the workshops going and avoid redundancies.

It undertook the manufacture of precision barometers, altitude meters and book-keeping machines, among other products, and short runs of such products as camp beds, kitchenware, and safety-razor components.

One day, an inventor and his agent appeared, to place an order for the manufacture of 10,000 frying pans – the world's best pans, of a new non-stick design. The excellence of the design was authenticated by a certificate from one of the best-known restaurateurs – the legendary Ekegårdh at the Operakällaren in Stockholm. He had tested the pan, and found it outstanding.

In the factory, the costs were calculated, and a contract to supply 10,000 pans was reached with a well-known wholesaler – part delivery of a couple of hundred units as soon as possible.

The first hundred pans were duly shipped and taken round by travelling salesmen, who would arrange demonstrations in the kitchens of prospective buyers. But after a week or two, the pans were returned, with an angry letter from the wholesaler cancelling the contract. The complaint was that when heated, the pans began to jump about, and in some cases they had even exploded, throwing bits of pork and herring about the place.

The explanation was simple. The frying pan had a double bottom, enclosing a layer of insulating material. The prototype had been made by hand, with the seam just hammered together. The seam was not air-tight, as it was when the pan was factory-made and the parts were joined by machine.

Worse – the insulating compound was a bit damp, so when heat was applied, steam was produced and the pressure soared to explosion point.

The wholesaler wanted to cancel, but

eventually, after the factory had improved the design, came back with orders for 500 pans at a time. Orders stopped when the 10,000th pan was shipped – but times were getting better, and LM Ericsson could return to making telephones.

159

Network construction

From the beginning, LM Ericsson has been engaged in the construction of the wire and cable networks, or outside plant, which form the backbone of any telephone network. In the very early days, the outside plant was built with open wires, strung up on poles or buildings. Later, the telephone cable came into use, and in the towns and cities the cables were laid in concrete ducts. A telephone cable could contain anything from some twenty to several hundreds of pairs of paper-insulated copper wire, all sheathed in a mantle of lead.

LM Ericsson salesmen were most often engineers. For a city or town with no existing network, the salesman and his team had to be capable of preparing a full project: outside plant, a suitable building, switching equipment, power plant with batteries and telephone sets.

For the outside plant, it was essential to know where the prospective subscribers were located: this meant maps of the town, and then physical inspection. The LME man would walk up and down the streets and note the number of households (making a guess as to whether they would want and could afford a telephone), shops, offices, etc. With all these data entered on the maps and taking into account suitable growth factors, the cable network was planned and costed: primary cables, distribution cabinets, secondary cables, distribution points.

In countries such as Mexico and Argentina, the concessionary companies naturally had outside plant departments, and network construction was an ongoing regular task. But when LME had sold a telephone exchange with network to a town in, say, Brazil, an engineer/foreman had to be sent out from Stockholm to arrive at the same time as the cable and other material; local labour would be hired for the digging and installation; and then another engineer/foreman would arrive, probably from Sweden again, to instal and test the switching equipment, power plant and all the little details that make up a working exchange.

In the 1930s, long-distance line-construction was added to the business of the outside plant department, which at that time mostly meant stringing wire along pole lines through the wilds of the country – forest, desert, mountains. They were tough people.

As business in a country grew, installers were permanently employed by the local company, and joined the community. At the directors' and salesmen's level, business contacts were maintained and carefully nurtured, and many friendships grew out of these contacts. And naturally, as a Swede, or a salesman of any nationality, got to know the local people, he made friends, learnt the language and became part of the LME/customer community.

Defraying expenses

LME people were naturally encouraged to maintain good relations with the customers' people. And, at times, it was appropriate for the company to be generous. One small incident from Bogotá is recorded:

Rune, a not exceedingly adventurous outside plant foreman, was instructed to invite his colleagues from ETB to a simple meal, for friendship's sake, and also to try and get some details of ETB's current plans.

The following day he presented his statement of expenses (5 guests).

1	paquete 'Luky' (Lucky Strike)	Ps.	0.35
2	paquete 'Piel Roja' (the favourite local cigarette)		0.30
6	piquetes (a Bogotá soup, very good)		3.00
66	Bavaria (local beer, very good)		26.40
	propina (tip)		3.45
		Total Ps.	33.50

(The Colombian peso at that time, 1943, stood at about half a US dollar.)

Just a few days later, we are told, Rune was able to use his contacts when the LME telephone service was suddenly interrupted. Rune was sent over to the exchange, and within 15 minutes service was restored.

Göte Fernstedt, Rune, and many other LME personnel in Latin America and elsewhere, were, of course, cut off by World War II. Home leave had to be put off, letters were slow and uncertain, the telegraph service was uncertain (and expensive). But few suffered any real hardships. In other parts of the world it could be much worse, but on the whole, as Sweden maintained its neutrality, Swedes for whom return to Sweden was impossible managed without undue suffering.

Artist's impression of LM Ericsson's
new headquarters and factory at
Midsommarkransen, 1940.

Some domestic matters

Housekeeping: Thulegatan to Midsommarkransen

For many years the Company's offices were at Thulegatan 5 and Södra Kungstornet, where the first factory had been built in 1885, while production was in the block of buildings corresponding to Thulegatan 15–19. Over time, the business took over the entire city block, and constructed a series of extensions to the existing building. By 1929, space was running out and overcrowding was severe. Further growth would soon require a new building.

In 1930, the Company bought a large piece of land in Midsommarkransen, an as yet undeveloped area about 5 kilometres southwest of Stockholm. Then came the difficult years of the 1930s and it was not until 1937 that the plans were revived. LME made an agreement with the Municipality of Stockholm that the Municipality should provide, among other facilities, roads, public communications, water and sewers; and

LME undertook to build a plant. A contract for the construction of the new plant was signed at the beginning of 1938. The move from Thulegatan to Midsommarkransen took place gradually during 1940.

The new premises had a factory floor area of 50,000 sq m (compared with 36,000 sq m at Thulegatan) and office space of 13,000 sq m (compared with 7,000 sq m). The facilities at Midsommarkransen are still the headquarters of the company. Substantial additions have been made, but today the original manufacturing areas have all been converted into offices.

Hans Theobald Holm outside the new Midsommarkransen office, with architect Ture Wennerholm.

Radiola
Radiola
Radiola
Radiola
FÅR EJ STROPPAS!
FÅR EJ STROPPAS!
Radiola
Radiola

CHAPTER 8

1940–1945

The war years

War!

The outbreak of war in 1939 had immediate repercussions for LM Ericsson, creating a whole new set of conditions and challenges. The Polish market and the PAST operations were lost immediately after the start of hostilities as Poland was overrun. Soon connections with many other markets were interrupted or seriously hampered. Circumstances in Sweden changed drastically as industrial conditions were increasingly determined by economic and political developments driven by the war.

The most notable impact of the war on Swedish industry came from military rearmament and the build-up of preparedness to meet potential hostile actions against the country, at the same time as trading channels with the rest of the world were disrupted.

Rearmament increased the Government's defence spending tenfold: during 1941–1944, about 60 per cent of the Government's budget was for defence. Another aspect was the build-up of government control of the country's resources and economic life.

Second World War in Stockholm. No petrol, horse-drawn delivery of Radiola radio sets. The horse´s name was Hallberg.

Vulnerable internationally …

As an international concern, LM Ericsson was vulnerable in several respects: property was destroyed or confiscated by the warring powers; parts of the Group were cut off, which made effective management and internal financial control difficult; and political change altered conditions for operations in many countries. The availability of many raw materials also became a problem for the manufacturing operations in various countries.

The following table illustrates how the Company's sales were affected during the war years. The amounts refer to sales by the parent company, including the Älvsjö cable works.

TABLE 9. WARTIME SALES (including cable)

	1939	1940	1941	1942	1943	1944	1945
	SEK m	SEK m	SEK m	SEK m	SEK m	SEK m	SEK m
Sweden	28.2	30.4	33.3	39.8	44.9	58.5	32.3
Exports	17.1	15.3	16.3	17.4	16.1	9.9	12.5
Total	**45.3**	**45.7**	**49.6**	**57.2**	**61.0**	**68.4**	**44.8**

From 'LM Ericsson 100 years', vol. II.

The figures show how the war increased the proportion of sales to the domestic market.

A closer look at a breakdown by area and country of the foreign sales (excluding those of the Älvsjö cable works in this instance) is given in Table 10.

As the war developed, shipping became more and more unpredictable. After April 1940, when Denmark and Norway were occupied by German forces, virtually all shipping from Sweden across the North Sea and the Atlantic was affected by the blockade. For a time, an alternative route was available via the port of Petsamo in Northern Finland. LM Ericsson was permitted to utilise the very limited freight space to export some 200 tons of telephone equipment and 50 tons of cable. When even that route was closed, there followed a period of six months during which the Company was able to export practically no equipment, the exception being a shipment of 30 tons to the Dutch East Indies via Leningrad, Baku, the Caspian Sea and Iran!

The Swedish Government held discussions with both the Germans and the British, and reached agreement on certain exports and imports. From the beginning of 1941, limited shipments were allowed through the west coast port of Gothenburg, the 'safe conduct traffic' ('lejdtrafik' in Swedish). There were of course numerous restrictions, among them one limiting Swedish ships to calling at neutral ports only. Until the entry of the USA into the war, this safe conduct traffic allowed shipments to the USA, and the South American markets could be reached. After the USA entered into the war, only Argentina and Chile were permitted as trading partners for Sweden, which meant problems for LME's shipments to Mexico and the other Latin American countries. There was an inevitable build-up of finished goods, though the Mexican company had taken large deliveries before the difficulties increased. The Latin American companies were even compelled to buy some equipment from the USA.

Within Europe, Spain and Portugal were accepted by Germany as trading partners, and played an important role in LME's exporting. Apart from the Gothenburg traffic, practically the only markets remaining for LME were the Axis powers and the territories occupied by them, and to some extent the company was there able to offset the loss of sales in markets controlled by the Allies. But as the war developed, trade with these areas too was increasingly disrupted.

TABLE 10. WARTIME EXPORT SALES FROM MAIN FACTORY, BY GEOGRAPHY (SEK million)

	1939	1940	1941	1942	1943	1944	1945
Europe	**8.3**	**6.6**	**7.7**	**9.4**	**10.3**	**5.4**	**4.6**
incl. Holland	1.2	1.0	1.3	1.6	0.6	0.3	0.1
Italy	0.6	0.9	0.7	1.2	0.5	-	-
Poland	1.5	-	-	0.02	0.3	0.3	-
Germany	0.09	-	-	0.8	0.6	0.1	-
Portugal	0.9	0.2	0.9	0.2	0.5	0.7	1.0
Rumania	0.1	-	0.08	0.3	1.6	0.2	-
Spain	-	-	0.1	0.7	1.1	1.1	-
Norway	1.1	0.9	1.1	0.9	1.0	1.1	1.5
Denmark	0.2	0.07	0.1	0.3	0.5	0.2	0.6
Finland	1.9	3.2	3.2	2.7	2.7	0.9	0.5
America	**4.6**	**6.5**	**7.0**	**6.9**	**3.3**	**4.1**	**5.7**
incl. Mexico	2.7	2.0	2.8	1.0	1.8	2.5	1.3
Argentina	0.9	0.4	1.5	2.8	1.2	1.0	1.2
Brazil	0.5	0.2	0.8	0.7	0.2	0.2	1.5
Bolivia	0.03	-	1.0	-	-	-	0.9
Colombia	0.1	3.6	0.1	0.08	0.1	0.02	0.4
Uruguay	0.08	0.1	0.5	2.2	-	0.06	0.1
Asia	**1.2**	**0.5**	**0.3**	**0.3**	**1.8**	**0.3**	**2.0**
Africa	**0.9**	**0.3**	**0.08**	**0.3**	**0.3**	**0.06**	**0.01**
Australia	**0.1**	**0.02**	**-**	**-**	**-**	**-**	**-**
Total	**15.1**	**13.9**	**15.1**	**16.9**	**15.7**	**9.9**	**12.4**

The numbers shown tell us very little about the value of sales. In today's money, it would, of course, be much larger. It should also be remembered that, especially during the initial years of the war, inflation was high in Sweden. A further observation is that the figures for 1945 were strongly affected by a metalworkers' strike from February to September of that year.

From 'LM Ericsson 100 years', vol. II.

During this period, Finland was LME's most important export customer. The demand was strong and the trade channels were kept open, though Finland's lack of foreign currency limited the import of telephone equipment. As a result, LME decided to expand its Finnish production, primarily of telephone instruments, and a new factory was constructed in Helsinki. At the end of 1944, this factory employed over 100 people.

Sales to the Company's telephone operating companies during the war years were, in absolute terms, roughly the same as during the years before the war. But as a proportion of total sales they declined, along with other export sales, due to the growing importance of domestic sales.

... healthy at home

By 1940, deliveries to Telegrafverket had fallen to less than SEK 10 m, from some SEK 15 m a year earlier; but by the following year, they had risen again, and reached about SEK 20 m in 1944. This represented about one third of the company's production. This was mainly due to the continued growth of the Swedish telephone network during the war years, in terms of added subscribers, expansion of the long-distance network, and conversion to automatic operation. By 1942, 50 per cent of the subscribers in Sweden were connected to automatic exchanges.

The bulk of what LME supplied to Televerket was automatic exchanges. The 500-point system was rapidly being installed in provincial towns; and extensions were carried out in major cities such as Stockholm and Gothenburg. In the late '30s, LME had also been manufacturing the Televerket crossbar system for rural exchanges, but this production ceased. Next in importance came loading coils and amplification equipment for the long-distance network, and deliveries of telephone sets. The telephones were of the bakelite type, and between 1941 and 1944 a total of over 270,000 sets were supplied.

Rearmament fuels expansion

The growth of the Swedish market was, however, largely attributable to the demands of Swedish rearmament.

Rearmament affected the whole Swedish engineering industry. About 25 per cent of Sweden's industrial capacity came to be engaged in the production of defence equipment, which in turn meant that almost 90 per cent of the equipment needed was manufactured within the country.

LM Ericsson's deliveries consisted of air defence and air raid warning systems; aeronautical and measuring instruments; telecommunications equipment, such as field telephones and field exchanges; and ordnance equipment.

The last item needs some explanation. As part of the national effort, the different engineering companies were assigned production quotas of specific ordnance material. To LME fell the manufacture of ammunition: by April 1940, some 15 to 20 per cent of the telephone factory's workforce was engaged in making ammunition and, increasingly, machine gun parts.

The company at first worked as a subcontractor to the Carl Gustafs Stads Gevärsfaktori, the government factory in the town of Eskiltuna producing rifles and small arms for the Forces. By 1940, LME was manufacturing complete machine guns – involving some 500 workers and 4,000 square metres of space, including space for testing the guns. This production reached such a scale that the new factory in Midsommarkransen became inadequate, and the company re-rented its former premises at Thulegatan. The machinery was mainly supplied by Gevärsfaktori on lease, but was later purchased and moved to Midsommarkransen.

By the Spring of 1941, the operation had reached a capacity of 15 standard machine guns per day.

The war also effectively cut off foreign competitors from the Swedish market. This favoured the position on the home market for several different LME products – it was referred to at the time as 'the greenhouse effect'. One example is electricity meters. The main competitor had been

An Ericsson wartime product.

Signaler som *måste* höras

Plötsligt skär tyfonernas korta, skarpa tjut genom bullret på gatorna ... det växer till ett enda infernaliskt fortissimo, som överröstar spårvagnarna

som efter hand vunnits, ha de ursprungliga anläggningarna förbättrats och utökats, så att vi nu ha fullständig trygghet inför alla rimliga eventualiteter.

Part of the war effort in Sweden: from an information booklet about air raid alarm systems.

Siemens & Halske, with a production capacity ten times that of LME. When the Siemens factory in Nuremberg was destroyed by bombing, the most serious competitor was out, and LME was able to capture the lion's share of the Swedish market. The disappearance of Siemens also opened up opportunities to sell limited numbers of meters in some other markets, such as Spain, Bulgaria and South America. It was decided to move meter production to new premises in Ulvsunda, a Stockholm suburb, and in 1945 a new company was formed, LM Ericssons Mätinstrument Aktiebolag, ERMI.

Aktiebolaget Svenska Elektronrör, SER, formed in 1938 as a fully-owned LM Ericsson subsidiary, had started manufacture of radio valves at the beginning of the war, and was another example of the greenhouse effect. Initially, this company produced valves for the telecommunications operations of the parent company – transmission equipment; but as imports dried up, it also began to make radio valves for the Swedish market. The technological difficulties were considerable, especially since it became necessary to find substitutes for certain raw materials that had become scarce. But by 1943, the company was becoming uncertain about its future after the war, when competition would return, and an application was made to the Government for tariff protection.

Similar uncertainties affected the makers of other components. Radio receiver manufacturers found it very difficult to obtain capacitors, for example – the only manufacturer was Ericsson's AB Alpha, and Alpha's output barely met the needs of LM Ericsson and Televerket.

There were, however, some entrepreneurial responses to the opportunities created by shortage. In 1942, the leading radio receiver manufacturers (Moon Radio, AGA Baltic, Gylling & Co. and Luxor, plus four smaller manufacturers) set up a new company, Radioindustrins Fabriksaktiebolag, in a modest workshop at Kungstensgatan in Stockholm to make electrolytic and mica condensers. Sales were good, but by 1945 the company had yet to make a profit. When the war ended, the radio manufacturers could return to importing their components, and lost interest in manufacture. Renamed simply RIFA, we shall meet their company again in Chapter 10.

An opportunity for diversification?

The SER operation provides an example of an operation which company management had to consider in the longer term: to what extent should LM Ericsson be involved in 'extraneous' business, which over time might not be viable?

During the first, uncertain, period of the war, the number of workers at the main factory gradually fell, from 3,500 at the end of 1939 to about 2,800 in the second quarter of 1941. The number thereafter gradually rose again, to equal the pre-war peak in the second quarter of 1942. For the rest of the war, LM Ericsson experienced what was, in effect, a war boom. On the whole, production capacity was fully utilised, and so the question of further diversification took on a different character: should other, non-telecommunications, production be enlarged to exploit the favourable, but no doubt temporary, conditions? Among activities started up at this time was the production of coin-counting and encryption machines; and there were, we are told, more or less serious discussions about introducing other new products – banknote counters, electric razors, record players. Part of management was eager to expand, another part recommended a return to 'pure' telecommunications.

Discussions of product strategy do of course come up periodically in a company such as LM Ericsson. The observation we may make regarding such deliberations in those times is that the problem to be solved was primarily that of filling the factory – we have a factory, can we make this or that item, and at a competitive price? Very little appears to have been said about the market – how do we market and sell these new products? The soul of the company was still in the factory, primarily a telecommunications factory.

As early as 1943, there was also serious discussion about a proposal to reduce the number of workers again gradually, to dampen the effect of a feared post-war depression. Such pessimistic views were not uncommon, especially among older managers who had experienced at first hand the depression years following the First World War.

But with the rising volume of orders from 1944 onwards, the company took a more optimistic view of the future. It became a very busy organisation, with its hands full in matching production to the inflow of orders, and the debates about diversification faded. This was a turning-point in the history of LM Ericsson. There was no longer time to invest in new activities, or the need to do so. LM Ericsson was developing into a company dedicated to telecommunications.

This change in direction coincided with the appointment of a new managing director. Hans Theobald Holm had come in as MD in 1932, after the Kreuger debacle. His job had been to clean up and re-structure the company, a task he had performed with a firm hand. Now, in 1942, he was succeeded by Helge Ericsson, an engineer who had worked in telecommunications all his life. From 1912 to 1928, he had worked at Telegrafverket, heavily involved in, among other things, the automatisation of the Stockholm telephone network. Then he was in charge of LME's telephone operations department for a couple of years, returning in 1930 to Telegrafverket as Director of the Nynäshamn factory. From 1939 to 1942, he was Director General of Televerket.

Once again, the company had a 'telephone man' leading it. He also brought valuable experience from his war-time work with the National Industry Commission, the government's tool for solving the acute supply problems that now beset Swedish industry.

Logotypes

From 1926 the parent company trademark was the well-known circular design with the classic telephone and the name Telefonaktiebolaget LM Ericsson. During the 1930s certain products carried a simpler logotype – the name Ericsson. This was also used as identification for several of the LM Ericsson subsidiary companies. Around 1940, the exact time is not recorded, a new official trade mark was designed, as shown.

This logotype, and the original classic circular design, existed together through to 1982 when the now well-known design was introduced (page 306). During this time there were also many variations on the theme in use and subsidiary companies marked their products and their company stationery in many different ways. Branding had not yet become a matter of life and death.

Helge Ericsson (1890–1953)

From 1942 to 1953, Helge Ericsson was the head of LM Ericsson, coming from a position as Director General of Televerket. Helge Ericsson guided the important relationship with Televerket, especially during the difficult war years when the company had to depend on the Swedish market to a large extent. During this period too, the crucial question of developing a new switching system was decided in favour of the highly successful Ericsson crossbar system. Helge Ericsson's time at the helm became a period of substantial expansion.

Helge Ericsson having a word with Marcus Wallenberg.

The effects of the war on LME's international operations

Poland and the loss of PAST

The loss of the Polish operation, PAST, at the beginning of the war was a serious setback for the company. Discussions were initiated with the German postal administration over compensation for LME's investments in the Polish networks. But despite the intervention of the Swedish foreign office, no agreement was reached. After the war, the new Polish government nationalised PAST in 1946, and again negotiations started over the termination of LME's involvement and compensation for its losses. A relatively favourable agreement was reached, including part compensation, a supply agreement for new equipment, and licence agreements.

LME also made claims on the government of the Federal German Republic in 1958, seeking compensation for losses incurred during the years of German occupation. For many years these claims were rejected on principle, but a final settlement was reached in 1966 with an award to LME of DM 1.1 m.

Through turmoil to the status quo in Italy

In Italy, the American-dominated operating companies in the three northern concessions were seized by the authorities early in the war, but the
German fourth zone and the LME concession in the fifth zone were permitted to continue operations. The FATME factory was partly reorganised
for production of war equipment. When Southern Italy became a theatre
of war in mid-1943, operations immediately became more difficult. During
the fighting, large parts of the network and many exchanges were destroyed, and in Rome the FATME factory was seriously damaged in 1944.

In the Spring of 1945, ITT suggested that all the Italian telephone networks should be consolidated under American management, which
would ensure American credits for reconstruction. This would mean that
LME might lose its operations, and LM Ericsson lobbied the Italian
government vigorously to preserve the old zone arrangement. By late
1945, the new de Gasperi government had injected greater stability, while
the American government was cooling somewhat in its support of ITT. In
New York, LME's managing director, Helge Ericsson, met Colonel Behn,
and the parties agreed to continue the cartel agreement from before the
war, which, it was pointed out 'had had an extremely beneficial effect on
the Italian market'. LME in Italy emerged relatively unharmed from the
political and military turmoil of the war.

The UK: increased independence, increased sales

In Britain, Ericsson Telephones Ltd was threatened with seizure under the
Trading with the Enemy Act of 1939 in the event of Sweden's being invaded by Germany. To minimise this risk, LME sold a part of its shares in ETL
in 1940, reducing its share in the British company to below 49 per cent.
This reinforced the British subsidiary's natural tendency to act rather
independently. ETL could now increase its sales in Britain and its colonies
– and indeed, at the end of the war, a review of the agreements between
the two companies gave ETL even greater freedom to expand its international business.

ETL's most important customer during the war was the Royal Air
Force. ETL supplied the RAF with radio equipment, while also undertaking large repairs of Post Office telephone equipment damaged by bombing during the Battle of Britain. The company reported satisfactory profits
through the war years. The subsidiary, British Automatic Totalisators Ltd,
was sold off in 1941.

A safe haven for Ericsson's assets in Latin America

In 1940 LME formed a holding company, Corporación Teleric, to which were transferred LME's shares in its Latin American operations, primarily those in Mexeric and Mextelco, and in CSTT in Argentina. Through these transactions, approved by the Swedish Exchange Control Office, practically all of the Company's assets in Latin America were taken out of Sweden. The purpose was to save these parts of the Group if ever Sweden were to be drawn into the war and cut off from its operations in the Western hemisphere. The move was initiated in February 1940, when the Finnish front was broken and Soviet troops were advancing, but the real threat was occupation of Sweden by Germany. Sweden managed to avoid direct involvement in the war, and so Swedish property could not be seized by either side as belonging to the enemy. Sweden, and LM Ericsson, continued to trade with both sides. LME factories in England and Italy for example became heavily involved in the manufacture of war material. But if Sweden had been drawn into the conflict, the balancing act would have become impossible, and the Group would probably have been cut in half. It was for this eventuality that Teleric was formed.

Teleric was registered in Panama, with its head office in New York. Complete duplicate sets of the company's product documentation (schematics, specifications and production documents) were included in the material transferred to security storage in New York.

The Government of Argentina was pro-German during the war. Exports from Sweden were accordingly permitted, and the Company's networks in Argentina could be expanded.

In Mexico, too, the situation for foreign investment improved when Mexeric was allowed to increase its call charges. But there was concern about the growing political and economic influence of the USA, and a risk was perceived that ITT might gain an advantage in terms of new concessions and financing. At this time of the war, 1941, Sweden was regarded by the US Government as part of the German sphere of interest, which made the company's bargaining position weak. The new Mexican Government was, however, not prepared to upset the status quo – and the telephone operations continued as before, with the two companies agreed on limited competition.

During the war years some new, small, concessionary companies were added to the LM Ericsson Group. In 1943, CSTT, the Argentine subsidiary, bought a majority shareholding in Sociedad Telefónica del Perú S.A. The acquisition enabled LME to supply a new automatic exchange to Arequipa, Peru's second largest city. The new company had its head office there, with other operations in Cuzco and Mollendo in southern Peru.

For similar reasons, LM Ericsson took over some minor concessions in towns in Brazil to which automatic exchanges had been supplied. The most important were those in Manaus on the Amazon and João Pessoa in northern Brazil. These concessions were sold in 1952 and 1955.

The withdrawal from Eastern Europe

During the 1930s, the East European countries had been systematically tied to Germany by trade agreements, and Swedish industry found it increasingly difficult to maintain its presence. With the war, conditions became even more difficult; and with the establishment of the Communist regimes in these countries, LME was forced to complete the withdrawal from Eastern Europe which had begun with the loss of the operations in Russia in 1917. We have mentioned the loss of the concessions in Poland and the sale of the Izmir network in Turkey. Now there were added the loss of factories in Estonia, Poland and Czechoslovakia, while the factories in Hungary and Austria had been sold and sales companies in Romania and Yugoslavia were closed down.

Lunchtime entertainment with the LM Ericsson men's choir 'Mikrofon', 1962.

A tough time for individuals

During the war years, large numbers of Swedish men were called up for military service for varying periods of time, in many cases more than two years. At LM Ericsson there was initially a generous compensation scheme for salaried staff, but by April 1940, new rules had been established. No salaries were now paid, but the Company introduced a benefit programme with the following undertakings:

No family to support	25 per cent of cash salary
One other person to support	50 per cent of cash salary
Two other persons to support	65 per cent of cash salary
Three or more persons to support	75 per cent of cash salary

The sum of these benefits plus the state allowances was not to exceed the normal salary from the company – if it did, the benefits would be adjusted.

In April 1940, 116 salaried staff and 419 workers were called up. Workers were not offered company benefits, and had to depend entirely on state allowances.

The numbers of LME people called up declined during the remaining years of the war, since the company became defined as part of 'the War Industry and of major importance for the country's military and economic defence'.

By 1945, there were 3,204 workers and 1,321 office staff employed at the parent company. For four years there had been rising discontent among workers in the Swedish engineering industry, over both the level of wages and the central control of wage-setting. Within the trade unions there were strong conflicts of opinion. The militant faction within the union was rooted in the communist party, which was gaining followers in the wake of Soviet military and political successes in the war – a fact also reflected in communist gains in the general election of 1944.

The conflict within the unions came to a head during wage negotiations in early 1945. It ended in a serious dispute and the most serious industrial action in Swedish history – some 119,000 engineering workers were on strike from 5 February to 7 July. The agreement finally reached resulted in an increase of the minimum wage by 8 öre per hour for certain categories of young workers, plus some other minor benefts.

Work at LME's factories was stopped for five months, and this had serious effects on the Company's business. Sales were 35 per cent down, and the efforts to keep production in step with growing demands were jeopardised. Profits from production dropped by some SEK 8 m. At first sight, LM Ericsson might not seem in the best shape for meeting the post-war boom – yet the next decade and a half were to see expansion on a greater scale than ever before.

CHAPTER 9

1945–1969

Expansion into crossbar

As peace returned, a much-changed world was slowly to emerge. For LM Ericsson, the first task was to re-establish normal relationships with its markets, and intensify marketing and development activities. It was again an open question whether the company could hold and increase its position in the markets. It became a time of technological revival, strengthening financial resources, and increased sales efforts.

In most countries, the need to rebuild, repair and extend telephone networks was urgent. By today's standards, telephone density worldwide was still dismally low, as Table 11 shows. There was plenty of potential.

Not only was the telephone density low, in 1950 a large part of the installed base still consisted of manual systems, dependent on operators. And even in 1950, virtually all trunk calls were still handled manually, though telephone network operators were beginning to foresee the change from manual to automatic working in long-distance traffic.

LME's main product for building automatic exchanges was the 500-point system, AGF. It was perceived as marginally more expensive to produce than the Strowger system, but maintenance costs were markedly lower. The same was true for the other large competing system, ITT's Rotary.

The installed base of AGF systems in 1945 amounted to some 1.2 million lines in operation. These networks would, of course, grow as new subscribers were added and continue to constitute a significant market for the company, but the system's advantages were probably no longer advanced enough to allow LM Ericsson to break into new markets.

Installing crossbar, London, 1971.

TABLE 11. TELEPHONE DENSITY
Selected countries and world total.

Number of telephones per
100 population.

	1930	1950	1970
USA	16	27	56
Sweden	8	23	54
Switzerland	7	18	45
New Zealand	10	18	44
Canada	14	20	44
Denmark	10	16	32
Australia	8	13	30
Norway	7	13	28
Great Britain	4	10	25
World total	**2**	**3**	**7**

By including figures for 1970, we get a picture of the dramatic extension of the telephone networks that eventually took place.

Selected data from 'LM Ericsson 100 years', vol. II.

The switching scene

In 1921, Televerket's system choice had set Ericsson off on its long and fruitful commitment to the AGF system. But the crossbar switch principle Reynolds had suggested in 1913 and Betulander and Palmgren had patented in 1919 had not been forgotten.

In the '20s in the US, the Bell System was using the 'panel system' – a machine-driven system with register control – for large metropolitan areas. But Bell Telephone Laboratories, BTL, was also probing new solutions to the problems of switching, and was aware of the work with crossbar systems going on in Sweden. In 1930, a study delegation from BTL visited Sweden and Televerket, and was able to purchase a few crossbar switches at the same time.

This, and no doubt other considerations, led to a substantial development effort at BTL. In 1937, there were articles in technical journals describing the new system, and certain BTL patents were recorded. The first AT&T 'Crossbar No 1' exchange was opened in Brooklyn, N.Y., in 1938. It was built with indirect control for large metropolitan exchanges, and the information available showed that Bell Labs had applied the link-connection principle with register and marker control that had been brought out by Betulander and Palmgren nearly 20 years earlier.

Meanwhile, Televerket, too, had been busy. It had installed crossbar in Sundsvall in 1926 and in Limhamn in 1928 in direct-driven, not link-connected, exchanges.

Televerket had perfected the crossbar switch invented in the US, while AT&T had perfected the link system with register and marker control, originally developed in Sweden.

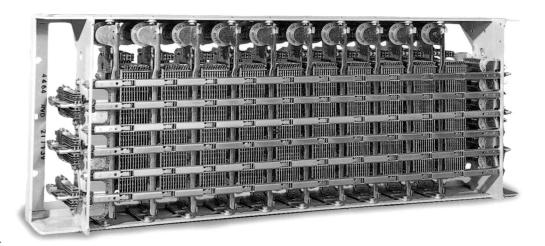

The crossbar switch.

By the '30s, even Ericsson had hands-on experience with crossbar. In 1935, it began the manufacture and installation of a number of rural exchanges for Televerket, though the crossbar switches were supplied by Televerket's factory. In 1940, when Televerket had introduced crossbar switches in the registers for the AGF system but had limited production capacity, LME had an opportunity to start making the new switches as well.

The Ericsson crossbar decision

Discussions within the company about the need for its own new telephone exchange system started during the war. In the early '40s, Ericsson was seeking a solution to the question of small switches, for rural exchanges and for private systems (PBX). Alongside the AGF, LME had the so-called XY switch, a step-by-step device, but it was proving costly in manufacture and XY systems had not shown themselves very competitive on the market. For small systems, the possibilities with crossbar seemed encouraging and in 1943 LME decided to start its manufacture of crossbar switches.

Certain modifications were worked out together with Televerket, but an important point was LM Ericsson's decision to build not only the 10-line capacity switch with 5 crossbars, but also a 20-line capacity version with 6 horizontal crossbars.

If the company were to follow the crossbar path into large systems, there were new problems to be solved. At the time, traffic engineering – in particular the dimensioning and structuring of linked switch arrangements – was not very advanced, and the Second World War had prevented any exchange of information with the USA.

Here, however, Ericsson had a major advantage in the work in Sweden of Conny Palm and Christian Jacobæus, two of the world's most advanced traffic researchers.

The father of traffic research was A.K. Erlang, a Dane, working in the first two decades of the century, who made important contributions to the understanding of the nature of telephone traffic and its representation in mathematical terms.

In Sweden a new generation of traffic researchers grew up in the late 1930s, led by Conny Palm. Starting in 1936, Palm tackled numerous problems in traffic research. In his doctor's thesis, published in 1943, he abandoned Erlang's concept of statistical equilibrium and found results of a more general nature.

Karlsson metering

Dr S. A. ('Svante') Karlsson became known for his invention of 'Karlsson metering'. In his doctor's thesis, he introduced a method of multi-metering (repeated pulses to the subscriber's call meter of a frequency to correspond to the distance of the call) which greatly simplified the equipment design by applying the start of the pulsing in a random manner. He proved that, statistically, the method was fair and did not cause over-charging.

The Swedish Traffic Machine

In his studies, Conny Palm included the traffic characteristics of 'gradings', typical of the electro-mechanical switching systems. Grading was a way of adjusting the hunting capacity of the selectors (in the 500-point selector system this was 20 outlets) to the required number of trunks in the route. As gradings of only limited sizes could be studied by theoretical methods, Palm suggested the construction of a 'traffic machine'. The Swedish Traffic Machine was built jointly by Televerket and LM Ericsson under Palm's guidance. It was designed for simulations of gradings with sequential hunting, as in LME's 500-point group selectors. The machine, completed in 1952, was a form of analogue computer, built specifically to study telephone traffic problems, and was the first in the world to produce results of sufficient accuracy.

Further steps for studying traffic engineering problems were taken by performing simulations in digital computers, the first results of which were presented by researchers at LM Ericsson in 1955.

When the war ended, Conny Palm visited the USA to study, among other things, how far Bell Labs had advanced in link-connection calculations. He found that Bell had used a pragmatic approach in deciding on its switch arrangements for the Crossbar No 1 system, and had been able to validate its rough approximations by measurements in the pilot Brooklyn exchange. But at LME, looking to an international market with very great variations in traffic handling requirements, it was desirable to find mathematical expressions that might directly be used for studying and defining linked switch groupings.

In the late 1940s, Christian Jacobæus of LM Ericsson was able to systematise crossbar link connections, and in his doctor's thesis published in 1950, *A Study of Congestion in Link Systems*, he presented methods for calculating traffic capacities with sufficient accuracy for practical purposes. His calculations were verified by extensive measurements, and were soon accepted by the international community of traffic researchers. His methods became a worldwide standard.

With these new tools available, LME was able to select different crossbar switch link arrangements for different applications and traffic capacities, and to engineer telephone exchanges to different customer specifications, using optimum quantities of switches.

Ericsson realised that the relatively large cost of the common equipment of registers and markers meant that small crossbar exchanges, rural and PBX, would be somewhat less economical in manufacture than the XY direct-driven system already available. But this cost would be off-set by the considerably lower maintenance costs for crossbar.

During the war years, Televerket's plans for automatisation of the long-distance traffic had matured, and by 1945 work had begun on the development of a crossbar transit exchange. At LM Ericsson, the 500-point system made up the bulk of switching system deliveries to the export

OPPOSITE:
Wiring crossbar system units,
Visby factory, 1960s.

markets, but in those markets, too, the developing need for transit equipment was obvious. For transit exchanges, requiring 4-wire switching, the 500-point selector was inadequate.

By around 1945, it had been decided that LME would develop a full range of crossbar switching systems for local, tandem and rural exchanges. It was also clear by now that within a short time there would be a demand for trunk exchanges to handle the automatisation of long-distance traffic. Since the long-distance networks required four-wire connections through the trunk exchanges, LME chose to standardise on both the 5-bar and the 6-bar crossbar switch for its new line of exchanges.

It was assumed that the 500-point system would continue to be sold for many years for extensions to existing exchanges and networks; but with a new and modern system product, LME would have a better chance of competing in new markets.

LM Ericsson's first crossbar systems

Since Televerket had its own crossbar exchange system in development and adequate manufacturing facilities, LME was looking to the export market for its new switching system. The competitive position in the aftermath of the war was favourable, since the main competitors were occupied in rebuilding their businesses. Siemens & Halske had suffered severe damage and needed to rebuild thoroughly, and its production would primarily be needed to re-equip and extend its home networks. ITT had similar problems. The British companies also needed much rebuilding and refurbishing, and their sales efforts were chiefly directed towards the protected home market. LME's problem at this stage was not the competition: it was the challenge of finding customers who were willing to invest in new, hitherto-untried technology.

In Finland, the Helsinki Telephone Company, HTF, or HPY in Finnish, needed to re-equip and extend its network of Siemens step-by-step exchanges. There were long waiting lists of new subscribers – and, most important, the upcoming 1952 Olympic Games were expected to mean substantial increases in traffic and demands for special services. HTF discussed its problems with LM Ericsson. Since any new exchange equipment had to be grafted into a step-by-step environment in an economical way, the group selectors had to be engineered for step-by-step working. This meant that the 500-point system would not meet the requirements. For LM Ericsson, one possibility could have been to offer an XY-switch based system, but instead it proposed crossbar – a step-by-step link-connected system (later designated ARF 50). The technical staff of HTF, headed by S.A. Karlsson, saw the advantages in flexibility and low maintenance costs of this solution, and requested a field trial in the network. The equipment was installed in 1948 and fulfilled all expectations. LME got an order for its first metropolitan crossbar exchanges. The first exchange of this contract was cut into service in 1950, and the remaining exchanges were in service in good time for the Olympic Games.

An interesting aspect of this series of events was that the development of the local crossbar system took place in LM Ericsson's export sales department. It was not, it should be pointed out, a case of what today is termed 'skunk work' – it was a management decision based on realities: the export department had its own technical staff. It was this department that maintained the technical discussions with the Helsinki customer and worked out the system solutions. The designs were built and tested in the central labs. The main (official) development organisation was fully occupied with the design of the transit and rural systems. Erik Lindström, the manager of export sales, supported by his boss, Cornelius Berglund, was the driving force behind this arrangement, which was unorthodox for its time.

A couple of engineers from the Helsinki Telephone Company transferred to Stockholm, foremost among them Gunnar Brunberg and, somewhat

The president of Lebanon, Camille Chamoun, inaugurates new crossbar exchange in Tripoli. On the right, the Minister of defence and communications, M. Majid Arslan.

185

later, Johan Borgström. They became the fathers of the new local exchange crossbar systems: ARF 50 for Helsinki; and, some 18 months later, ARF 10 for Denmark and, eventually, a very wide range of countries.

In the Netherlands, the Rotterdam telephone exchanges were severely damaged in air attacks during 1940. During the war, LME had been able to supply equipment and staff for rebuilding the local 500-point exchanges; now, after the war, the Dutch Telephone Administration presented its requirements for a large automatic trunk exchange. LME proposed a link-connected crossbar system, designated ARM 10. There was also a requirement to add equipment to all the Rotterdam local exchanges, so as to allow subscriber access to the new trunk system. This equipment, too, was based on crossbar solutions. It became known as the Rotterdam 'by-pass'. The Rotterdam installations were cut into service in 1952.

In Denmark, the telephone companies in Copenhagen, KTAS, on the island of Funen, FKT, and in Jutland, JTAS, plus the government-owned long distance operator, P&T, still had manual service in the 1940s. Joint planning for conversion to automatic started during the war. The Danes in their preparatory studies had become convinced of the advantages of crossbar and since at this time only LME was in a position to offer such equipment, negotiations soon began.

In 1949, JTAS placed its first orders, for crossbar local exchanges (ARF 10)

Wartime destruction in Rotterdam, 1941.

and a crossbar trunk exchange (ARM 20). A little later, KTAS and FKT also ordered numbers of crossbar exchanges for both local and trunk service. For several years, Denmark was LME's largest market for crossbar systems.

LME worked closely with its customers' technical experts, both during the design of the crossbar systems and in their continued development. In this way, LME gathered valuable operational experience early. It was also of the greatest value to have these installations at hand as references for demonstrations to new customers. The Finnish, Danish and Dutch administrations were only too pleased to show off their networks and discuss the various advantages (and also, alas, occasional disadvantages!).

During the 1950s, LME completed the development of a full range of crossbar systems for both public and private networks (PBX). An important application was the system version for handling telex traffic. Right up to the end of the 1970s telex was the main text communications medium, until it was completely overtaken by telefacsimile, today's 'fax'.

The competition now realised that crossbar was giving step-by-step and Rotary systems a hard time, and set up their various development programmes to bring out more modern systems. Siemens presented the ESK (Edel-metall Schnell-Koppler) system, based on link-connected relay matrices; ITT's French company, CGCT, developed the link-connected crossbar system, Pentaconta; and the Japanese companies, particularly Nippon Electric, obtained the rights to manufacture the crossbar systems developed by Bell Labs of AT&T.

'No noise, no time, no maintenance'

LME began discussions with HTF (the Helsinki Telephone Company) in around 1945. The key person on the LME side was Sven Weber, MD of the LM Ericsson company in Finland. We've mentioned S. A. Karlsson, Technical Director, representing HTF; and one of the driving personalities from LME in Stockholm, Erik Lindström. HTF wanted direct interworking with the existing step-by-step exchanges (Strowger, supplied before the war by Siemens); common use of the existing power supply of 60 V (LME's systems to date were designed for 48 V or 24 V); and deliveries on time. LME realised that, with a new system, built on the crossbar switch, all these requirements could be met. For HTF, LME offered a solution; for LME, HTF pointed a way into the future.

In Denmark, the situation was different. The Danish telephone networks were predominantly manual: it was virgin territory for automatic exchanges. The four Danish administrations spent time and effort studying the available switching alternatives, and the Jutland Telephone Company actually placed orders with LM Ericsson for 500-point selector systems.

Lars Christian Nørrelund was the MD of LME's Danish company. During the last few years of the war, he had cooperated closely with the Danish administrations in drawing up post-war plans for automation. He also made it his job to stay well-informed about the crossbar plans emerging at headquarters in Stockholm. It was he who brought out the crossbar slogan: 'no noise, no time, no maintenance' – referring, of course, to the characteristics of the switches – no contact noise, fast operation, and low maintenance costs. He eventually convinced the Jutland customer to convert its exchange order to crossbar, and that, in turn, confirmed LM Ericsson in its decision to put every effort into developing and marketing its crossbar systems.

New ventures for the crossbar era

Initially, sales efforts were directed to established markets, including the remaining telephone concessions. A look at three markets will show how substantially they developed as a response to the crossbar stimulus.

Australia

LM Ericsson had a strong market in Australia in the old days of the magneto telephone, but when the Australian Post Office standardised on Strowger for its networks, the market came to be dominated by the British manufacturers. The return of LM Ericsson to this market was largely the result of one man's efforts.

In New Zealand, ASEA Electric was the agent for LME, and Les Rowe was responsible for the LME business. This business was small, since the New Zealand Government had made a bulk supply agreement with the British manufacturers. There was just one exception to the agreement: the Post Office would buy equipment from other manufacturers if it were produced locally. In 1949, Les Rowe set up a small assembly shop, under ASEA management, and made efforts to introduce small locally-made crossbar exchanges for rural areas. But there was a change of Postmaster General, and the new man had a different interpretation of the bulk supply agreement. The loop-hole was closed, and Les Rowe transferred to Australia.

In the late 1940s, two British manufacturing plants were set up in Australia. One belonged to Standard Telephones & Cables Pty Ltd (STC), the other to a combine of British companies called Telephone & Electrical Industries Pty Ltd (TEI). Both were in Sydney. In 1948, the APO entered into a ten-year supply agreement with these companies, which effectively closed the market. During this period, the Australian telephone system, including the long-distance network, underwent substantial expansion. As the networks grew, the limitations of Strowger technology began to become evident, and the APO became increasingly aware of the need to find more practical solutions for expansion.

An LM Ericsson sales company was formed in Melbourne at the end of 1950. Soon after, Les Rowe approached the APO Director-General and presented him with a small demonstration-model crossbar exchange – originally sent to New Zealand, but now shipped on to Australia. A few months later, Rowe made a proposal for a crossbar exchange, but the offer was declined.

Undeterred, Rowe kept up his talks with the APO. Since the APO was unwilling to purchase any crossbar equipment, in 1953 Rowe offered to provide the administration with a 60-line Crossbar Rural Automatic Exchange (ARK 313) as a gift, for use in its laboratory. (This exchange had originally been sent to New Zealand in 1952, but the NZPO would have nothing to do with it.) The gift was gracefully accepted by the PMG, and the APO engineers made extensive studies and tests. These were so positive that a 60-line extension was ordered in early 1954 – the APO's first actual order. Later, the exchange was moved from the laboratory and installed at Panton Hill, near Melbourne, where it was incorporated in the network. That year, the APO signed contracts for two 600-line crossbar (ARF 50) exchanges, for Sefton outside Sydney and Tempelstowe outside Melbourne – though it was not until 1957 that these installations were completed and cut into service.

By this time the APO had come to the conclusion that the Strowger system must be replaced by a new standard in both Sydney and Melbourne. A committee was appointed, which carried out a worldwide search and study, and eventually concluded that LME's crossbar systems were superior. (At the time, ITT was offering the Pentaconta system, and Siemens the ESK.)

Crossbar exchange in Papua, New Guinea, manufactured by Ericsson, Australia 1977.

Confirmation came when a Member of Parliament from the town of Toowoomba made a strong case for bringing modern telephone service to his home town. In 1958, the APO sent out an international invitation to tender for an exchange for Toowoomba. There were 12 tenders, 9 of them offering crossbar systems. Toowoomba became an important test case in the international telephone industry. LM Ericsson won the competition, and the APO ordered a 6,300 line crossbar exchange. It was delivered in 1960.

By now it was clear that the APO intended to choose the LME crossbar system as the standard for Australia. In September 1959, agreements were made, first with TEI, and soon after with STC, for the manufacture of LME's crossbar systems by these companies under licence. The only question was whether LME, too, should start up crossbar system manufacture in Australia.

The two Australian companies had supply agreements with the APO in force until 1963. LME decided that there was room for a third factory.

In 1960, LME bought Trimax Transformers Pty Ltd, outside Melbourne. In 1961, the name was changed to LM Ericsson-Trimax Pty Ltd, and the company began to produce telephone equipment. Late that year, it was decided to build a new factory, and a plot of land was purchased at Broadmeadows, outside Melbourne.

LME now argued that from September 1963, when the purchase agreements with STC and TEI expired, the APO's ordering of exchange equipment should be based on competitive tendering. This proposal naturally caused fierce opposition from the two Australian companies, who wanted to extend the supply agreements and so exclude LME from contracts. In November 1962, the PMG decided that the supply agreements would not be extended and that, after a transitional period of two years, future orders would be awarded on a competitive tendering basis. It now became very important that the new factory building should be completed and set up for crossbar production, and it was opened on 28 September 1963. LME had now, assuming successful tendering, secured about one-third of the rapidly-expanding Australian market for public exchanges, and a quarter of the private market (PBX, etc.). There were also orders for trunk exchanges (ARM 20) for Melbourne and Sydney, delivered from the Stockholm factory.

At the end of 1962, the name of the company was changed to LM Ericsson Pty Ltd (EPA). In the late '60s, LME acquired interests in two other companies, Conqueror Cables and A.E.E. Capacitors Pty Ltd. LME had built up a new strong presence in Australia.

Mexico

When the war ended, there was still no solution to the management question of a merged operating company jointly owned by ITT and Ericsson: the status quo continued; and discussions continued. At one stage, LME offered to sell its telephone interests in Mexico to ITT, if this would pave the way for consolidation of the operations. At another point, Colonel Behn, in Stockholm this time, considered the possibility of LME's buying ITT's Mexican interests. This scheme was approved, and a formal agreement was drawn up, but then, in July 1947, the Colonel broke off negotiations – again.

Enter Axel Wenner-Gren.

In 1947, Axel Wenner-Gren, at that time one of the best-known industrialists in Sweden, had obtained a large sum of money in Swedish kronor from the sale of interests in Svenska Cellulosa AB. He wished to transfer these funds abroad, and approached LME to see whether he could collaborate in the Mexican telephone operations. The outcome was a series of agreements between Wenner-Gren, LME, Mexeric and Teleric (the LME holding company in New York) in the autumn of 1947. Under the terms of these agreements, a Mexican telephone operating company was to be formed, to which Mexeric's operations would be transferred.

The new company was named Teléfonos de México S.A., referred to as Telmex, and started operations on 1 January 1948. It was guaranteed technical and administrative assistance from LME, and a ten-year supply agreement was also set up.

Interconnection between the two networks in Mexico City was finally implemented during that same year, 1948, but negotiations with ITT and Behn had still not led to results. The solution came in 1950 with an agreement between on the one hand, the Mexican Government, and on the other hand, LME, ITT and Axel Wenner-Gren. By this agreement, Mextelco, like Mexeric two years earlier, was merged into Telmex, and the three parties, LME, ITT and Wenner-Gren, each contributed one third. Based on the respective sizes of the merged operations, LME and ITT obtained supply agreements: LME 65 per cent and ITT 35 per cent of the value of orders.

Five years later, in 1953, Wenner-Gren sold his interests in Telmex to LME and ITT. LME and its fiercest competitor were sole and equal owners of Teléfonos de México.

The Mexican Government was anxious that the telephone service should be expanded, but Telmex and its owners did not find it easy to raise the necessary capital under the existing conditions. Then the Government backed the introduction of a telephone tax (15 per cent on local calls, 10 per cent on long distance calls), which was loaned back to Telmex to support the financing of expansion.

Still the need for new capital continued. In 1954, LME and ITT subscribed for parts of a new issue, and shares worth 22 million pesos were placed on the Mexican market. In consultation with the Government, Telmex introduced a subscriber financing system in 1957: new customers had to subscribe for bonds and shares in order to obtain a telephone. The system gradually reduced the percentage of shares held by the main owners – LME's holding at the end of 1957 was 37 per cent.

It was becoming increasingly difficult to raise tariffs, a problem especially difficult for foreign-owned companies, so it seemed logical to start looking for ways to transfer the ownership to Mexican interests. Discussions began in the early summer of 1958, and in June an agreement was signed by which LM Ericsson and ITT transferred ownership to a Mexican syndicate headed by Messrs Eloy S. Vallina and Carlos Troyet. The agreement also included supply contracts for ten years, at unchanged price levels, and an extension of agreements for technical assistance.

This agreement finally ended more than fifty years of LM Ericsson's presence as a telephone operator in Mexico. Its legacy was the modern telephone service it had built.

The sale also marked the final solution to the problems discussed with ITT ever since 1932. But notwithstanding the supply agreements, it raised the question of telephone equipment manufacture in Mexico.

Network expansion took off after the Mexicanisation of Telmex. In 1954, there had been a total of 334,000 subscribers. By 1959, there were 470,000; and in 1960, 500,000. Seven years later, the number had reached 1 million – 2 million by July 1973.

Wiring crossbar equipment.

After 1960, most of the new exchanges supplied by LME were of the crossbar type, while ITT introduced the Pentaconta system a few years later. During the same decade, an increasing proportion of the long-distance traffic became up-graded to automatic, including the traffic to and from the USA. The conversion of the long-distance routes to automatic meant that LME was also able to sell increasing amounts of transmission equipment.

In 1956, LME and ITT each subscribed one half of the capital for the formation of Industria de Telecommunicación S.A. de C.V. (Indetel). The new company started up production of telephone sets in 1958, with parts supplied from Sweden. But there were increasingly strong demands for domestic manufacture of major equipment, for which the jointly-owned Indetel company would not be suitable, and LME had to consider building its own factory – which might well cause a break with ITT.

Strictly, the rest of the story belongs to later chapters of this book, but it's included here to bring the picture of LM Ericsson's presence in the important Mexican market up to date.

Late in 1963, Teleindustria S.A. de C.V. (TIM) was appointed as subcontractor for the wiring and testing of exchange equipment. In 1964, LME sold to ITT its interests in the joint company, Indetel, which was not functioning well. It decided instead to have its own production facility in Mexico, and on 1 January 1965 took over Teleindustria. By now, when full production got under way, LM Ericsson had about two thirds of the sales of telephone exchanges and multiplex equipment to the rapidly-expanding Telmex company, while ITT had one third. These proportions were to remain stable through the 1970s.

Meanwhile, LM Ericsson continued to add to its manufacturing strength. In 1965, it acquired 51 per cent of the cable manufacturer Latino-americana de Cables S.A. (Latincasa, LCM). Later, LME increased its shareholding to 87.5 per cent.

In 1967, it acquired from Teleconstructora, a locally owned service company, its exchange installation business, which LME organised as a separate company, Telemontaje S.A. de C.V.

In 1968, Mextron S.A., MXM, a company manufacturing loading coils and power-supply equipment, was acquired.

By 1972, Teleindustria had completed a new facility – factory and offices – and moved from Naucalpan to Tlalnepantla on the northern outskirts of Mexico City. By now, the company had over 1,500 employees.

Alongside the acquisitions, there were also times when it seemed expedient to be less dominant, and from 1970 onwards, portions of LME's shareholdings in its Mexican companies were sold to Mexican interests. In 1975 LME owned 70 per cent of Teleindustria. In subsequent years the proportion of ownership has varied as a consequence of changing financial and political conditions.

Brazil

Before World War II, the Companhia Telefônica Brasileira, CTB, the dominating operating company in Brazil, bought its telephone equipment from British and US suppliers, including Standard Electric and Automatic Electric. At the end of the war, Ericsson do Brasil, EDB, was able to offer short delivery times for automatic exchanges and managed to obtain orders from CTB for the towns of Rezende (1946) and Vassouras (1948), both in the state of Rio de Janeiro. Later in 1948, EDB also secured a large order for a 10,000-line exchange in Belo Horizonte; and two years later, an order for a 5,000-line exchange for Pelotas, a city in southern Brazil.

Henry Clausen transferred to Brazil from Argentina as a salesman in 1950. Clausen's sales area included the regions around São Paulo, and here he introduced a novel sales concept: auto-financing. EDB made contract arrangements with the telephone companies, whereby the exchange equipment was paid for by the subscribers, as part of the monthly subscription fees. The projects often involved the replacing of old magneto exchanges. Competing with other suppliers – notably with ITT – Clausen managed to secure contracts for automatic exchanges with new customers, located in those parts of the São Paulo, Paraná and Mato Grosso states that were outside the range of CTB. Once local exchanges had been set up, trunks between them were required. Similar sales activities were performed by Hans Lieberenz in the Minas Gerais region; and Wolf Kantif, whom we have already met in the 1930s, was still building valuable sales through his excellent connections.

Then, in 1952, the Brazilian Government, which had been raising the matter of national production, refused EDB import permission for telephone equipment. It insisted that LME should begin manufacturing parts of its equipment within Brazil. An agreement was reached that LME should begin by manufacturing a portion of its telephone sets – about 30 per cent – within the country. Thereafter, by degrees, domestic manufacture should be raised to 70 per cent. LME felt obliged to comply with these demands, and in doing so it reckoned on obtaining contracts for switching systems from CTB. ITT already had a factory, SESA, with a capacity of 100,000 sets a year, and CTB was keen to bring in a competitor.

At the end of 1952, LM Ericsson decided to build a new telephone factory in São José dos Campos, outside São Paulo, and the facility was completed in 1954. In the same year, LME's efforts to reach a closer business relationship with CTB resulted in large contracts for transmission equipment, plus a 14,000-line extension of the Belo Horizonte AGF exchange.

British suppliers, led by AT&E of Liverpool, still dominated the large CTB market, while ITT and LME shared the market outside the CTB areas. Siemens made efforts to enter, but could not at this point offer crossbar exchanges.

CTB was a subsidiary of the Canadian company, the Brazilian Traction, Light and Power Co. Its telephone concessions would expire in 1957, and it had been announced that the company would then be transformed into a purely Brazilian concern, which among other things meant that CTB's purchases of telephone equipment would be paid for in cruzeiros. This move made it clear that also switching equipment would have to be manufactured locally. Furthermore, CTB announced that it had decided to use crossbar systems in future, which meant that AT&E would be out of the running for the time being.

In 1955, LM Ericsson had already won a first crossbar order for the city of Santo André. In 1957, production of crossbar systems started in São José dos Campos. From now on LME's Brazilian business grew strongly.

Investments in the plant, inflation, and requirements for financing customer credit all made severe demands on the financial management of the business, and for several years EDB was operating at a loss. In 1961, the

Installing crossbar, Medellín,
Colombia, 1970.

company was reorganised and more stringent accounting was introduced.

In 1960, EDB and LME supplied all the telecommunications equipment for the new capital of Brasilia, including radio link carrier equipment between Brasilia and Rio de Janeiro.

The 1960–65 period in Brazil was difficult, due on the one hand to continued inflation, and on the other to fierce competition from ITT and CTB's traditional suppliers in Great Britain and the USA. But in the new political and economic climate following Castelo Branco's election as President, EDB's long campaign for crossbar technology bore fruit. In December 1965, CTB signed orders for 85,500 lines of crossbar exchanges for São Paulo and 50,000 lines for Belo Horizonte, where the new equipment replaced existing LME 500-point and ITT Rotary gear.

In 1966, the Government purchased CTB and also set up a federal operating company for interstate and international traffic, Embratel. A period of rapid expansion followed, and in 1967–68 the EDB factory in São José dos Campos was extended, while the administrative offices of the company were moved from Río de Janeiro to São Paulo.

Substantial orders continued to be placed with EDB for local and long-distance switching and for transmission equipment. The plant in São José dos Campos was further extended, and two new factories were established in the states of Minas Gerais and Río Grande do Sul. LM Ericsson also bought an interest in a cable factory, FICAP (Fíos e Cabos Plásticos do Brasil).

In the course of two decades, and in the face of keen competition, LM Ericsson had built up a significant telephone industry in Brazil and reached a market share of around 50 per cent.

Sven Ture Åberg (1903–1974)

Sven Ture Åberg succeeded Helge Ericsson in 1953, and was MD until 1964. Åberg joined the company in 1927 and had spent most of his time with LM Ericsson out in the market, particularly in Latin America. Since Åberg at the time was practically unknown, inside or outside the company, his elevation to MD raised some questions; but at a time when the company needed a true salesman, it was undoubtedly a good choice. Sven Ture Åberg guided the company back into the international markets, at a time of increasing competition, and it was during his time that the company concluded the first series of crucial contracts for its new crossbar systems. It was also a period during which research and product development were intensified – the transistor became available, and important first steps were taken in electronic switching systems and PCM transmission.

Emperor Haile Selassie of Ethiopia, King Gustav VI Adolf of Sweden and S.T. Åberg.

Manufacture abroad: 1946 and after

By 1946 LM Ericsson had manufacturing companies in eight countries outside Sweden.

TABLE 12. MANUFACTURE OUTSIDE SWEDEN: 1946

Denmark	Dansk Signal Industri A/S (DSI) and Telefon Fabrik Automatic (TFA)*
Norway	Elektrisk Bureau (EBN) and Norsk Kabel Fabrik (NKD)*
Finland	Oy LM Ericsson A/B (LMF)
The Netherlands	Ericsson Telefoonmaatschappij BV (ETM)
France	Société des Téléphones Ericsson (STE)
Great Britain	Ericsson Telephones Ltd (ETL)*
Spain	Compañía Española Teléfonos Ericsson (CEE)
Italy	Fabbrica Apparechi Telefonici e Materiale Elettrico (FATME or FAT)*

The acronyms in parentheses are the internal LME codes. An asterisk indicates that LME did not own the majority shareholding, but the company was regarded as belonging to the Group.

The Hungarian and Austrian companies had been sold in the late 1930s, while those in Poland, Estonia and Czechoslovakia had been lost as a result of the war.

Since 1940, LM Ericsson's shareholding in the British factory had been gradually reduced. ETL was chiefly producing the Strowger system for the British Post Office, a product which LME now considered outmoded and which did not fit its crossbar strategy. The remainder of the shares of Ericsson Telephones Ltd were sold in 1950 and 1951.

The French company, STE, had mainly been manufacturing Rotary equipment for the French PTT. In the early 1950s, STE started development of a French version of crossbar, with Folke Ek as design manager. Ek came from Televerket and crossbar development there. The new French system, designated CP 400, was approved by the PTT in the mid-'50s. In the 1960s, the French network was rapidly expanded and STE's sales grew strongly.

FATME manufactured a range of LM Ericsson equipment for the Italian market which soon included crossbar exchanges, and the company grew fast.

In 1951, LM Ericsson acquired 60 per cent of the North Electric Company (NEC), in Galion, Ohio. Part of the reason for this acquisition was that LME still felt the need to strengthen its presence in the Western hemisphere, to reinforce the position established with Teleric: 'in the event of a blockade the American company could take over manufacturing responsibilities for LME's American markets.'

North Electric manufactured a range of equipment, including telephone sets and exchanges for the independent, non-Bell, operating companies in the US. After its acquisition by LME, production and sales of the 412L electronic telecommunications system for the US Air Force (see chapter 13), were transferred to North Electric from Stockholm, and North Electric developed a version of the crossbar system for the US market.

The company had difficulties of various kinds, and profits were unsatisfactory for several years, but – to complete the NEC story – operations took a turn for the better in 1965, when large orders were received from United Utilities. UU was the aggressive holding company of a number of telephone operators and grew to become the third-largest of its kind in the USA, after AT&T and General Telephone.

In 1966, LME sold its majority interest in NEC to United. It kept 32 per cent of the shares and made new licence agreements, but in 1967 there was a serious disagreement between the managements of LME and UU, and LME sold its remaining shares in the North Electric Company.

Close technical relations between the parties continued, however, for several years, providing LME with an important presence in the US telecommunications community. But an LM Ericsson venture aimed at becoming a recognised supplier to the US telecom companies had failed – for the second time. It may be worth recording here that several years later United sold North Electric to ITT.

But as we have seen in Australia, Mexico and Brazil, crossbar could give local manufacture new life – in many countries, governments required local production as a condition for obtaining orders. From a technical point of view, this suited LME very well, since the crossbar system was comparatively easy and cost-effective to manufacture, even on a relatively small scale. Local manufacture became one of the key selling arguments; the others were the operational robustness of crossbar, and the low costs of maintenance.

Licensing crossbar know-how

A market could be attacked by hard direct selling and export, by the development of local manufacturing, or by licensing. The first licence agreement was reached with the Nicola Tesla Company in Zagreb, in what was then Yugoslavia, in 1953. Nicola Tesla initially produced LM Ericsson's crossbar systems for the Yugoslavian telephone network, but later expanded its business into other markets within the Soviet block, including the Soviet Union. Other licence agreements were set up during the following decades – with Egypt, for example, in 1960, and Hungary in 1968.

OPPOSITE: *Crossbar exchange installation in Tunisia.*

Crossbar Private Branch Exchanges

By the mid-1950s, LM Ericsson's public crossbar system had been installed in a number of markets – outside Sweden. They had been found to
operate extremely satisfactorily and as crossbar production increased
steadily, it was natural that the same technology should be applied in
private branch exchanges. During the '50s, a series of crossbar PBXs was
developed, the ARD range, of which the ARD 561 for 50–270 extensions
and 10–40 exchange lines became a strong seller. The ARD became a
standard item of supply for several large telephone administrations. It
was manufactured not only in Sweden, but in LM Ericsson factories in
Italy, Norway, Spain, Brazil, Mexico and Australia. By 1975, PBX switches
with a total capacity of more than 1.4 million extension lines had been sold.

The PBX operator consoles were still of the traditional cord and plug-
and-jack types, with jack multiples for larger sizes. With the new ARD
PBX, new operator consoles were introduced. They were cordless and all
operator functions were performed with keys, plus a dial or key-set. The
consoles for the ARD system were typical of their time – a straight-for-
ward design in white plastic.

In the early 1960s, development started on an additional line of PBX
systems, based on the new code switch (see following section). These
included a smaller version for 30–50 extensions, as well as the larger

Operator's console for a 1970s PBX.

AKD 791 system with from 300 to 9,000 extension lines. The AKD operator consoles were attractively designed in wood. These PBXs, too, were a success on many markets, and were not replaced until electronic switching and computer control arrived.

We should remind ourselves that until about 1980, when the subscriber equipment markets began to be liberalised, the majority of all PBXs were sold to the telephone administrations, which in turn would lease the equipment to their customers.

Cordless trunk switchboards,
St John´s, Antigua, c. 1970.

201

Meanwhile, the code switch

Despite strong indications, particularly from Bell Labs in the US, that development work on systems with electronic control and new switch concepts was under way, in 1958 LME decided to develop a new electromechanical switch, the code switch. Under the circumstances, it was not an easy decision, and outside expertise was called in to evaluate the new design. A thorough study was carried out by Bertil Bjurel, then Deputy Director of Televerket, and Dr S.A. Karlsson, Technical Director of the Helsinki Telephone Company. It was the general view in LME that it would be at least another ten years before electronic systems would be ready for exploitation in non-military applications.

The code switch, the brain-child of Harald Alexandersson, was an extremely compact electromechanical device. It provided flexibility for different switch configurations; large multiple capacity; pulse operation with mechanical latching; and excellent contact properties. And, most important, the code switch was designed for automated manufacturing.

The equipment racks for code switch equipment were of a novel type – 'hanging racks', on the bookshelf principle. The racks ran on rollers in the ceiling, and were connected by flexible cable bundles so that a rack could be pulled out for inspection and repair. By this method, the floorspace required for a code switch exchange was reduced by about two thirds, compared with crossbar.

The first code switch application was in a new large PBX system, the AKD 791, briefly mentioned above. The first AKD 791 switchboard was installed at the LM Ericsson headquarters at Midsommarkransen in October 1962. Initially, there were some embarrassing production problems in the switches (the LM Ericsson Telephone Company could not receive telephone calls!), but within a few days it all worked well.

The AKF 11 code switch system for very large public exchanges followed. AKF systems were installed in Copenhagen in 1964 and Stockholm in 1965, and in a few other places.

However, customers were finding that the hanging racks involved certain added costs and made installation more complicated. Furthermore, many of LME's factories had invested considerable sums in tooling up for manufacture of crossbar systems and were not ready to go over to a new system. The hanging-rack design was abandoned, but the code switch itself was to have several other applications, initially in rural and additional private branch exchanges, AKK and AKD respectively. And, as we shall see in later chapters, LME's first stored program controlled exchange system used the code switch.

Harald Alexandersson explaining his code switch to Sven Ture Åberg.

Looking back at crossbar

What, it's worth asking in hindsight, were the factors that drove LME's management to the decision to develop crossbar?

One factor was undoubtedly the recognition that crossbar technology, as brought out by Televerket, was a superior technology compared with all the systems based on switches with moving contacts. This recognition was underpinned by the extensive reports coming in at the time from Televerket and AT&T and its Bell operating companies.

A second factor was the ease of production – compared with the 500-point selectors, crossbar switches were so much less complicated to manufacture (and the core of LM Ericsson was still very much in its factories).

But it seems that the most important input came from LME's interaction with the market – or, to be more precise, from its interaction with a few key customers. First of all, there was close cooperation with Televerket. Televerket made the crossbar switch design available to LME, and the two parties worked closely together in perfecting the switch and following up results from operation and maintenance. But Televerket had developed its own first crossbar system and was working on further versions. It had its own production resources and was not a potential customer.

The important customers were the Helsinki Telephone Company and the Danish administrations, all of which became proactively involved with LM Ericsson in the development of crossbar for their networks. In other words, the 'crossbar decision' was very much taken *with the market*. It was taken at a favourable point in time, when strong market potential was clearly visible. It was several years before this potential could be fully exploited, during the 1960s and 1970s, so it was a brave decision to choose the crossbar road. It was certainly to move LM Ericsson into the premier league.

By 1965, LM Ericsson had significantly grown in the market for public network equipment – switching and transmission systems – and its market share had increased. The company was now again a recognised and major international telecommunications concern.

This situation was due partly to the company's emergence relatively unhurt from the war, and largely to the timely bringing to market of a more modern switching system, crossbar. The key words are 'bringing to market'. The company made strategic investments in system development and in rational production. But the key to success was the dedicated way in which the new system was introduced to the markets. Working close to the customers, understanding the customers' problems and working out solutions together. To a very great degree, the customer-vendor relation was a matter of engineers talking to engineers.

This in turn meant that very often, after the successful cut-over and sometimes an initial period of worry while teething troubles were sorted out, the customer became a champion of the system. The early crossbar installations became important reference points; visits of potential new customers would be arranged – and often enough, the LM Ericsson representative would, gratefully, find that his customer was making the sales pitch.

This mode of marketing became the model for many years. It was further strengthened through 'maintenance conferences' arranged in a cycle of English, Spanish and Nordic language yearly sessions. Operation and maintenance staff from telephone administrations were invited to these events, to share experiences – positive and negative. In later years the conference format was changed with the introduction of the AXE User Club in the 1980s. In this connection, the contribution of Televerket to LM Ericsson's marketing of public exchange systems should be acknowledged.

Stockholm, direct call operator (namnanrop), c. 1945.

The vanished world of the '40s, '50s and '60s

There are plenty of people still alive and working who remember vividly what it was like to be in business in those decades after the war.

Even in such comparatively civilised centres as Stockholm, London and New York, life was unimaginably different from today's, less than half a century later.

Engineers, and salesmen, used slide-rules – who remembers this handy tool today? There were no personal computers before the '80s; no faxes or word processors before the '70s; no xerographic copying machines, even, before the '60s. It was a world of carbon paper; Tippex and Liquid Paper and erasers; stencils for office printing; and jelly spirit duplicators. A database was likely to be a manual affair, manipulated on edge-punched cards with needles, or kept on thousands of individual metal printing plates. Accounting, where it wasn't manual, was handled by 'punched-card operators' on Burroughs machines. Both internal and external phone calls might well need to be set up by an operator, and in a company of any size, desks had at least two phones.

If, of course, they had any at all. And when you left the civilised centres, you could never be sure. Communications within countries could be very difficult, and communications between countries sometimes seemed virtually impossible. Telex, telegraph and cable, with all their limitations, were the most reliable media available. Telex meant an expensive machine at each end, and even in Sweden, cables and telegrams were delivered by boys on bikes. To set up an international phone call, it was quite usual to book a time in advance with the operator. To be sure someone would be there to answer when you called might well involve a cable saying when you proposed to call, a return cable saying that would be OK, and then an interminable wait at the appointed time while the operator was 'trying to connect you, caller'. And intercontinental voice quality …

Physical movement was just as difficult. Planes salvaged from the war, held together by applied faith, were by no means restricted to Latin America and the remoter parts of Asia. Most railways had received no investment of any but the most basic kind for ten or twenty years. Petrol was often difficult to find. Hotels were downright primitive. Decent food was a permanent problem. In many territories, bandits were reluctant to abandon the way of life that had proved so profitable and entertaining during the war.

Yet somehow, on foot, on mules, in unreliable buses shared with goats, crossing their fingers over the Alps or the Andes, skirting precipices in ex-GI jeeps, LME's field engineers and salesmen criss-crossed the world. In the '70s, it was estimated that at any one time there were 12 Ericsson people in flight, somewhere over the globe.

It was always an adventure. Sometimes, it meant real hardship. Occasionally, it was very dangerous – you'll read about a couple of horrifying experiences in Iraq, later on. Most Ericsson people accepted these adventures as an occupational hazard.

But when you meet these people – often a bit grizzled, these days – and hear them cheerfully (but endlessly) reminiscing about the hazards and experiences of 'the old days', don't feel impatient with them. There are such things as real heroes.

And while you're thinking of heroes, remember that not all dragons are slain in a fair fight for a fair lady's hand, before crowds of cheering spectators. Many an Ericsson hero has slain his dragon during hours alone in a laboratory or in a customer's exchange premises, wrestling with some insoluble system problem, long after the lights are out and everybody else has gone home.

Sometimes, the dragon slayer earns the hero's recognition, and he gets a medal. But again, remember that for every Ericsson person who earns a medal, there are probably hundreds of others who deserve one. And if you're ambitious, don't worry: life will keep the dragons coming.

CHAPTER 10

Growth in Sweden

Decentralisation of Swedish production.
A lesson in Swedish geography.

Until the end of World War II, LM Ericsson in Sweden was a Stockholm company. The parent company's employees worked in Midsommarkransen and at the nearby Älvsjö cable works. Other Group companies were scattered over the greater Stockholm area.

In 1946, a factory facility was leased in the town of Katrineholm, where the local textile industry was in decline and female labour was available. The coil winding department was moved from Midsommarkransen to Katrineholm, and in the following year work was started on a new factory.

Other moves were instituted to create more space in the main factory: electricity meters moved to Ulvsunda in 1945, cash registers to rented premises on Döbelnsgatan in 1946, and signalling equipment to Gröndal in 1947, all locations within the Stockholm area.

In this post-war period, the Swedish economy suffered from a period of unexpected inflation and a currency crisis. To avoid overheating, the Government imposed strict control over construction work, and since there was a shortage of both labour and housing in the Stockholm area, it was practically impossible to obtain permission to build new factory premises there. The company's plans for extensions in Stockholm had to be shelved for the time being. On the other hand, the Government indicated that it would support the establishment of production in certain specific parts of the country that had a labour surplus.

A new LME factory was completed in Söderhamn in 1948, and in Karlskrona LME was able to take over factory premises from Tobaksmonopolet (the State Tobacco Monopoly) when that company moved its production of snuff to Nässjö. In 1947, the production of telephone instruments moved to this factory. These moves showed the company's good intentions, and the Government was now willing to grant certain

OPPOSITE: *A quartz glass pre-form prepared for drawing. The result – a 40-kilometre optical fibre.*

A 1950s view of LM Ericsson at Midsommarkransen.

building permits in Stockholm. The main factory at Midsommarkransen was expanded (the so called 'Tower Building', Tornhuset, was added at this time) and the Ulvsunda factory was extended.

The decision to expand the company's production facilities outside the Stockholm area was not solely attributable to Government restrictions. The company needed new labour, preferably less mobile, and to a large extent female; and building costs and wages were lower outside the Stockholm area.

In 1955–56, production of 500-point switches was transferred completely to Söderhamn, while the assembly of crossbar switches was transferred to Karlskrona, where facilities were extended.

In 1955, LME purchased the premises of Örgryte-verken in Mölndal, close to Gothenburg. To this factory was assigned the production of the company's military systems, beginning with radar and followed by space electronics, computer equipment, laser and IR systems, and road and rail signalling equipment. Military security considerations prompted the location of this production away from Stockholm, but equally, or more, important was the availability of qualified staff through its proximity to the Chalmers Institute of Technology.

The 1960s were a period of vigorous growth in the company's business and increase of production capacity continued through further decentralisation – in eight years, twelve new factories were added in the provinces. LME favoured the south-eastern parts of the country, where labour was available, wages low and transportation distances not too great. This strategy resulted in new factories in Olofström, Visby on the island of Gotland, Ronneby, Norrköping, Kristianstad, Ingelsta outside Norrköping, Oscarshamn and Vedeby.

The Government pressed for investment in the northern parts of the country, where unemployment was greater, and offered favourable Government loans and even straight capital subsidies. But for LM Ericsson, the most interesting form of Government control was the use of investment funds. Limited companies were allowed to make certain tax-free allocations to special funds that could only be used with Government approval. Under this scheme, LME established factories in Delsbo, Östersund, Hudiksvall and Piteå.

By 1974, the parent company had more than three-quarters of its production capacity located outside the Stockholm area.

The technology of the times

Apart from the manufacturing facilities of the parent company, two of LM Ericsson's major subsidiaries, each contributing advanced technology in its field, developed in a similar way. In this section, we'll follow both their stories some way into the future.

RIFA

The first of them is RIFA, last met in Chapter 8 as Radioindustrins Fabriks-aktiebolag, an unprofitable manufacturer of electrolytic and mica condensers for several radio receiver manufacturers.

In 1946, ASEA took over the company, but soon LM Ericsson came in as a 50 per cent owner and the name was changed to just 'RIFA'. The partnership did not work out well, however, and on 1 January 1947, RIFA became a fully-owned subsidiary of LM Ericsson. The following year the company moved to Ulvsunda, into a former biscuit factory.

Electromechanical components on the move. Stockholm factory 1960s.

Initially, production was focused on capacitors of various types. Volumes grew rapidly, and in 1960 some old factory buildings were acquired in Gränna, to which the manufacture of electrolytic capacitors was moved in 1961. But the facilities at Ulvsunda soon became too small again, and a new factory was built in Kalmar. It opened in 1964 to manufacture miniprint capacitors, spark quenchers and fluorescent lamp condensers. In 1968, RIFA started making capacitors in Australia as well, and in 1971 a factory was opened in France.

SER, LM Ericsson's electron tube company, was merged into RIFA in 1967. The key product now became semiconductors, primarily diodes, which SER had started to manufacture in its factory at Bollmora, outside Stockholm.

RIFA had built up an important external market for capacitors, and this business grew strongly, with sales to consumer product manufacturers and makers of industrial electronics. RIFA's own products were complemented by a vigorous resale operation, representing several well known manufacturers (including General Electric, Thomson-CSF, Panasonic, and others) and marketing through RIFA subsidiaries in several countries. In 1981, RIFA acquired the Norwegian company Sverre Höiem A/S, and the Hitachi Nordic agencies.

In 1971, RIFA concluded its first cooperation agreement, with National Semiconductor – an agreement which was to be very important for RIFA's future development of integrated circuits.

In 1977, the different activities of RIFA in the Stockholm area moved into new facilities at Kista. This move marked the end of a period of very heavy investment. Profitability was down, and the capacitor business was starting to decline, but RIFA had started to develop expertise in the new IC technology, with a focus on MOS (metal oxide semiconductor) and gallium arsenide.

RIFA went on to play a most important part in Ericsson's successes of the '80s, where we'll pick up its fortunes again.

From Sieverts to Ericsson Cables

Early cable technology

The merger with SAT in 1918 brought to the new company important experience, from Sweden and abroad, of planning, building and maintaining telephone outside plant.

The replacement of open-wire telephone lines by cables began in the city networks, but open wires were still in use well into the 1960s (mainly for long-distance links and in rural networks). Telephone cables were built

Cable making.

with paper-insulated copper wires, sheathed in a lead cover. The thickness of the wires was progressively brought down to 0.4 mm, and the maximum number of pairs was eventually to reach 3,000.

After World War II, the use of plastics increased, with polythene instead of lead for sheathing.

For long-distance networks, cable runs may be very long, and this increases attenuation and the risk of crosstalk. Hence, paper-insulated conductors remained in these networks.

Transmission systems using multiplex technology came into use in the 1930s, and allowed substantial increases in the number of channels carried by each pair, or rather two pairs (quad), of wires in a cable. But this technology had its limits: the maximum number of channels per quad was 120.

Coaxial cable – an external cylindrical conductor and a central inner conductor, insulated from one another by air – also arrived in the 1930s. The first coaxial route in Sweden was installed in 1947, supplied by a foreign manufacturer. LM Ericsson started manufacture of coaxial cables at the Sieverts cable works and developed a series of corresponding transmission systems. A less expensive and more flexible small-diameter coaxial cable was first manufactured in 1962, and became a great success on many markets.

Coaxial cables marked a giant step forward in network construction, making it possible to arrange for high numbers of simultaneous connections to be set up over increasing distances. And at the same time, digital PCM transmission rapidly took over as the dominant carrier technology.

But the need for higher capacity continued to increase. And by the mid-1970s, other media, such as data transmission, had started to clamour for capacity in the telecommunications networks. It was time for optical fibre.

Submarine cable.

Opto cables

Two researchers in Britain, C. K. Kao and G. A. Hockham, are credited as the first to recognise the potential of light guided through a glass fibre as a medium for transmitting large quantities of information. Their findings were first published in 1966. The key to low attenuation was sufficiently pure glass, and by 1970, D. Maurer at Corning Glass in the US had successfully produced glass fibres with an attenuation of under 20 dB/km. Since then, attenuation figures for glass fibre have steadily been reduced.

In 1979, Drs Kao and Maurer received the LM Ericsson Prize for their pioneering contribution to optical telecommunications technology.

By the mid 1970s, LM Ericsson had started up studies of optical transmission systems and the development of technology for the manufacture of optical fibres. In 1979, Sieverts provided optical fibre cables for the first Swedish field trial; and from 1982, the business expanded rapidly.

Basically, an optical-fibre transmission system includes a transmitter, which is a laser or a light-emitting diode, the fibre, and a receiver, a photo diode. In the transmitter, the incoming digital electrical signal (PCM or other digital coding) is transformed into a corresponding train of light pulses transmitted by the laser.

Power cable

Traditionally, power cables used copper conductors. Though there were attempts in the 1950s to use aluminium instead of copper (because of its lower density), jointing proved difficult and the idea was abandoned. But by the mid 1960s, copper prices were beginning to increase steadily while the price of aluminium was stable, and this time the industry switched over to aluminium for gauges over 50 square millimetres.

Copper, aluminium, nickel, sodium ... the periodic table of cable manufacture

By the beginning of the 1970s, the price of copper had reached over SEK 10 per kilo and there was serious concern that copper was being priced out of power cables altogether. Sieverts Kabelverk started up an extensive development project, that resulted in a new product: nickel plated aluminium, SINIPAL, for use in installation cable and wire instead of copper. By the time SINIPAL was fully developed and standardised, however, the price of copper had returned to more normal levels, while that of aluminium, due to an increase of the cost of electric power, was on the way up. The Sinipal project was discontinued – but is available should the price of copper again go up.

In the US in the early 1970s, a cable with sodium conductors was introduced – a superbly light and inexpensive new type of cable, according to the accompanying publicity. Sieverts contributed with test installations for determining the new cable's characteristics, and during the trials it was soon found that the difficulties in producing, handling, installing and scrapping such cables were just too great. As long as copper (and aluminium) are available, sodium is not an alternative.

Sieverts Kabelwerk: growth in Sweden ...

Though Sieverts Kabelverk suffered during the war years from lack of raw materials, by 1944 there was a turn for the better. Sales were exclusively to the Swedish market, and the company's operations were all concentrated in the original location at Sundbyberg, a town adjoining Stockholm, where new building and reconditioning continued during the 1950s.

New plants for making lacquered wire (Öregrund, but later transferred to an LM Ericsson factory in Vedeby, Blekinge) and cable sleeves and other cable accessories (Alingsås, 1956) began the transfer of operations away from Sundbyberg, and in 1965, government permission was obtained for the construction of a plant at Öjebyn, just outside Piteå in northern Sweden. In the same year came a breakthrough with new cable technology: aluminium replaced copper as the conductor in high-tension cables. Sieverts' PEK aluminium cables with polythene insulation became a success both on the Swedish and the export markets, and the old design with copper conductors, paper insulation and lead sheathing was quickly squeezed out.

Sieverts and ASEA were the dominating manufacturers of cable and associated products in the limited Swedish market, and to avoid duplication an agreement was concluded between the parties in 1968 by which certain products were 'exchanged'.

In the late 1960s, competition from imports was becoming severe. 'To rationalise the structure of the electric supply sector' an agreement was reached with a number of suppliers on cooperation under the umbrella of a new company, Svenska Elgrossist AB, Selga. Sieverts' subsidiary retailers were organised in a separate company, which became a part of Selga, and LM Ericsson became the majority owner of Selga.

The parent company had its telephone cable factory in Älvsjö, in southern Stockholm. A new factory was added in Hudiksvall in 1966. In 1970 the Sieverts telephone cable operations were sold to LM Ericsson and transferred to Hudiksvall. Not long afterwards, in 1972, parts of Sieverts' power cable manufacture were transferred to a new factory at Falun.

The 1970s saw a series of acquisitions. Among them was Thorsman & Co in Nyköping, a company specialising in installation equipment, including the well-known 'Thorsman Plug'. Again, most of these activities, by Sieverts, ASEA and others, were moves to protect the Swedish market from foreign competition.

By 1976, further rationalisation was achieved when the LM Ericsson telephone cable division (Älvsjö, Hudiksvall and Piteå) was transferred to Sieverts Kabelverk and formed a second division of that company, parallel to the power cable division. At the same time, mainly as a consequence of the world recession, the Älvsjö cable operations were discontinued.

The 1980s saw further structural changes in the Swedish cable industry, but by now, LM Ericsson and Sieverts also had international interests.

In 1985 the name of the company was changed from Sieverts Kabelverk to Ericsson Cables.

... and internationally

As early as in the 1920s, LM Ericsson had expanded its cable operations outside Sweden when it acquired an interest in Elektrisk Bureau and its subsidiary Norsk Kabelfabrik in Drammen.

The next expansion did not come until 1948, when Industrias Eléctricas de Quilmes in Argentina was acquired. The Quilmes factory has played an important role in LME operations in Argentina, with a broad selection of power and telephone cable products.

In the late 1960s there was a strong expansion drive, and LM Ericsson became owner or part owner of cable operations in Australia, Colombia, Brazil and Mexico (some of which have since been divested).

With the 1980 joint venture with ARCO in the US, Ericsson took a step into the US cable market, when the old Anaconda cable company became a part of the joint venture. It soon became obvious that Anaconda-Ericsson should focus on telecommunications cable, and the power cable operations

Testing cable, Latincasa, Mexico.

were sold off. The US cable operation, although not as lucrative as had been hoped, became an important component in Ericsson's establishment on the US market. But operations suffered from low profitability, and after a slump in the market during 1987 most of the remaining cable operations were sold off.

Employing local labour.

OPPOSITE: *Network construction, Libya.*

King Carl Gustaf and LM Ericsson Managing Director Björn Lundvall.

Björn Lundvall (1920–1980)

In 1964, Björn Lundvall took over as MD. He was an engineer by training, had worked in design of transmission systems, and at the time of his nomination was head of the transmission department, where his natural instincts as a salesman had come to the fore. Again there were some raised eyebrows. LM Ericsson's soul and heart was still that of a telecommunications factory, served by dependent product development and sales departments, and speculations, inside the company and out, had been that a production person would be chosen.

But, again, history has proved that it was a shrewd choice. Lundvall was to oversee the long and arduous development of the first computer-controlled telephone exchange system, AKE; the formation of the Ellemtel development company in partnership with Televerket; and, eventually, the first AXE system in service and the first major AXE contract, for France. In sales terms, crossbar systems still dominated, both in public and private exchanges, and Lundvall's years (1964–1977)

were a period during which the company moved up the ranking list of international telecommunication equipment manufacturers.

In 1976, Björn Lundvall hosted the company's 100-year anniversary, which in spite of the somewhat difficult times became a great event, with a balanced mixture of solemnity and fun. But difficulties there certainly were during his time. The first oil crisis had a severe effect on the world's economy. It came at the time when the telecoms operators were already hesitant about the introduction of computer-controlled switches in their networks, and it resulted in a dramatic downturn in orders, stockpiling at the LM Ericsson factories, and the threat of lay-offs among employees. On top of all this, there were considerable increases in the costs of labour. This period of stress lasted until 1978, when Björn Svedberg had taken over as MD, while Lundvall succeeded Marcus Wallenberg Jr as Chairman of the Board. Sadly, Björn Lundvall fell victim to a peculiarly Swedish hazard: he was killed when his car collided with an elk in the road.

Telephone instruments

The bakelite phone

For obvious reasons, the LM Ericsson product best known to the general public has always been the telephone. From 1931 on, this was made in black bakelite, a thermo-setting resin named after the chemist L.H. Baekeland, a Belgian working in the US. The design and styling were the result of work at LME's Norwegian subsidiary, Elektrisk Bureau. Not only was the styling new, the circuitry was based on extensive new calculations and measurements in the laboratories. The transmitter included a new anti-sidetone transformer for the first time.

The new telephone was fully on a level with the best foreign designs, and with its practical construction and advanced external form it set a standard in the industry for many years to come. It was adopted by Televerket and the British Post Office, among other administrations.

The desk set was the instrument most commonly in use, but a full range of different types for different uses was soon available: a wall-set, a 2-line set, a set with built-in amplifier, a house exchange telephone, and so on.

First-generation bakelite desk set, 1931.

Luxury telephones for Thailand.

Second-generation desk telephones 1947.

At the new headquarters and factory at Midsommarkransen, the telephone department set up a modern electro-acoustic laboratory with a sound-insulated anechoic chamber and advanced test facilities. It produced a second generation of bakelite sets in 1947, with softer lines in the design, improved transmission characteristics, and a plastic dial.

The Ericofon

While the bakelite telephones were still being developed, other ideas were germinating. By the mid 1940s, great advances had been made in materials research. New thermoplastics, well suited for telephone set design, and new ferromagnetic materials became available, as did new light metal alloys for constructional details. It was becoming possible to reduce the weight and volume of the component parts of a telephone set. There were various ideas for a radically new design.

An early example of such ideas was the 'Unifon', proposed by Hans Kraepelin as early as 1944. The Unifon, of which Kraepelin had built two prototypes in his home workshop, was a one-piece telephone with the dial incorporated in the 'handle'. There was no immediate reaction from his colleagues.

The Unifon

OPPOSITE: *The 1931 set: a promotional image.*

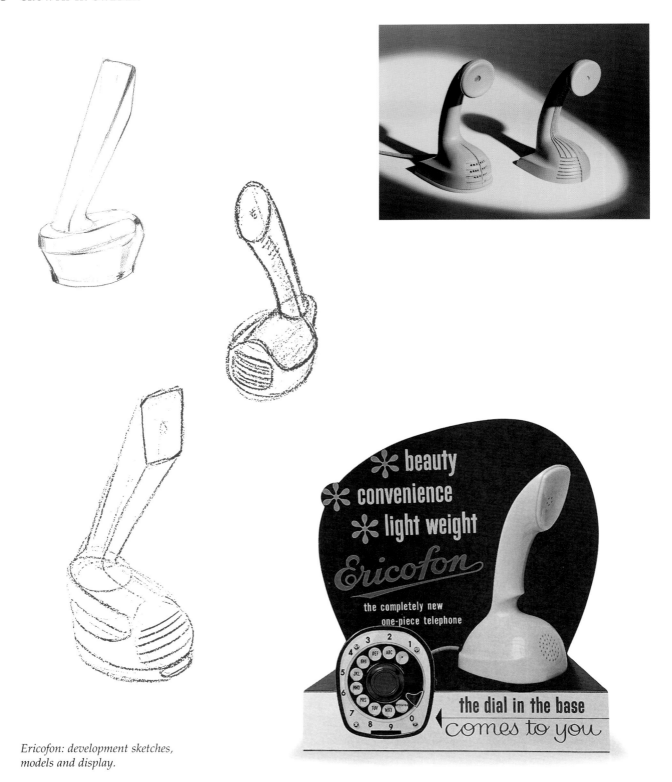

*Ericofon: development sketches,
models and display.*

Billboard advertising in Canada.

The following year Kraepelin took over as manager of the New York office, and in 1954 he became President of the LME-owned North Electric Co., in Galion, Ohio. He left LME in 1958. But his Unifon had been a subject for much discussion over many years.

As early as 1939, LME discovered that Siemens was working on a new one-piece telephone. Hugo Blomberg, then technical manager at LM Ericsson, took this information seriously, and the following year, after a switch of jobs, he got in touch with a young Stockholm designer, Ralph Lysell. Together, in 1941 they produced two models of a stand-up one-piece telephone with the dial placed under the stand, or foot. They applied for a patent for their concept, and called it the 'Erifon'.

The covering patent was not awarded, however, since Siemens had already obtained a patent in 1931 for 'a standing handset with dial'. Hugo Blomberg moved to the USA, where his job was to track technological development, while Lysell turned his talents in other directions.

Blomberg returned from the USA in 1946, and became Chief Engineer, assigned to reorganise a development department. In 1949, a phone technology group was organised headed by Gösta Thames, and the one-piece telephone turned into a drawn-out battle: There were still two basic concepts, the Unifon and the Erifon, and there were major problems with many details. Debates were, apparently, fierce, but by the spring of 1950, the Unifon had been discarded. A way was found to fit a receiver into the top of the Erifon stand, and work began to fit the transformer and condenser inside the phone as well, rather than in a wall plug.

Blomberg became MD of Svenska Elektronrör in 1950, while Thames and his group moved back to the telephone department. With a newly developed transformer and condenser, and with a new microphone design, the final shape was given to what was now called the 'Ericofon'. Gösta Thames holds the honour for developing the final styling.

The first pre-production Ericofon was presented to Televerket at its centenary festivities on 1 November, 1953. In 1956, shipments began of the revolutionary new one-piece telephone, and interest quickly spread throughout the world. In 1972, the Ericofon was nominated by the Museum of Modern Art in New York as one of the best examples of industrial design in the 20th century.

The 'dial-in-handset' principle was later adopted in several advanced designs by competitors, with the well-known Bell System 'Trimline' model foremost among them.

Ericofon in promotional leaflet.

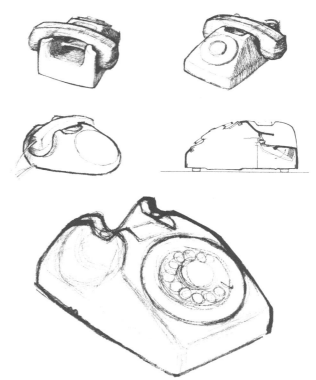

The 1962 Dialog.

Dialog

Even with the success of the Ericofon, it was clear that many large telephone administrations also wanted telephones of the traditional type, but in a more modern design. In the early '60s, LM Ericsson cooperated with Televerket in the development of a new model. It appeared in 1962 under the name 'Dialog'.

The casing of the Dialog was of thermoplastic material, available in several colours and very light. The loudness of the bell could be adjusted, and the electric transmission level was automatically regulated to match the length of the subscriber line. To simplify production, several new solutions were introduced: all the components were slotted into a frame, connected by plug and jack, and the whole was fixed inside the casing with a single screw.

Keysets for indicating numbers had been in use for many years, typically in operator consoles, test equipment and so on, but in telephone sets the dial ruled. LM Ericsson brought out its first keyset telephone instrument in 1969, incorporated in new versions of the Dialog and Ericofon models. The standard signalling used was two-tone: when a key was depressed, a combination of two tones was transmitted to the exchange. The telephone exchange had to be equipped with corresponding tone receivers. For connection to older exchanges, not equipped with tone receivers, telephones with electronically-produced dial pulsing were offered.

1959 Ericovox loudspeaking telephone.

'Now hear this': loudspeaking telephones

The first loudspeaking telephones were produced in the mid-'40s. The microphone and speaker were separated, there was a mains-connected wall-mounted amplifier, and the telephone set had extra buttons for switching between normal and loudspeaking conversation. It came to be used mainly in executives' offices – in pre-transistor days, it was a relatively expensive piece.

Ten years later, in 1959, the Ericovox loudspeaking telephone was introduced. In Ericovox the loudspeaking equipment was integrated with the remainder of the telephone in a single unit. Ericovox had two amplifiers, one for each voice direction, and both of these were voice-controlled – a technical first. For normal, non-loudspeaking, conversation an Ericofon was used, placed beside the Ericovox.

'Now look who's talking': the picture telephone

In 1927, the Bell System demonstrated picture telephony over a line from New York to Washington. A primitive picture of the speaking parties was transmitted in each direction, appearing on a square screen about 6 cm x 6 cm, with 50-line scanning by means of a rotating disc. The light source was a neon lamp. Later, in the '30s in Germany, other trials were made with picture telephony between Berlin and Leipzig.

With the advent of television, new technology became available, and in the '50s Bell Labs was able to demonstrate satisfactory picture transmission. Semiconductors in the next decade paved the way for commercially-viable picture telephony services. The first public system went into use in Chicago in the early '70s. The quality was defined by the requirement that the speakers should be able to see each other. For a reasonable picture of a person's face, BTL chose a bandwidth of 1 MHz, 267 scanning lines and 30 frames per second.

LM Ericsson decided that the system was too costly if used only for seeing faces. They decided that for a picture telephone system to be economically warranted it must be possible to display documents and drawings over the same system. With this in mind, LME chose to develop its own system with higher definition, and decided on the European television standard of 625 lines and 25 frames per second at 5 MHz. This made it possible to make use of commercially available TV cameras, monitors and tape recorders. In the transmission network, broadband channels would be required.

Swedish prime minister Tage Erlander trying out the picture telephone. His called party is radio and TV personality Lennart Hyland.

LME's picture telephone station consisted of the actual picture telephone (a TV screen with camera and mirror mounted above), a loudspeaking telephone and a normal telephone.

The official introduction was in 1971, in conjunction with the opening of the Nordic earth station for satellite communication. Conversations were exchanged with Washington via the Intelsat IV satellite, over one telephone and two TV channels. Other demonstrations were conducted between Brazil and Sweden and between Australia and Sweden. In 1972, in a field trial conducted in cooperation with Televerket, picture telephones were installed in a number of offices. A major project was also carried out at the LME offices, with some 100 people participating over a period of two years.

The field trials were positive in all respects. Certain office functions were greatly facilitated by being able to read and discuss documents over the phone. But commercially, the picture phone never took off. It was an expensive piece of equipment, and above all it required a lot of costly bandwidth for transmission.

The picture telephone provided a lot of glorious PR. It was demonstrated to the international press, at shows and conferences and became literally a conversation piece. But the technology was all analogue – and the picture phone was 30 years ahead of its time.

CHAPTER 11

1950–1980

Diversification

During the post-war period, the Ericsson Group developed, manufactured and marketed a wide range of products. This range was partly the result of exploiting telecommunications know-how in new applications, and partly a legacy of the efforts during the lean pre-war years to exploit production capacity. The manufacture of arms and ammunition had naturally been abandoned at the end of the war.

Products at SRA

Consumer products

During the 1930s, Swedish architecture and furniture design had developed a famously simple, functional style: LM Ericsson's Midsommarkransen headquarter premises are today a protected example of the architecture of the period. The furniture became known as 'Swedish Modern', and in 1939, SRA cooperated with professional designers to bring out out the first of a new series of radio receiver sets for home use. These Radiola sets became popular after the war, as the economy improved and home-building began again. They were followed by radio gramophones, radiograms, which by the '60s even included a tape recorder.

With the advent of the transistor came transistorised radio receivers, which were introduced in 1958.

In the 1920s, John Baird in Britain started experiments with television broadcasts. In the US, Vladimir Zworykin invented the iconoscope, the first camera tube based on the cathode ray principle. By 1935, SRA had

OPPOSITE: *Installing railway signalling in Sri Lanka.*

229

reached an agreement with the German radio firm Loewe for the patent rights in Sweden of their television technology. In December that year, there were successful demonstrations in Stockholm. By the end of the war, the ground was prepared for the introduction of regular TV broadcasting services.

In Sweden, interest in television was slight. LM Ericsson was, however, keen to get things moving. In 1946, it set up a foundation for the promotion of television research, and sent two engineers from the Royal Institute of Technology to the USA to study television. In the following year, LME provided funds for experimental equipment. These activities led to the formation of the 'Committee for Television Research', with representatives from Televerket, the Royal Institute of Technology, the Defence Research Establishment, and LM Ericsson. A few years later, the Swedish Broadcasting Corporation and a group of radio manufacturers also became members.

A first 1 kW TV transmitter was built at the Institute of Technology, and a TV camera was purchased from the USA. The transmitter was built for 625-line scanning and was the first in Europe to operate on this system, which was later adopted as standard by most countries inside and outside Europe. And a pioneering group of television engineers had been created.

Still the Government remained indifferent to starting a regular TV service, and it was not until September 1956 that the Swedish Broadcasting Corporation initiated regular broadcasting. After the long waiting period, public interest in the new medium was immense, and as the broadcasting network expanded the demand for television sets increased rapidly. Soon, Sweden had the highest television density in Europe.

As early as 1952, SRA set up a department for the design of television sets, and the first Radiola TV set was launched in 1954. It was a floor model, in Swedish Modern style, with a 17" picture tube. Even though at that time only trial programmes were being broadcast, demand was keen. A similar 21" set and a 17" table model soon followed.

By the late '50s television sets had become the main product of SRA. In the peak years, some 1,000 TVs left the factory every week. 23" picture tubes and printed circuit boards came into use, and in the early '60s the sets had two channels – in preparation for the coming of the Swedish second programme.

But SRA was becoming increasingly aware that its future should not lie in consumer products, and that its resources in technology and production

Home entertainment from Radiola.

should be devoted to telecommunications. In 1964 the radio and TV business, including the Radiola trade mark, was sold off to AGA (who in turn sold it to Philips a few years later). The focus was switched to communication radio and development projects for the Swedish defence forces.

Land mobile radio

The first organisation to make widespread use of mobile radio in Sweden was the police force. Experiments during the 1930s with UHF equipment led, as so often in Sweden, to a Commission of Inquiry, and in 1943 an initial decision was taken to set up regulations for the development and manufacture of mobile radio in Sweden. The Commission also investigated the modulation principles of the time, and decided in favour of frequency modulation rather than amplitude modulation.

SRA developed a first police mobile radio system, and deliveries began in 1944. The fire and ambulance services soon became customers, and in the early '50s, SRA provided a network of fixed radio stations to the Swedish Civil Defence authority which were also used by police and fire brigades. By the end of the decade, this network covered the whole country, eventually forming a base for the expansion of other mobile radio services.

The early mobile radio sets were bulky and heavy, but with the introduction of transistors in the 1960s, dimensions could be reduced substantially.

The power companies were the first commercial enterprises to introduce mobile radio, but soon many other businesses, and particularly the transport industry, became important users. An interesting example is the Swedish forestry industry. Timber from the logging areas in the forests was traditionally floated down the rivers to the mills along the Baltic coast. But now, trucks were taking over, and mobile radio became an important means of controlling and directing the transportation fleets. Between 1969 and 1974, SRA provided a network of fixed radio stations and relay stations covering most of the forested area of the country.

Mobile radio grew strongly in Sweden. In 1960, there were some 10,000 vehicles equipped, rising to about 100,000 in the 1970s.

Land mobile radio systems also became an important export product for SRA, while provision to the Swedish military forces continued. And the experience and skills in mobile radio technology that SRA built over the years would eventually be the base for moving into mobile telephony. But that is a later story.

Police mobile radio on duty.

Intercom and LMS

In Chapter 7, we saw the establishment of LM Ericssons Försäljnings-aktiebolag, FÖB, to handle sales and installations on the private market. In 1943, the parent company took over development and production, and FÖB became a pure sales company. In an attempt to expand sales, by 1945 FÖB had taken up the marketing of several additional products, including electric fencing, electric locks, heat measuring instruments, paper-counters, centralised alarm equipment, visual paging systems and intercom systems.

By 1952 it was again time for a change of the company's name, to LM Ericssons Svenska Försäljningsbolag, marking a new focus on the Swedish market.

In 1961, the central alarm systems business was sold to Svenska Vakt AB. In 1965, it was decided that the company again should take over the

The loudspeaking telephone from the UK's Ericsson Telephones Ltd, 1938.

international marketing and sales of all LM Ericsson's private market products, excluding PBX and PAX. Per Bertil Jansson became MD and the name of the company was changed to LME Telematerial AB, with the internal designation LMS.

The new company focused on development and sales within three product areas: security systems, time control systems (both described below) and communications systems (intercom).

Intercom (popularly known as a 'squawk box') is a particular type of telephone for use in offices, hospitals, etc. The concept really started with conference telephones. In 1933, Ericsson Telephones Ltd introduced a loudspeaking telephone in the UK. It had two great advantages: both your hands were free while you were speaking on the phone (well, the early systems were simplex, which meant you had to throw a key between speaking and listening); and more than one person could speak into it. In its original form, the system consisted of one loudspeaking phone for the boss, with up to 16 ordinary telephone subsets.

By the following year, LM Ericsson in Sweden had developed a system of its own which allowed the linking of several loudspeaking phones within the office, and connection to the public network. By today's standards, the system was bulky and had to be used with a certain discipline to avoid acoustic feedback and howling.

In 1945, a new conference system was brought out, less bulky and with a special conference console. This, in turn was replaced in 1965. Conferences were still very much reserved for the executives.

LM Ericsson's first true intercom system appeared in 1942, but it was not until a second generation came on the market in 1948 that there were any significant sales. It was called the 'F system', and it was a simplex, 'one-at-a-time', system consisting of a master phone and up to ten slave stations.

The F system used multi-wiring, which became a drawback when customers started asking for larger systems. Any future system would need to be based on some sort of central switching device and would have to be upgraded to duplex working. With a switch there was also the advantage that the amplifiers could be located in the central equipment.

When two competitors appeared on the Swedish market, AB Gylling & Co. (Centrum products) and Svenska Reläfabriken AB (Sinus products), LM Ericsson had to speed up development of its duplex system. It appeared in 1962, named DIRIVOX. Depending on system size, the switch was built on crossbar or code switches.

The DIRIVOX series was improved and extended during the '60s, until the largest system had a capacity of 5,400 extensions.

Meanwhile the Gylling company had acquired the Sinus business (from the estate of Axel Wenner-Gren) and the two companies' products had been amalgamated. In 1967, an agreement was reached and LM Ericsson

OPPOSITE:
Ericsson's popular ERICOM, which could be used as a loud-speaking intercom, or, when picked up, as a regular phone. Stockholm, 1972.

Ericsson's DIRIVOX loudspeaking intercom.

took over the Gylling telecom products. Further radical rationalisation followed, making use of the early experience in time division multiplex that had been gained in the System 412L work (see Chapter 13).

The first fully electronic intercom exchanges were delivered in 1971, and sales of LMS intercom telephones and systems expanded quickly.

But the company was finding that there were certain problems with intercom. One difficulty was learning to operate and use all its services: it took time, and was easily forgotten. There were too many buttons, with confusing symbols. And, moreover, customers were demanding intercom telephones that could also be used for making regular calls.

The first systems of a new generation were delivered in 1972, the ERICOM system. ERICOM immediately proved successful and became an all-purpose office communications device.

In 1983, the name of the company was changed to Ericsson Security and Tele Systems AB, ESS. Further change came the following year, when the ESS product development and manufacturing operations were transferred into the new Ericsson Information Systems, EIS. The installation activities were moved into the new Ericsson Network Engineering AB, as were the sales to the Swedish market (for which the name Ericsson Telematerial was retained), and the security business was sold off to a Swiss company, Cerberus.

In the mid-'80s, further sell-offs followed, and the activities focused on intercom systems. Ericsson Telematerial was transferred to the short-lived Ericsson Sverige company, then moved into what is today the enterprise system organisation.

Odds and ends

This section brings together descriptions of a collection of LM Ericsson products and businesses which seemingly have little or nothing to do with telecommunications. But in their time they were important elements in the company's business – to keep factories working, to compensate for business lost because of economic depression, or to contribute to Sweden's re-armament during war. Virtually nothing of these activities remains within Ericsson today.

Railway and road signalling

Even before Lars Magnus Ericsson brought out his first telephone, he was undertaking the repair of railway telegraph instruments. The telegraph provided a critical support function for train services, and both pointer telegraph and Morse telegraph were used. After a few years, L M Ericsson started his own production of such apparatus, supplying not only the railways, but also Telegrafverket, the Swedish Army and the fire brigades. Pointer telegraphs were used by the railways in Sweden up to 1913, and the Morse telegraph was not completely replaced by the telephone until the 1940s.

An early patent was awarded to two LME engineers in 1910 for 'an electric signalling device for railway crossings and the like'. A train passing a level crossing caused a contact to be closed which in turn set a warning bell ringing.

In 1915, when equipment from German suppliers was difficult to obtain, LME started to develop and manufacture equipment for signal boxes, and a railway signalling department was set up which soon gained

Cranked mechanical signal box for medium-sized railway stations.

a strong position. In 1929, the Förende Signalverkstäderna was taken over and combined with the signalling department in a new company, LM Ericsson Signalaktiebolag, SIB. In 1968, SIB was transferred to the then MI Division of which it formed the Signalling Department.

Railway signalling, as it developed within LME, may be roughly divided into the following categories:

- Signal boxes with interlocking functions – for supervising and routing trains in yards;
- Line block equipment for supervision and control of trains between stations;
- Automatic Train Control equipment, ATC – with direct signalling between track and train to ensure greater safety and cost effective operation;
- Centralised Traffic Control equipment, CTC – for the supervision and routing of trains within an entire traffic zone, including both lines and yards.

Signal boxes with interlocking functions

Security requirements for railway signalling are even higher than for telephony, since a fault may cause stoppage or even accident. With its long experience in telephony, it was natural for LM Ericsson to enter railway signalling, but it was a long time before exports reached any significant level.

The first generation of signal boxes was mechanical. The first electrical signal box was supplied to Moscow, in 1916, and the following year the first was delivered to the Swedish Railways. For delivery to Malmö, LME entered into cooperation with the British firm of Westinghouse Brake and Saxby Signal Co., which provided the frames. Electrical interlocking was first delivered to the Hässleholm region in 1925–26.

A key element in railway signalling systems was the safety relay. Through its cooperation with Westinghouse Brake and Saxby Signal Co., LME obtained access to such a relay design – initially imported, but later manufactured by LME. The first equipment was installed in 1934, followed by, among other installations, the Madrid Underground Railway in 1936, and the Stockholm Östra station on the Roslagen line in 1941. During 1941–43, 25 plants were supplied to the Swedish State Railways. The systems based on electromechanical safety relays underwent continuous development, to reduce the size of the equipment and rationalise installation. The introduction of computer control began in collaboration with the Swedish State Railways in 1973. The first computer-controlled system went into operation in 1976.

Line block equipment

Line block systems were introduced in order to prevent collisions between meeting trains and to prevent a following train running into one in front. After the introduction of track circuits, it was possible to divide the lines into block sections. At the entry to each block section, signals were set up to show whether the sections immediately ahead were free from trains or not.

Automatic Train Control, ATC

Automatic line block systems made it possible to increase traffic capacity: the rolling stock could be used more effectively, and average speeds could be increased. The first automatic line block system was introduced in 1927.

A further development of the automatic block systems was the introduction of line-to-locomotive signalling used to activate the brakes automatically. A first system was designed for the new Stockholm Underground Railway, but the order was lost to a competitor. LM Ericsson was however able to return at a later stage and has supplied electronic locomotive equipment since the end of the '60s. Apart from the Stockholm Underground, 100 units were supplied in 1975 to Muni Metro in San Francisco.

Chi Tu marshalling yard, Taiwan, 1970s.

Centralised Traffic Control, CTC

First introduced in the USA in the twenties, CTC puts the signals at the stations under the control of a train dispatcher in the central office. Control signals are sent to the station interlocks and information from the stations is returned. The safety of train movements on the lines between stations is secured by automatic line blocks, and stations may be left unattended.

Signalbolaget built the first CTC plant in Europe for the Saltsjöbaden line in 1938. This plant was in use for about 30 years before it was replaced by electronic equipment.

In the late '40s and early '50s, Signalbolaget developed a new CTC system, based throughout on relays. This system was adopted as standard by the Swedish, Danish and Norwegian railways.

Railway traffic control centre in Melbourne, Australia.

In further development stages, a computerised CTC system which uses one computer for remote control in each direction, and a third computer as an 'electronic train description system' was introduced on some of the main Swedish railway routes.

Road traffic signalling

As early as 1868, trials were made in London with signals to control road traffic, and the first traffic lights installed in the '20s in Stockholm were manufactured in Britain. Each crossing was equipped with sets of lamp standards and a controller. LM Ericsson Signalaktiebolag delivered its first traffic signalling plant to the city in the mid-'30s.

Four-year old boy to father: 'Daddy, when the policeman turns green we can go'.

In the late '40s, after studies in London and elsewhere, the Stockholm city authorities decided to introduce more intelligent signal control which could adapt minute-by-minute to traffic conditions. The vehicles ran over a rubber pad in the street surface, with internal air channels. When they were compressed, a pneumatic relay was actuated. Pulses from the relay were acted upon by the central controller.

The rubber pads tended to be damaged by vehicles and snow-ploughs, so a new device was developed, consisting of a detector loop buried in the street. As a vehicle passed over it, the direction of the magnetic flux was reversed and an electric pulse was delivered. This system was first installed in 1949. Over time, the whole system was transistorised and gained considerable intelligence.

In 1989 the rail and road signalling operations were sold to Elektrisk Bureau A/S of Norway, as part of a larger deal which also involved Ericsson's acquiring EB's telecommunications business.

Security systems and time control

Air raid warning systems

Under the threat of war, the Swedish authorities started to consider systems for warning the population of air attack. After an investigation by LM Ericsson, it was decided to base a warning system on a pneumatically-operated siren, or hooter, the so-called TYFON. This device was manufactured by Kockums, a Malmö shipyard, and an agreement was concluded giving LME the sole right of sale for all applications outside maritime use.

At three o'clock in the afternoon of the first Monday of every month, we still hear the TYFONs being tested, all over Sweden.

In the alp valleys of Switzerland the coming of spring means a risk of very sudden flooding as the melting snows swell rivers. To warn the com-

Tyfon air raid public warning system, Cairo.

munities along the river banks TYFON systems have been set up with a special type of sensor (developed by Kurt Klöpfer, MD of the Swiss Ericsson company) which detects rising snow and water levels.

Fire telegraph

In the Lars Magnus Ericsson workshop in 1876, the fire brigade was among the first customers. L. M. Ericsson decided that existing equipment could be improved and developed a system of his own, the 'pointer telegraph', which was widely used right up to the 1910s.

In 1917, the company introduced a magneto generator system for use in smaller communities. When the glass was broken, a crank handle fell forward and the person raising the alarm would crank the magneto – as instructed. The signal actuated bells in the homes of the firemen, a specific code for each alarm box so that the firemen would know from where the alarm had been sounded.

For larger cities with permanently manned fire-stations, more sophisticated equipment was developed, based on the 'double Morse system'. The work started as early as 1909, and the system survived right up to the 1940s, when telephone-based systems could replace the telegraphs.

Automatic fire alarms

Early automatic fire alarm devices, based on contact thermometers, existed in the 19th century. Siemens & Halske marketed such a system in Sweden, but it was never a success. As insurance companies in those days paid compensation both for direct damage and for loss of profit, it was not considered good business to spend money on things that reduced risks covered by insurance. The exception was the protection of human life. Thus in Stockholm the law required installation of automatic fire alarms in, for example, theatres.

In the mid-'20s, LME developed its first automatic fire alarm system in cooperation with the Stockholm Fire Brigade. Together with the Fire Brigades, LME entered into negotiations with insurance companies, suggesting some form of rebate on insurance premiums in cases where an automatic fire alarm was installed. Over time, the insurers consented and provided LME with a strong sales argument.

In the 1940s, a new type of device, the ion detector, was developed in Switzerland, and LME obtained the sales rights for these detectors in Sweden. Later, a flame detector added coverage, and the little fire detectors became common in all types of buildings – offices, factories, restaurants, and so on. And still are, of course.

Early fire alarm box.

Members of the Stockholm fire brigade and LME meet to discuss the development of fire alarm systems, 1910s.

Time control

After the end of the First World War, time control in industry became general practice. A first electric time control system was designed at the Industriaktiebolaget H. T. Cedergren in 1918 when, after Televerket had taken over the SAT telephone operations, the company was looking around for new products to manufacture. The first installation was at Norrahammars Bruk in 1921, by when the company had been merged into LM Ericsson.

By 1934, the company had difficulties in filling the factory and had to look for alternative products to manufacture. The newly-formed LM Ericssons Svenska Försäljningsaktiebolag (FÖB), which had been given the task of selling the time recording systems, now also took over the manufacture of the recorders. The parts were made by the LME factory in Vienna and assembled in an attic (such were the times!) in Drottninggatan in central Stockholm. Development responsibility, however, stayed with the parent company.

In 1940, after the move to Midsommarkransen, the manufacture of time recording systems was transferred back to Sweden.

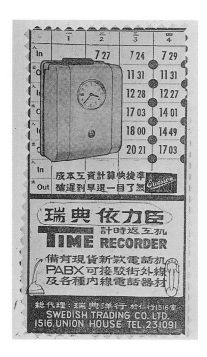

Ericsson time recorders advertised in Hong Kong.

Cultural conflict and cooperation

A market for time recorders also developed in Britain, where Telephone Rentals was keen to handle them. Conditions required local manufacture, which was located at the Beeston factory. Plans were drawn up to rationalise production of the piece parts by sharing the work between Vienna and Beeston. But these plans fell through because Vienna used the metric system, while in Britain, naturally, they lived and died by the inch.

All components for the British market had to be made at Beeston.

OPPOSITE: *Stockholm nostalgia from the beginning of the century – with automobile, policeman, fire alarm box and a telephone wire tower on the roof.*

Just In Time – the dynamising effect of a punched card time recorder.

Process Control

The Centralograph

In 1931, LME acquired the patent rights for a device called a Centralograph, originally designed for the control of textile machines. On a tally roll, the Centralograph would print in columns the status of a number (up to 30) of machines. A later version would also signal and record the causes of stoppages. Over time, the Centralograph found many other applications: in the engineering industry, in steel works – and in telephone exchanges. In the crossbar systems, it was used to record faulty or non-completed connections, and for traffic metering on trunk routes. As late as 1965, a Centralograph was installed at the heavy rolling mill of the Sandvik AB steel works. 33 years later, in 1998, it was still in service (and probably is today).

The Centralograph process control device.

Computer-based process control

For the Swedish AJ-37 Viggen aircraft, the Defence Matériel Administration specified a test centre installed in a bus. An aircraft would be connected via a multi-pin socket for programmed testing of all the different electronics. MI Division, at this time not very familiar with 'ones and zeros', had to work hard to develop a real-time computer to control the testing. It was named the UAC1601. The product was proudly presented to the Board of Defence, but it appeared that there had been some sort of clash of personalities – and the order went to Hewlett Packard of the US. The prototypes that MI had produced went to SAAB and served for several years, and a consolation was that HP became severely delayed in fulfilling the contract.

At the same time, around 1970, the need arose for a 'front end' computer in data communication networks, inserted between the data links and the main computer. This was a computer application well within the sphere of interest of a telecommunications company. And it had also become clear that such a computer could be used with advantage for the control of industrial processes. The UAC1601 computer developed by MI Division was upgraded into the UAC1610, and came into production in 1971. The new product was well received, both in data network and process control applications.

But since ASEA had also become active in process control, it was soon obvious that two competing companies in a limited market was one too many. The competitors formed a new company, ASEA-LME Automation AB, ALA, of which LME owned 40 per cent. ALA took over the sales of the UAC1610, but the marriage did not last long: it broke up in 1975, and ASEA took over LME's share. LME retained the rights to the UAC computer for applications other than process control.

Living on borrowed time

A special piece of 'humane engineering' was a new coin-operated meter introduced in the late '30s. It had an extra little device which made it possible to 'borrow' current if the user lacked a coin or token. It apparently filled a real need and became very popular.

The UAC 1610 computer would play important roles in the telecommunications world in later years. The first such application was in international exchanges, in which it came into use for handling the clearing of accounts between countries. The second application came later, in operation and maintenance solutions for a new generation of switching systems. But that story belongs to a later chapter.

Electricity meters

In the '30s, these meters were important in utilising factory capacity during the world recession. Production continued, and new and improved meter designs were brought out.

Research and development were transferred to the central R&D department, FUA (Forsknings och Utvecklingsavdelningen), in 1931, and in 1933 the marketing rights were assigned to ASEA. FUA was dissolved in 1934 and a separate electricity meter department was formed.

There followed several years of intense development work, which introduced a whole string of new products – mainly single- and three-phase AC meters and a new ampere-hour meter for DC. The Meter Department also developed special-purpose meters for such customers as the National Power Board, the Stockholm Electricity Works and ASEA.

In the period after 1945, efforts concentrated on improving the functions and cutting the costs of the meters. Meters with a wider range (up to four times the rated current) and higher accuracy were introduced.

In 1945, the Meter Department and the production of meters were transferred to Ulvsunda, a Stockholm suburb, and a separate company was formed, LM Ericsson Mätinstrument AB. Ten years later, this company changed its name to AB ERMI. It soon emerged that Ulvsunda was not the best location for a factory of this type, and ERMI moved to specially-adapted premises in Karlskrona in 1961.

In the 1970s ERMI was sold to the Swiss company, Landis & Gyr. Its electricity meter operation was sold to Bergman & Beving in 1969.

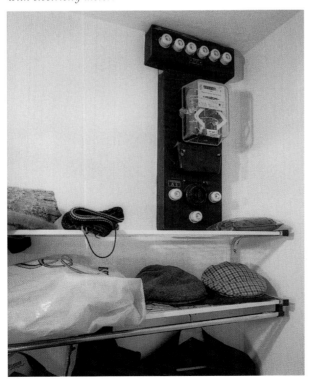

A typical Swedish front hall – with electricity meter.

Measuring instruments

Among the large collection of bygones at LME there is a 'tangent galvan-ometer', designed by Lars Magnus Ericsson in 1878. From the '80s and '90s, there are further examples of the firm's early development of meas-uring instruments – necessary tools in the telephone business. But this production remained small in quantity, and by the turn of the century spe-cialised companies had become too competitive.

Nevertheless, production continued, and as WWII approached, it be-came clear that Sweden would require a domestic source of measuring instruments in the event of a blockade. The Government encouraged LM Ericsson to start up development and production. The measuring instru-ment business, for civil and military purposes, was to prove of great value during the war. It included thermal instruments for the measurement and recording of heat, gas and steam in heating plants, steam power generat-ing plants and steelworks; instruments for flue-gas analysis; and a line of machines for balancing rotating steel shafts.

For the military sector, the company became expert in designing instru-ments for aircraft. These included voltmeters and ammeters, oil-pressure gauges, thermometers and meters for measuring fluid quantities.

In 1946, the measuring instrument and meter departments were joined together in the new LM Ericsson Mätinstrument AB, which, in 1955, be-came ERMI. By the end of the '60s, LM Ericsson was beginning to realise that its strategy must focus on telecommunications. In 1969, The electrical instrument operation was sold to AB Charles Westerberg in Nyköping, while the special aircraft instruments were transferred back to the parent company.

Shockproof

An odd product for ERMI was, for several years, electric cattle fencing. In the early '60s, this electric fence, along with a selection of telecom products, was included in LME's stand at a trade show in Moscow. The fence became the centre of interest when the Soviet Premier, Mr Khruschev, visited, tested and approved of its function. He was not easily shocked.

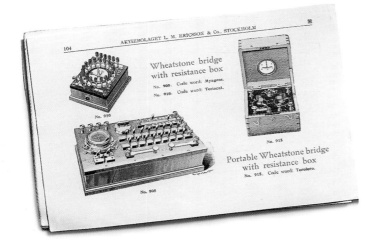

From 1910 catalogue:
Wheatstone bridges.

CHAPTER 12

Products for defence and space

F rom the early days, LM Ericsson was engaged in making and exporting field telephones and field telephone exchanges for military use. In the company's total turnover however, these products never played a significant role.

But during the Second World War, SRA made some early experiments with 'echo radio', which would, eventually, lead to a Swedish radar industry. A tentative start was made in the '50s, but it was in the '60s that LME radar equipment of very high quality was developed.

In 1887 H.R. Hertz had discovered that radio waves, like light, are reflected. In 1922, two Americans found that ships could be detected by means of radio waves; and in Britain, in 1927, E.V. Appelton and M.E.F. Burnett were able to determine the altitude of the ionospheric layers by using reflected radio transmission.

Early experiments used continuous waves, and it was not until the principle of transmitting directed radio waves in short bursts, pulses, was adopted, that accurate range-measurement and direction-finding could be achieved.

Work was going on in several countries, but it was in Britain that working pulse radar equipment was first introduced. In 1937, a chain of early-warning systems directed across the English Channel was set up, which was to play a decisive role in the Battle of Britain.

The first systems used a wavelength of 10 metres. The British then developed smaller equipment using a 1.5 metre wavelength, which could also be carried in aircraft and used to detect surfacing submarines.

With the development of the magnetron as a transmitter tube, even shorter wavelengths could be achieved. When the German Navy countered with radar warning receivers, the Americans developed the magnetron

OPPOSITE: *Control, command, COMMUNICATE! Ericsson tactical radio in action.*

251

further, using wavelengths down to 3 centimetres.

With the application of the 'doppler effect' (named after the Austrian physicist Christian Johann Doppler) radar techniques were refined further, so that echoes from moving objects could be separated from those from stationary objects.

As we've seen, LME had worked on an echo radar during the war. At the end of the war, the company was commissioned by the Swedish Defence Authorities to manufacture under licence a French search radar for the Swedish army. The licence arrangement came to involve both tracking radar for anti-aircraft use and aircraft radar for the Swedish A-32 Lansen aircraft.

The MI Division started, in 1956, as the Radar Section within the parent company, which in 1959 was elevated to a Department, MI. From 1965 through 1986 it was the MI Division.

In 1987, MI was formed into a separate company, Ericsson Radar Electronics AB. In view of the growing importance of products for civilian applications and as microwave systems were becoming the dominant business, in 1994 the company's name was changed to Ericsson Microwave Systems AB.

Airborne radar

In the second half of the 1950s, development of the first all-Swedish airborne radar started for the D version of the F-35 Draken aircraft. Close cooperation was established with SAAB and the Air Force, and SAAB developed the aiming computer. Radar equipment of this first type was delivered in 1961–65.

The transition from sub-miniature tubes to semiconductors happened in the next phase, the airborne radar equipment for the F version of the Draken aircraft. Deliveries took place in 1964–70.

The specifications for the development of the Viggen aircraft were even more exacting. LME was responsible for the airborne target-sensing equipment, and the most sophisticated radar went into the fighter version of Viggen to search for, track and determine the range of targets. This required the use of doppler radar and a digital signal processor. The entire avionics system was built around a central digital computer. First deliveries of this radar system took place in 1970.

For the interceptor version of Viggen, JA-37, a contract for type definition development was received in 1973. A proposal was presented to the defence authorities, FMV, the Defence Matériel Administration – and immediately and unanimously rejected as being too conservative. So back

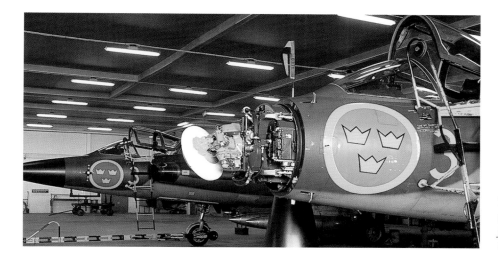

The first Ericsson-developed pulsed radar, PS-03/A, for fighter aircraft J-35 D Draken (Dragon), late 1950s.

The British Sea Harrier is equipped with radar subsystems from Ericsson.

to the drawingboard, and to extensive development work and new technology. The first Viggen radar was delivered in 1978, the last in 1987.

During the late 1970s, studies began of radar systems and FLIR, Forward Looking Infra Red, for a new aircraft to follow Viggen. In the spring of 1980 the Swedish Parliament allocated funds for project studies for a new plane, named JAS, which became known as the JAS-39 Gripen (Griffin). An industry group was formed for the project, Industrigruppen JAS, IG JAS, with SAAB-Scania, Volvo Flygmotor (aircraft engines), LM Ericsson, SRA and FFV, the Swedish Defence Manufacturing Agency.

The contract was signed in 1982. It was an extremely complicated document, and for several months it was questioned whether any individual existed who had mastered the whole content and its interpretation.

Electronic display system in the JAS-39 Gripen aircraft. Three head-down and one head-up CRT displays using diffraction optics.

The JAS project led to cooperation with the Ferranti company in Edinburgh as system parts supplier; and, later, the MI Division was selected as the subcontractor for system modules for the British Blue Vixen radar for the Sea Harrier aircraft.

Permanent land radar installations are vulnerable to air attack and have a limited range within which they can detect low-flying targets, such as cruise missiles. This led to the development of a flying surveillance radar, the Erieye, for cooperation with ground radar stations.

A first airborne radar for civilian applications was supplied in 1977. Its initial use was for detection of oil spills at sea, but other uses, such as ice mapping, have been developed since.

Sticking its neck out

During 1975 there was a competition within the MI Division to give PS-70 a suitable name. After drawn-out deliberations, the name 'Giraffe' was chosen, suggested by five individuals. The more stylish and descriptive 'Eriction' was rejected.

Surface radar

The first surface radars were reconnaissance and range-finder systems for the Swedish air defence.

In 1968, the first pulsed doppler radar for anti-aircraft guns was contracted to the Swiss Contraves company for its Skyguard system.

ECSTRA, Ericsson Coherent Search and Track Radar, was installed in an old bus in 1970 to carry out demonstrations.

The following year, MI demonstrated automatic tracking of several

independent moving targets by means of ESA, an electrically controlled antenna. ESA was the result of a joint development programme with the Chalmers Institute of Technology.

Cooperation was set up with Marconi Radar Systems Ltd of the UK for the development of radar components for fire control systems for naval use. First orders were received in 1975.

In 1972, the development of PS-70, now known as 'the Giraffe', started. This was a pulse-doppler search radar for inclusion in the Swedish RBS 70 missile system. The radar is mounted in a cabin on a truck and is characterised by a 12-metre hydraulically-operated mast. PS-70 was first demonstrated at the Air and Space Show in Paris in 1975.

Radar systems:

LEFT: *Giraffe 40, mobile reconnaissance and tracking pulse doppler radar.*

RIGHT TOP: *HARD, Helicopter and Airplane Radio Detection, a 3-D local surveillance radar, first introduced in 1984.*

RIGHT BOTTOM: *ARTHUR, ARTillery HUnting Radar, a mobile system for determining enemy artillery and missile firing positions, 1995.*

Weather radar system, PROMIS 90 in service in Italy.

The Giraffe has been continuously developed, and several new versions have appeared. It has become a success both at home and in export markets. A sea-borne version, SPIRA, was first supplied to the Swedish navy in 1981. Subsequent orders have come from the navies of Canada and Australia.

During the 1980s, the Helicopter and Aircraft Radar Detection, HARD, system was developed. The anti-aircraft system RBS-70 DARK, based on HARD, began to be ordered in the late 1980s.

A civilian special radar, christened PROMIS 90, was developed as an aid to more accurate local weather forecasting, and the first system was inaugurated at Norrköping in Sweden in 1984. The PROMIS weather radar was also sold to Denmark, and a few years later Spain had become the largest market with over 90 per cent of the country covered.

In the early 1990s ARTHUR is introduced, a radar system for locating enemy artillery firing positions. ARTHUR stands for ARTillery HUnting Radar: it detects an incoming missile quickly, measures and analyses its trajectory and defines the position of the enemy weapon firing it.

A special radar application is the RACON beacon, a maritime navigational system. RACONs have been supplied for, among other users, the approaches and mouth of the St Lawrence Seaway in Canada.

OPPOSITE: RACON radar beacon on Swedish west coast.

An engineer's dream

The early work with the new radar technology was assigned to the Transmission Division in Stockholm. However, the expansion of Swedish industry in the years following the Second World War created a lack of trained engineers in the Stockholm and Västerås (ASEA) areas. Young electronics engineers leaving Chalmers in Gothenburg, on the other hand, were having a hard time finding jobs in the western part of Sweden.

LM Ericsson decided to move the development activities of the fledgling defence section (MI) to Mölndal, near Gothenburg, so as to be able to tap that source for staff. And no doubt, radar technology and electronics were seen as something of an ugly duckling at a time when the company's main business was building electro-mechanical telephone exchanges.

The MI Department, which became a Division in 1965, developed its own culture from the beginning. The MI engineers worked at the high-tech front end of technology, and they knew it. They referred to the business in Stockholm as winding coils and bending bits of metal. Mölndal became the answer to an engineer's dream: no economics, no admin, and production managed from Stockholm – just well-equipped laboratories to be enjoyed. And good work was done.

Optronics

Researchers at Hughes Aircraft Co. were the first to demonstrate a workable laser (Light Amplification by Stimulated Emission of Radiation). The possibilities of producing radar-like characteristics in the optical domain led to intense development efforts in many parts of the world.

At the MI Division, studies of the new technology were started up in 1962, with the aim of designing optical rangefinders. The first tests were performed between two of the buildings at the Mölndal facility. The first prototype was delivered to the Swedish Navy in 1967.

Marine, coastal defence, artillery, airborne and other laser applications were brought out over several years, and supplied to several countries. In 1978, lasers were purchased by Sperry in the US for the fire-control system, Sea-Archer 2.

New applications have followed, for the Bofors BOFI anti-aircraft system, as a light-weight version for artillery use, and as a laser zone pipe for the Sidewinder missile.

When the Swedish defence authorities were interested in infrared technology, the leading nations were reluctant to transfer it. The LM Ericsson MI Division was accordingly requested to develop a prototype for an imaging IR camera. Tests were positive, but that particular project was discontinued. Instead, it was the Swedish Army that brought out plans for providing the RBS-70 with scotopic vision (ability to see in the dark). The provision of heat cameras to Bofors commenced in 1990.

In 1996, the optronics activities were sold to SAAB Dynamics.

Space technology

For LM Ericsson, the emerging communications satellite systems were naturally of interest as they pointed towards a new trans-ocean telecommunications medium. Initially, the market was dominated by US enterprises, but in 1964, ESRO was formed to promote the European development of systems for space research, and ELDO for the development of launchers. The two organisations were merged into one, the European Space Agency, ESA, in 1975. LM Ericsson, along with SAAB-Scania, has received substantial commissions from ESA over the years.

Ericsson had a share in the so-called F9 ESRO project, a launch to test repeater equipment for communications satellites. LME was responsible for the development of oscillator and frequency-conversion equipment for the 4 GHz radio carrier on the sender side of the repeater. In 1970, 18

Chilean operator Entel´s satellite earth station in Punta Arenas for telecommunications with the Antarctic.

months delayed, the satellite was launched from the Woomera rocket test range in Australia. The three rocket stages functioned as planned, but the nose cone failed to separate from the third stage and the satellite never went into orbit!

A second launch took place the same year – the scientific satellite TD1. LM Ericsson had supplied telemetry transmitters and telecommand receivers in the VHF range. This satellite stayed up.

For the communications satellite MAROTS/INMARSAT, LM Ericsson provided the local oscillator system for the transponder, in 1973.

In the mid-'70s, LM Ericsson became more interested in the satellite earth stations. Earth stations were seen to offer a larger business potential than the relatively few and critical satellites. The main competitor was Nippon Electric, but by 1977, the company had received orders for six earth stations in five different countries. The customers were European PTTs, preparing themselves for the European satellite communications systems, ECSS, which was being planned at the time.

In 1977, two satellites with Ericsson equipment on board were launched – an OTS satellite, which had to be blown up, and sank in the Caribbean

MiniLink has found its way all over the world. Here, it overlooks the harbour at Gothenburg.

Sea; and the ISEE-B (for measuring radiation and magnetic fields surrounding the Earth), which was launched, successfully, from Cape Canaveral in the US.

In the late 1970s, interest in TV satellites began to grow in Europe. The Swedish government increased funding for space research, and plans for a Swedish TV satellite started to taken shape. By 1981, the first contract for TELE-X was signed with the Swedish National Space Board. TELE-X became the largest space project in which the MI Division has been a partner. MI has now become a leading supplier of satellite antennas using carbon-fibre technology.

TELE-X became a Pan-Nordic project (though the Finns abandoned it before the launch). It was launched in 1989 with a French ARIANE II rocket from French Guyana. About thirty earth stations were in operation, ready to start data and video communications.

The space ferry Discovery was launched from the Kennedy Space Center in Florida in 1990. On board was Ulysses, the satellite programmed for solar research. Ulysses communicates with Earth via his Ericsson antennas.

In January 1992, a new company, SAAB Ericsson Space AB, was formed by merging the space activities of Ericsson with SAAB Space AB. Ericsson holds a 40 per cent share.

Radio links

In the mid-'60s, the MI Division took over from Elektrisk Bureau a fledgling project for an analogue radio link. The development was originally for the Swedish defence authorities, but when the system was introduced in 1970, the military changed their minds and placed contracts for a large number of links from Lenkurt in the US. This radio link was, incidentally, the first MI product to use semiconductors throughout – no more valves.

Through the Transmission Division in Stockholm, however, MI Division was able to sell some quantities of these links to Yugoslavia, Iceland, Ecuador and other countries for use in a variety of applications – though not primarily in telecoms networks.

By the mid-'70s, it was decided that the proportion of the Division's non-military business should be increased, and attempts were made at a large range of high-tech civil applications, such as burglar alarms, electric fences, velocity measurement, and so on. But eventually the signal came through – the LM Ericsson company's main business was telecommunications. A new product, the digital MiniLink, was brought out, and went

into various applications – still, however, not in telecommunications networks.

The breakthrough finally came in the mid-1980s, with a large order from the US Army. Supply went on for about five years and, apart from the business generated, the customer provided important support in production technology and quality control.

By the time the task of supplying the US Army came to an end, another large market had emerged – the mobile telephone operators. Digital radio links offer many advantages to cellular operators, particularly in ease and speed of installation: it is crucial for an operator to get 'airborne' fast, and to start generating revenues.

The key concept of LME's MiniLink is the all-in-one container, which houses the complete system (radio, antenna and transmission) and is pole-mounted. Today, Ericsson Microwave Systems is the leading link supplier in the world.

More recently, a variant has been introduced, the point-to-multipoint MiniLink, which enables operators, especially cellular network operators, to add flexibility and streamline their network building further.

After the long years of slow business, repeated suggestions that the MiniLink line should be discontinued, and insistent questioning by top management, the MiniLink digital microwave has turned out to be a most important and successful product line. Today, it is one of Ericsson's core products.

OPPOSITE: MiniLink again – this time in Malaysia.

Encryption

'Gentlemen do not read each other's mail.' So said Henry L. Stimson, the US Secretary of State, in 1929. And how wrong he was!

In the period leading up to the Second World War, and even more during the war itself, the states involved increasingly built their strategies and tactics on information gathered through signals reconnaissance. Eavesdropping methods became increasingly sophisticated, and special attention was naturally paid to radio communication.

Similarly, all sides became increasingly adept at working out methods for protecting their own information. Here, we are chiefly concerned with coding and encryption.

In most countries, information protection and signals reconnaissance were the not-much-publicised responsibility of government and military authorities. With the increasing dependence on data communication, these disciplines are also important today – in business, in banking, in

An Ericsson encryption machine, encrypting.

industry, and in just about every conceivable activity in the modern world.

Among the western powers during World War II and the years following, the encryption of alpha-numeric text was largely dominated by a mechanical construction originally developed by a Swedish engineer, Arvid Gerhard Damm, and later improved on by Boris Hagelin. The Germans had developed their own machine, called Enigma. For speech encryption, used for telephone conversations between Roosevelt and Churchill, among other people, simple scramblers were used: these were analogue and based on the principle of inverting the speech band. The use of coding (as opposed to encryption) was still widespread.

In Sweden, the defence level of the encryption in the Hagelin machines was gradually raised, but as better and better methods for breaking the encrypted messages were developed, it was realised that newer, more secure systems were needed. There was also a need to adapt the encryption machines to new forms of communication, such as teleprinters, for which 'on-line' encryption was needed. The technology available was still mechanical and electromechanical.

At the Radio Section of the National Defence Radio Centre (Försvarets Radioanstalt, FRA), work by four engineers, P-E Ahlman, Åke Lindegren, Vigo Lindstein and Bengt Florin, led the development of two promising machine types, HC and SA.

The authorities recommended that a private company should be set up to carry out the further development and, later, manufacture of the machines. One of the reasons for this move was security: in a private company it would be easier to keep the work secret.

The company was formed in 1951, named AB Transvertex, TRX, with Vigo Lindstein as managing director. The shares were owned by Lindstein, P-E Ahlman, Bengt Florin and Olof W. Jonsson.

AB Transvertex

During the '50s and '60s, business was primarily based on the two machines, SA and HC. During the first few years, finance for product development was provided by the Defence Authorities, and thereafter chiefly through supply contracts. This period was the 'golden age' of Transvertex: the order level from the military, civil defence and other Swedish customers was high, results were above average, and in the mid '60s a leading business magazine selected the company as one of the ten most profitable in the Stockholm area.

The first electronic encryption machine, EC-2, was developed during the second half of the 1960s. In 1966, on a laboratory EC-2 machine, TRX demonstrated encryption of telefacsimile pictures with a transfer speed of about 2.4 kb/s. This achievement led several other firms to take an interest in Transvertex, including LM Ericsson.

Attempts were also made to export the company's products. There were some formal problems, since the two original machines were based on secret patents, but these obstacles were overcome through alternative development or as the patents expired over time. But the main difficulty was that available markets were nearly all members in NATO – countries which used exclusively NATO-approved equipment. Sweden was not a member of NATO.

By 1969, the market for TRX in Sweden was weakening as advanced machines produced by competitors were taking over. Since attempts at the export market had not been hugely successful, the business would not be able to finance the heavy product development costs foreseen, and the Transvertex Board decided that it was time to sell the operation.

In December 1969, LM Ericsson acquired all the shares of Transvertex.

Why was Ericsson interested?

LM Ericsson had itself been working with encryption for some time. At the end of the previous century, the company had already built encryption devices, one of which used so-called Wheatstone discs. Information is, however, scarce, and this area of activity never had much impact on the company's business.

But in the late '60s, the MI Division started development of an encryption machine intended for civil application in radio telephony. This project never got beyond an experimental model, but by now the company had become seriously interested in a new military project, called SN210. Preliminary studies soon showed that access to experienced cryptological know-how would be essential to continue in the project. The fast way to build expertise was through an acquisition – and the only specialised company in Sweden was Transvertex.

Within the Ericsson Group, Transvertex continued operations under its old name. The company developed rapidly, thanks both to a renewed and more successful export drive, and, above all, to the dramatic development of microelectronics.

Its portfolio also included several types of encryption equipment for non-military data communication.

In 1980 TRX ownership was transferred from LM Ericsson to SRA. At that time, SRA was successfully selling tactical radio systems on the export market, including radio links and VHF radio. Among products produced for these applications should be mentioned a multi-channel encryption equipment for the new digital MiniLink system. In 1984 TRX was transformed into a division within Ericsson Radio Systems. The Transvertex trade name has been retained for the encryption line of products.

CHAPTER 13

1950–1970

The lure of electronics

As early as the 1930s, there were discussions and experiments in Britain and the USA investigating the replacement of the electromechanical elements in switching systems by electronics. LM Ericsson made attempts with a specially-designed cathode ray tube, in which the electron beam could be locked into different multiple positions and used for speech transmission. The work demonstrated the possibility of electronic switching, but also showed that it was still a long way from any commercial application.

In the mid-'40s, there were experiments on the use of the 'trochotron', an invention by Hannes Alfvén and Harald Romanus. The trochotron was a tube with an electron beam which could be set to one of ten positions by crossing electric and magnetic fields. The difficult areas in these investigations were the transmission of speech and signals, and finding electronic contacts that could also transmit speech current and ringing signals to the telephone. It was still not easy to find solutions that could compete with electromechanics.

Around 1950, ideas for switching speech signals in time division multiplex, TDM, were floated in the USA and Britain. The analogy with mechanical switching was now no longer possible: in its simplest form, TDM transmits all conversations through a common point known as a highway. The speech signals are coded; and each conversation is allotted a time slot. The TDM principle showed some promise, but trial systems built in the labs showed that while it was possible to use TDM to build switches, it was not a commercial proposition.

In 1954, LME completed a TDM-based trial exchange called the Electronic Multiplex Automatic Exchange, EMAX, using diodes and cathode ray tubes. EMAX used the principle of 'resonant transfer', invented

OPPOSITE: *Death of an old friend: Malte Patricks, Senior Director at LM Ericsson, and Bertil Bjurel, Director General at Televerket, muse over the relics of some pole lines. All over the world, 'telegraph wires' are coming down, replaced by copper cable and optical fibre buried underground.*

by Gunnar Svala and Bertil Hård, which provided speech transmission practically free from loss. This in turn meant that TDM systems could be built without amplifiers and with a single-wire speech network. Resonant transfer came to be used in several applications at LME and elsewhere.

However, with the appearance of the transistor in 1950, and particularly after the introduction of the junction transistor in 1954, it became clear that here was a technology offering much greater possibilities. The development of semiconductors, which rapidly led to integrated circuits, produced results unimaginable just a few years earlier. It was the first sign of radical change in telecommunications (and in most areas of electrical engineering, for that matter).

After EMAX, preparations were made for development of a new TDM switch based on semiconductors. Efforts were also made to introduce electronics into existing systems. In the early '50s, voice-frequency tone signalling had been adopted for the transmission of numerical signals, primarily in long-distance networks, which meant electronic signal generators and receivers in transmission equipment. These were an early target for a change to transistors.

Gunnar Svala (left) and Kurt Katzeff (centre) are awarded medals by the Swedish Academy of Engineering Sciences for their pioneering work in electronic switching. Also in the picture is technical guru Dr Christian Jacobæus.

Transmission and the introduction of digital technology

Soon after the end of the war, LM Ericsson brought out its first transmission system for coaxial cable, working at 4 MHz with 960 channels. The first system was installed in Sweden in 1950 on the Stockholm-Gothenburg route. In the '50s, a 12 MHz system was introduced, providing 2,700 speech channels. It was the first in the world with this high capacity, but it represented the maximum that could be achieved with electron tube technology. In 1964, LME started development work using semiconductor technology, transistors, on a 60 MHz system, and brought out terminal equipment for 10,800 channels. This was first installed in 1972 – again in Sweden.

The transistor brought a radical change to transmission through its low power consumption. The cable repeaters, or amplifiers, became smaller and more robust, were installed underground, and were powered from remote points.

A small-diameter coaxial cable was introduced around 1960, and LME developed a transmission system for 300 channels, later followed by products offering 960 and 2,700 channels. A large seller was a system for small, single tube, coaxial cable, which was often used in aerial form, strung up along existing pole routes on which earlier open wire had been taken down.

In carrier equipment, LME was to focus on frequency division techniques, initially for cable. With modifications to the terminal equipment, the same systems were adapted for open-wire lines and for radio relay links.

From the 1950s, transmission equipment took on an increasingly important role in the company´s business with the PTTs. This meant that local manufacture became important, and production was started up in several subsidiary companies, notably Norway, Italy, Mexico, Brazil and Portugal. There were also licence agreements with non-LME companies in several countries.

The start of the digital revolution in telecommunications

Until the mid-'60s, transmission systems were built on the frequency division multiplex principle, meaning that the speech channels were assigned to different 'carrier' frequencies within the available band. Now, a new technology emerged, called time division multiplex, which made use of pulse code modulation, PCM.

PCM was proposed in 1937 by Alec Reeves, an Englishman working in Paris for ITT. But the technology to make PCM a commercial proposition was just not available at the time. It was the invention of the transistor and the development of integrated circuits that brought PCM into commercial use during the 1960s.

Two international standards evolved, one at 1.5 Mb/s with 24 speech channels per line, and the other at 2 Mb/s with 30 channels plus two channels used for signalling purposes.

LME introduced a first, 24-channel, PCM transmission system as a trial in 1963, but soon followed with a 30-channel system. It was to take several years before PCM transmission was generally accepted on the markets and its heyday was not to come until the 1970s.

Testing PCM, Oman.

LME and Televerket:
an attempt at a coordinated approach

Televerket had kept up vigorous research and development activities in telephone switching (among other fields) since the 1920s. In the 1950s Televerket's labs were also working on electronic switching, and in many ways the activity paralleled what was going on at LME. In 1956 the two parties came to an agreement to coordinate their work in this area, and a joint 'Electronics Council' (Elektroniknämnden) was formed. The results were not particularly impressive, since the interests and characters of the two parties were diametrically opposed – on one side, a state monopoly; on the other, an international commercial concern. And the vendor-customer relationship was of course tricky to handle at times.

There was some exchange of information and ideas through the Council, but it soon became evident that the parties were aiming in somewhat different technical directions: Televerket was an advocate of space division switching, while LME was concentrating its efforts on time division.

The US Air Force and a successful electronic switch

Late in 1959 LME's plans for developing a full-scale TDM switching system (without, as yet, computer control, SPC) had matured. Meanwhile, the LME subsidiary in the USA, North Electric, a well-established supplier to the US Armed Forces, had received an enquiry for all-electronic exchanges for a tactical communications system for the US Air Force. The specifications required advanced traffic-handling, very high operational security, fast switching and flexibility – plus the requirement that one of the versions should be transportable by helicopter. NEC succeeded in getting the supply contract, with LME as subcontractor. It was a major success for LM Ericsson.

The system became known as the 412L. Company lore has it that at the last minute, en route to make a presentation of the system to the customer, the Swedish team realised that the product had to have a name, and 412L was the number of the SAS flight from Copenhagen to New York.

The project proved to involve more effort than had been anticipated, but the first 412L all-electronic switches were delivered on time and successfully incorporated in the US Air Force tactical system.

The 412L represented a substantial advance in many ways. LME was able to try out electronic switching in a real and complex environment. The leading brains in the development of the 412L were Gunnar Svala and Kurt Katzeff with a cadre of young electronic switching engineers growing up around the project. They later became a core resource for future developments in stored program control and digital switching systems.

The equipment functioned to the full satisfaction of the US Air Force, and as additional orders were received over time, the system was modernised in several stages. For many years, there were 412L systems in operation, not only in North America, but also with NATO elsewhere in the world. LME was never told exactly where they were – such is the nature of defence work – but the 412L was a commercial success.

Stored Program Control – the major advance

Back now to the Electronics Council. By 1963, though the managements of Televerket and LME still shared a desire for closer cooperation, the lack of real cooperation at the working level had become embarrassing.

It was Torsten Larsson, the newly appointed Technical Director of Televerket, who came to the conclusion that instead of trying to force the two organisations into a shotgun marriage, it would be more practical to accept the fait accompli. At a meeting between the managements of the two parties he reported his thoughts and it was formally decided that each party would dedicate its efforts to its respective system developments. Televerket would continue with a system for large city exchanges – the A210 project; and LM Ericsson would devote its efforts to a system for smaller towns and rural areas – the AKE 12 project. There would be certain shared work in basic technology, such as memories.

With hindsight, we can see that this was a wise decision. If the parties had been forced into some form of joint development it would have meant much controversy; and with the technology available at the time, the results would undoubtedly been both slow in coming and disappointing in performance. Instead, the two organisations gained tremendous experience individually, experience which was to become a critical asset in a later stage.

At LM Ericsson, development of the AKE 12 system went ahead, with Lars-Olof Norén as project leader. The key feature was the method for controlling the system, called Stored Program Control, SPC. With SPC, the switches and all the elements of the exchange are supervised and controlled by a computer. And not just any computer: the nature of telephone traffic, in which subscribers pick up their phones to make a call at any time and where calls arrive from other exchanges at any moment, requires a computer working in 'real time'.

The switch element chosen for AKE 12 was the code switch. In 1968, the first AKE 12 exchange went into service in Tumba, a community about 30

*The first AKE 12 to go into
service was the exchange in
Tumba (shown here) in
Sweden in 1968.*

kilometres outside Stockholm. Testing the installation became a lengthy business, since software development continued right through to the day of the cut-over (and after).

At the same time as the Tumba installation was cut over, a similar SPC exchange (with 4-wire speech paths) was provided to the Swedish Air Force. These were the first working SPC exchanges outside the United States.

In the meantime, LME marketing and sales people had been busy introducing the AKE system to customers around the world. There were, of course, many references to what was going on in the US, and the exciting new technology coming out of Bell Labs, and the response was keen and favourable.

In many countries there was a growing need for switching equipment for large transit exchanges, stemming from the fast growth of semi-automatic and fully-automatic long distance traffic. This led LM Ericsson to start up a second SPC-based development programme for a larger system with a more powerful, multi-processor, control system. This was named the AKE 13 system, designed for large national and international transit exchanges. The first orders were booked in 1966.

273

An early warning

In 1968, the Australian Post Office (as it was then) issued an international invitation to tender for a large transit exchange, Pitt Street in Sydney. This was precisely the sort of application for which AKE 13 was being designed. Together with its Australian company, Ericsson Pty Ltd, LM Ericsson worked out a proposal. The APO specification listed large numbers of requirements that made stored program control an obvious choice. AKE 13 was well under way and would meet all these requirements.

The only other contender for the order was ITT, which had now introduced its Metaconta system. The offers were submitted in January 1969. The LME team felt optimistic about the outcome – but in September the APO announced that it had chosen Metaconta! It was a serious blow, but it was recognised as a clear indication of the way the telecoms world was heading.

Other SPC applications

During the 1960s, and indeed the 1970s as well, most telephone exchange sales were crossbar. LME's crossbar had become the system of choice in many markets, crossbar was being produced in many countries, and the installed base continued to grow in a very satisfactory way. It was natural to look at the potential for modernising the crossbar systems to increase functionality and make the system more useful – more flexible and more cost-effective – for the customers.

There was an early attempt to replace the logic of the crossbar systems – markers and registers, largely made up of relay circuitry – with electronics. The result was not encouraging. Indeed, it demonstrated that any significant upgrading of features and performance would be achieved only by introducing stored program control, a solution which would also add a new level of facilities for operation and maintenance.

The new SPC marker-register product for the crossbar systems, first installed in the early 1970s, was named ANA 30. With ANA 30, the local exchange system ARF became ARE 11, and the transit system ARM became ARE 13. ANA 30 was also sold separately for upgrading existing installations of ARF and ARM.

The 1960s, as we have seen, were years of very strong growth in telephone networks, worldwide. The number of subscribers grew, cities expanded and long-distance automatic traffic increased. A particular problem arose in metropolitan networks, which called for the introduction of large local transit, or tandem, switching systems. For this metropolitan environment, LME developed a new tandem system called the ANC 11,

*Local and transit crossbar
exchange at Saida, Algeria.*

which could be incorporated into the existing ARF crossbar exchanges or
set up as stand-alone tandem switches. The ANC 11 used electronic control and the code switch, though the code switch was eventually replaced
by reed relay matrices.

275

CHAPTER 14

1970–1984

A switch in time

AXE and the emerging information age

125 years down the line, it's clear that Ericsson is part of a world that Lars Magnus could never have envisaged. It's a world created by a revolution even more fundamental than the industrial revolution – the information revolution – and Ericsson was one of the revolutionaries.

This new information age is digital. It's service-driven and market-driven. It's relationships-based. It's transparent. It involves cooperative efforts and joint ventures and agreed protocols between purchasers and vendors, customers and competitors, governments and business, and the man and the woman in the street.

It began with computer technology. It came to include telecommunications technology, as computers came in to control telecoms equipment.

Both technologies, and many of the other elements – relationships, protocols and regulations, cooperation, and so on – are present from the beginning in the story of LM Ericsson's first great contribution to the information age: the architecture of the AXE digital switch.

But back in 1970, Ericsson, like the rest of the world, was not aware of what was to come. The market was still a rigid structure, defined largely by government rules and monopoly operators. Ericsson had made, and continued to make, substantial inroads into new areas of this market, and its success was above all based on technology.

Ericsson's decision to develop a new switching system, including computer control and digital switching technology, was taken as a natural evolutionary step in a well-known and stable world. The company could not foresee the liberalisation and global market of the future. But in defining the characteristics of its new switching system – which much later became known as the AXE system – the company showed exceptional foresight.

OPPOSITE:
AXE exchange in Kuwait.

An early attempt at joint development

It didn't look like that in the beginning, of course. In the 1950s and '60s, Ericsson and Televerket had tried cooperative development, but as we've seen, the attempts at coordination were not a success. The Electronics Council was ahead of its time, the necessary culture didn't exist, the results were minimal, and the two parties went in their own respective directions. In Ericsson's case, this meant continuing to develop SPC code switch exchanges, the AKE system.

By the late '60s, it was time for a review. What had Ericsson learned from the many years put into stored program control?

True, it had learned how to build, manage and operate SPC systems. And it was clear that the added functionality offered by stored program control was becoming appreciated by customers – was, indeed, becoming a prerequisite. But Ericsson had also learned that the current generation of SPC, as it existed in the late '60s, was expensive and complex – worthwhile in major national and international transit centres, but not obviously cost-effective for local exchanges in large numbers over wide areas. The disadvantages were above all in the high costs of handling – design, testing, modification, fault-correction, production, installation, and operation and maintenance.

Furthermore, the code switch and crossbar content of Ericsson's SPC systems was beginning to look outdated. And the Pitt Street decision was pointing the way …

Televerket was having similar experiences and encountering similar difficulties. Both organisations were also realising that switching system development costs, traditionally measured in tens of man-years, were starting to be measured in hundreds of man-years. The rules of the game were changing.

Establishing Ellemtel

It was time to look at cooperation again, but in a new way – a joint venture, with its own individual programmes and objectives, single-mindedly developing systems that both parents could use. A venture that could develop its own individual culture and with a high degree of independence.

In May 1970, Ellemtel (Ellemtel Utvecklings AB) was formed as a 50/50 joint venture development company. The baby had four main godparents: Björn Lundvall, President, and Fred Sundqvist, head of the

Switching Division, at Ericsson; and Bertil Bjurel, Director General, and Torsten Larsson, Technical Director, at Televerket.

And the baby was born with its future all mapped out: among the first tasks defined for Ellemtel was a project with the code name AX, the development of a proposal for an SPC local exchange system which would offer positive cost benefits.

Network construction in Thailand.

First step: the requirement specification

It's important for any organisation given a system to design to leave designing till the last sensible moment. The early effort is best directed at agreeing what the 'deliverables' of the system must be – and then getting sign-off – before the hideously expensive business of designing starts.

These deliverables are collected in a requirement specification, and Ellemtel got two of them, one from Televerket, one from Ericsson.

Ericsson's requirement specification was written by a small working group in the marketing section of the Switching Division, headed by Inge Jönsson. The group was formed in the autumn of 1970, and its activities represented a breakthrough in the history of Ericsson – in some ways even more significant than the development of AXE itself.

Traditionally, technology companies wrote requirement specifications from a technology point of view: 'What can we do, and how can we do it?' Inge Jönsson's group decided that the specification should be 'written by the market' – not 'What can we do?' but 'What do they want, and what will they buy?'

Today, it seems natural to start a marketing exercise by considering the market. In 1970, and particularly in a large engineering company, it was trail-blazing. It was the beginning of marketing in Ericsson.

Design ping-pong

Throughout 1971, the requirement specification and Ellemtel's responses to it went backwards and forwards. It was not a smooth process – it could hardly be so – but slowly some crucial guiding principles and a modification of the initial brief emerged.

The brief to Ellemtel was more complex than it seemed. To begin with, there were the two requirement specifications, one from each parent. Televerket was concerned to get a switch developed that would specifically fit the Swedish network environment. Ericsson had worldwide export in view. To a degree, the specifications were in conflict. The more closely any switching system would fit the Swedish environment, the more work would have to be done to make it fit the very varied markets where Ericsson had ambitions. Adaptations are expensive, and the whole point of the brief was to keep costs manageable.

The solution was to build up the system in such a way that features and functions, or function packages, were designed in blocks – modules – any of which could be included or omitted or modified without affecting the rest of the system. The modular principle had begun to emerge in connection with AKE, for different reasons. As 'functional modularity', it was to become one of the central defining features of AXE, later adopted by every designer of switching systems in the world.

The second guiding principle was ease of 'handling', the experience that the first-generation stored program control had so clearly pointed up – the new system must be easy to design in hardware and software, easy to manufacture and test, easy to instal, easy to document, easy to teach to operating staff, easy to operate and maintain.

Any such system would surely also be easy to sell ... and if so, why make things harder by sticking to the brief for a local exchange? In the long run, would any administration be interested in a system that, however attractive, could be implemented only in local exchanges?

And what effect would functional modularity have on the structure of the network? It should be easy to separate the group switch function set from the subscriber switch function set, and if some of the subscriber stages could be remoted, it could mean significant savings in the cable network. Perhaps it was time to abandon the restrictive concept of a monolithic local exchange, and think of it as two more or less autonomous parts: the subscriber switch subsystem, and the group switch subsystem.

This concept in turn highlighted the switching technology itself. Initially electromechanical, how long would it be before it went digital? Shouldn't the design allow digital switching technology to replace electromechanical technology without altering the system concept? A digital group switch in particular would offer significant advantages to operators by cutting the investment in building a network.

Almost a year went by as these arguments went to and fro, but by the end of 1971 a single joint requirement specification had been worked out together with Televerket, and accepted by Ellemtel ...

- an SPC system which could support a host of end-user services;

- a system capable of implementation as a local, rural, tandem or transit exchange, with remotable subscriber stages, adaptable to any network in the world;

- a system with a traffic-handling capacity (as a local exchange) of up to 40,000 subscribers, with a traffic load of 0.12 Erlang per subscriber and with 90–100 seconds average call-holding time (for traffic engineers, this translates into 144,000 BHCA, Busy Hour Call Attempts);

- a functionally modular system, able to accommodate new technologies and support new services without fundamental system changes (future-proof);

- and above all, a system easy to handle, offering low handling costs.

Ellemtel's 20-year get-together 1990: John Meurling, Bertil Bjurel and Bengt-Gunnar Magnusson all dressed up.

Red, amber, GREEN

It was an attractive specification, but it meant a vast amount of work, and represented an agonising decision.

Ellemtel and Televerket were eager to go ahead with the design and development of the new switch. But the decision for Ericsson, with its global market – and its global competition – was difficult.

ITT and Northern Telecom had SPC products in service. The Japanese D10 system was a year down the road, Siemens was a year behind the Japanese, and Philips a year behind Siemens. If Ericsson chose to develop the new AX product, it would be a year behind even Philips with a working commercial system installed – 1976 at the earliest – and most of any SPC market there was might well have been taken. Plus, there was the little matter of the $ 30 m or 1,200 man years it would take to develop AX …

(Note that the $ 30 m dollars and 1,200 man years were just to cover the development of a first prototype: naturally, in the 30 years following, many times those numbers have been invested in the development of AX.)

On the other hand, Ericsson was well on the way in the development and sales of the AKE13 transit exchange system, and had started up a second development program, AKE11, for local exchange applications. If Ericsson chose to stick to these code switch SPC systems, supplemented by ARE crossbar, it could get its first local exchanges into service in 1972. But that would mean seriously postponing any new switch, and going into service with systems which had known limitations: the loss to ITT in Australia loomed large.

How significant a market was there for SPC systems? Would one develop? Where and when?

And what about digital switching? Many people were exploring different concepts of digital switching. CIT-Alcatel had actually introduced its E10 – at this early stage a small system, but undeniably with a digital switch. And digital technology was looking more and more promising as the price of memory chips started to fall: the fourth of the principal requirements listed above foresaw what had to come.

Bengt-Gunnar Magnusson had been the driving force behind Televerket's A210 stored program control development project during the '60s. In 1968 he had transferred to LM Ericsson, and had been given the task of working out a new SPC system proposal, pulling together the experience of Televerket and LME. He was recognised as the leading expert in the field, also as a no-compromise doer – and something of a character. His system proposals (there were two of them by 1970) had formed part of the input to the new Ellemtel company, as had Bengt-Gunnar himself, who became head of the X Department. X Department was to be responsible for development of the new system, once the partners had reached agreement on what it should be.

Early in 1972, the decision was taken. Hans Sund, who had been appointed from head of the Defence Division to head of the Switching Division less than two years before, pressed strongly for the development of AX. At the crucial LME meeting, Björn Lundvall, the President, asked searching questions, and to the very end, the decision was acutely difficult. Nevertheless, there was no attempt to fudge or compromise, and when it came, the decision was quite clear: the AX switching system should be developed along the lines proposed by Ellemtel, with an in-service date for the first pilot exchange in 1976. Work on AKE11 was stopped.

What did the herald angels sing?

To introduce a new product to potential customers there is no reference or argument as valuable as a working exchange. Presentations may be persuasive and elegant, documentation excellent, and the lunch delectable, but nothing beats a working reference installation.

The site for the first AXE exchange to be installed was the subject of serious deliberations. It would have to be in Sweden, of course, and Televerket had strong views on location, and how it should fit into the Swedish telephone network. Ericsson felt it must be within easy reach of Stockholm, accessible to prospective customers. It wanted premises spacious enough for groups of visitors to be taken through. And it asked for a separate room in the same building, to hold about 20 people, which could be used for presentations.

Both sides got almost everything they hoped for. Södertälje, a town some 50 km from Stockholm, was to be the site of the first AXE exchange in the world. Södertälje was to be the name on everyone's lips. Södertälje was to herald the coming of the new-born babe, the second-generation SPC switching system.

Only one thing had been overlooked: more than 95 per cent of the visitors would be from overseas, and nobody from overseas can pronounce, let alone spell, the name of the city of Södertälje …

Kick-off

The name AXE has become firmly attached to Ericsson's digital switching system. It's easy to forget that the pilot AXE exchange that went into service in 1976 was analogue. It was not until 1978 that the first AXE exchange with a digital group switch came into service at Turku in Finland. Ellemtel was charged to develop not a new technology, but a new switch structure (today we would call it an architecture) that could accept new technologies as they came along.

As we've seen, AX system development was the responsibility of the X Department within Ellemtel, headed by Bengt-Gunnar Magnusson. Two other individuals should be mentioned here as providing key contributions to the design of the system. Göran Hemdahl, a man with a truly innovative mind, provided much of the basis for a new software structure, the software signalling principles and a new programming language. Soon after the completion of the project and the cut-over of the first installation, Göran left Ellemtel, due to an unfortunate tiff with Ericsson management, and joined ITT. Today, he is running his own successful business. Ivar Jacobsson was not part of the AXE development team (he had been working with the AKE13 system) but he made the very important contribution of the 'block concept', the structuring of the system into self-contained functional blocks, with all interworking between blocks performed by software signals – the concept of functional modularity that has over time become an industry standard. Ivar Jacobsson went on to a doctor's degree, left Ericsson and started his own software company. Ericsson became a part owner, then the company was sold to Rational Software, and Ivar moved to California.

Ellemtel had not, of course, been sitting idle since 1970, waiting for agreement to proceed. It had been heavily involved in the ping-pong game, and had made its first design recommendations. These were rejected by Ericsson on three grounds – cost (too high, particularly for the smaller exchanges); capacity (too low, at a maximum of 32,000 subscribers, instead of the 40,000 in the requirement specification); and reliability (below industry standards in some respects). When the decision to develop AX was taken in Spring 1972, Ellemtel had proposed ways to meet such criticism, at least on paper, but they persisted as critical development benchmarks through 1973 and beyond.

1973 was in many ways the turning point in the development process. It was the year in which the name AXE was finally adopted, and in which Södertälje, just outside Stockholm, was selected as the site of the pilot exchange, and the year in which efforts began to 'market' AXE internally within Ericsson. It was also the year in which Ericsson made its first, low-key, presentation of AXE to a customer, the Helsinki Telephone Company.

By 1974, Ericsson could with some confidence start to expose its new switch to selected customers and prospects – adopting what became known as the 'canine concept': as a dog marks certain trees to establish its territorial claims, Ericsson would try to get as many of its customers as possible to commit to one 'model' AXE exchange. It was some years since Ericsson had introduced any serious new systems. It could still not hope to make any sales at this early stage, but it might persuade some Administrations to wait and see how AXE would turn out, instead of making an instant system choice from one of Ericsson's competitors. In all, Ericsson made some 20 customer presentations of AXE in 1974.

The same broad pattern, but now broken by the first AXE contracts, continued throughout 1975, though by the Autumn Ericsson felt able to display one rack of AXE at the world's premier telecommunications exhibition, Telecom 75 in Geneva. It aroused considerable interest.

Then at last, late in 1976, the pilot exchange in Södertälje went into trial service, for debugging, before its successful official cut-over on 1 March 1977.

AXE was in business.

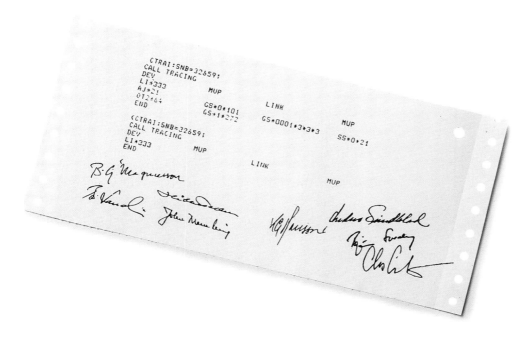

Print-out, recording first call through an AXE switch.

Control room of the Turku AXE exchange, 1978.

Behind the Turku decision

25 years after the Turku conversion, everything sounds fairly simple and straightforward. In real life, things were a little more complicated. Veikko Tähti, the General Manager of the Turku Telephone Company (owned by the local authority) is a gentleman and friend of great charm, but tough as nails. In 1969, Mr Tähti had ordered an AKE 13 exchange to handle transit and tandem traffic, and in 1970 this contract had been complemented by an order for an AKE 11 local exchange for 4,000 subscribers. By 1973, and before presenting AXE to other Finnish customers, it was necessary to inform him that his new local exchange was not only delayed, but would in fact never appear. In its place, Hans Flinck offered an AXE local exchange. Veikko eventually agreed.

A couple of years later, the digital AXE group switch was in development, but the engineers claimed they desperately needed a customer order to justify putting more effort into the development programme.

It was time for Hans Flinck to pay another visit to Turku. Veikko Tähti, obviously, asked, 'What on earth do I need a digital switch for? I don't have a single PCM transmission system in my network.' Hans suggested that the Turku administration would wish to demonstrate to the rest of the Finnish telecoms community that it was a truly modern, forward-looking administration. 'But how can I defend such a decision?' 'Well, since you need more transmission, why don't you buy some PCM?'

So Veikko bought some PCM systems

from Nokia, but then he said, 'I can't defend the outlay for a second pair of processors.' (The tandem was going into the same building as the local AXE.) 'All right,' said Hans, 'the processors will not appear in the specifications: they are free of charge.'

To get the new digital tandem into traffic as soon as possible, and since the programmers were worried about covering a large variety of signalling interfaces, it was further agreed that the new tandem would initially handle only overflow tandem traffic, and only PCM connections.

This arrangement also had the advantage that in demonstrations the switch could be manhandled fairly roughly without losing calls – a quality that was to become most useful.

Setting off into the digital world

During this worrying time, when Ericsson had primarily crossbar to sell, and nothing that was new to offer (while its competitors claimed to have so much) one piece of luck came Ericsson's way. At the end of 1973, the first big international oil crisis hit the world. By the end of 1974, as the world economy slowed down, telephone administrations found themselves short of funds – which meant postponing decisions to invest in new systems on any large scale. For Ericsson, it was a valuable breathing space.

And though the time was worrying, it was not completely barren. Even before the official cut-over of Södertälje, Ericsson had two firm orders for AXE, and one that was conditional on a successful cut-over of the pilot ...

In 1973, Ericsson persuaded the Turku administration in Finland, with which it had a long-standing and very warm relationship, to cancel an order for AKE 11 (the code switch SPC system on which development had been stopped), which the administration had placed in 1970, and replace it with an order for AXE. An analogue local AXE exchange for 4,000 subscribers was duly delivered in 1977 (the first commercial AXE exchange ever installed), followed by a digital tandem exchange in 1978 (the first digital AXE exchange ever installed).

The next order came from France, which in 1975 was looking for a second supplier of analogue SPC exchanges to complement the CIT-Alcatel E10. It was a condition of the order that the exchanges should be manufactured in France, and any companies tendering should be French. After an enormously complicated round of musical chairs, in December 1976 the French government chose Thomson-CSF to manufacture and supply AXE under licence. It was a large order, and for many years France was the market with the largest number of AXE lines installed – virtually none of them supplied by Ericsson!

Just two serious orders: not a vast amount to show for the years of anxious toil.

Meanwhile – down under

Quite a lot has been said about the digital switchblocks for the AXE system. As a matter of fact the first, and basic, digital switch development was performed a long way from LM Ericsson and Ellemtel – in Australia.

LM Ericsson Pty Ltd (EPA), at Broadmeadows outside Melbourne, had built up a strong competence, including an R&D department of keen young engineers. Their first exploration into digital switching technology used the so-called FADM concept, Fast Attack Delta Modulation. They built a prototype switch, documented it and travelled, with switch and documentation, to Stockholm to present it. Reception of the prototype was somewhat cool: LME and Ellemtel engineers had a touch of the NIH (Not Invented Here) syndrome. But it did provoke some serious discussion, the two concrete outcomes of which were decisions that the digital switch for the AXE system must be designed for pulse code modulation (PCM); and that EPA should go ahead and develop a prototype.

A year later, 1974, a couple of engineers from LME and Ellemtel travelled to Australia on a sort of exchange programme: they were to learn about the technology developed at EPA; and to teach their EPA colleagues about the structure of AXE and the hardware and software interfaces necessary for the introduction of a digital switch into the system. In 1975, the EPA design was transferred to Ellemtel and a new prototype was produced and inserted into an AXE test-bed.

Since that time the EPA R&D group has undertaken a number of development tasks, including a rural AXE exchange version.

'A hellish year'

In 1976, LM Ericsson celebrated its centenary.

It was decided to include the launch of the new AXE system as part of the celebrations. Hard times or not, the company was determined to 'put out more flags.' During a week in May, LM Ericsson laid on banquets, receptions, a seminar on telecommunications, and visits to some of the facilities in the Stockholm area. As guests, customers from around the world were invited, along with dignitaries from the ITU, and representatives of the industry. There were important speakers from every continent, and a film was produced for the centenary. Called *Linking People Together*, it had its world première during this hectic week.

A scholarly three-volume company history was produced, tracing the evolution of LM Ericsson from the early workshop days of Lars Magnus Ericsson all the way through the many ups-and-downs of the business.

Fundamentally, LM Ericsson was celebrating a hundred years of electromechanical technology. True, it had been working with electronic technology and products for many years – transmission equipment; defence electronics such as radar; microwave; satellite electronics; and components. For the centenary, it even produced a fully-electronic one-piece telephone – every guest received one, gold-plated. But its largest product area, and the one for which it was most famous, was the telephone exchange. And in 1976, this still meant crossbar.

AXE was at an early test stage in Södertälje. Cut-over was six months away, but bravely Ericsson put the exchange on display over a television link, with a 25-minute review by Björn Svedberg, later CEO but at that time Chief Technical Officer. The exchange performed gracefully. It was the beginning of a new Ericsson, but few of the people watching the display realised just how soon that new Ericsson would emerge.

At the end of that year, Björn Lundvall, the President, referred to 1976 as 'a hellish year', and times were unquestionably hard. Following the oil crisis, customers were coy. They cut back on purchases, which severely affected the company's production volumes in crossbar; and they held off from test installations of AXE.

The chief trouble spot, as far as LM Ericsson was concerned, was Brazil. Very substantial orders for crossbar equipment had been received to implement the large expansion programme of the Brazilian telephone networks, with production in both the Swedish and the Brazilian factories. Then the Brazilian economy went sour, and the large orders were cancelled. As the stocks of goods for shipment piled up, LM Ericsson was facing the difficult decision to cut back on its work force. At this point, the Swedish government stepped in by encouraging Televerket to place early orders for digital AXE exchanges (10 exchanges with a total of 240,000 lines) and PCM transmission equipment. This meant that plant closures were avoided, at least for a time, and it also meant that the AXE reference list looked a good deal healthier.

And at last, as 1976 moved on into 1977, relief was on the way.

Network construction in Thailand. From anniversary film Linking People Together.

A balancing act

At this point, we may as well take a break in the AXE story and see what happened to AKE and ARE.

As we saw in the last chapter, marketing of the AKE 13 system commenced in the mid '60s, and the first exchange was cut into commercial service in 1971, in Rotterdam. This was followed by installations in Denmark, Sweden, Finland, Mexico and other countries. AKE 13 was specifically designed for applications as large national and international transit exchanges – the switchblocks (code switches) could be grouped for up to some 40,000 terminations (lines connected), and with a multi-processor control system a very high call-handling capacity was ensured.

Automatic international telephone traffic was on the increase, and AKE13 became something of a flagship for LM Ericsson during the period from 1969 to around 1976, a time when the main competitors were not able to offer comparable equipment.

But it was a rocky road, and the first customers did suffer some serious delays. One example was Copenhagen: international and national transit traffic was growing fast, and the AKE 13 exchange ordered from LM Ericsson did not appear on time. But customer relations are most important, and LME supplied and installed sizable quantities of ARM crossbar switches to tide Copenhagen over. Free of charge, of course.

AKE 13 exchanges were sold to a total of ten countries, and in 1988 there were still over 430,000 lines in service – the number has naturally gone down since then.

Like AKE, ARE was marketed throughout the 1970–1978 period. And ARE did become an important marketing tool at a time when many customers were hesitating about taking the step into the unknown world of 'full SPC'. A 'delicate' example was Spain. LM Ericsson (in partnership with Telefónica) and SESA, the ITT company, were the local manufacturers. LME wished to introduce the AXE system, but Telefónica declared that it was much too early (this was in 1975) and that there would be no new system until SESA was ready to offer its System 12. But Señor Rebollo, the Telefónica Engineer in Chief, was very interested in computer control in the crossbar exchanges, and initiated a programme for updating the installed Ericsson crossbar base to SPC status, ARE.

The ARE systems can be said to have performed two important roles. On the one hand, ARE was a kiss of life for crossbar – it prolonged the crossbar system's useful existence, both for LM Ericsson and for its customers; and on the other hand, ARE was a gap-filler in some critical markets. For the times, the ARE volumes sold were considerable. Over 6 million lines of ARE were sold and in 1988, there were over 4.3 million lines of ARE 11 still in service and about 100,000 lines of ARE 13.

Which switch?

At the time of the centenary in 1976, LM Ericsson sales people were actively marketing AKE 13, ARE and AXE stored program control switching systems. In press releases, in advertising, at exhibitions and in sales brochures, the Company promoted the three different switching products in parallel. No wonder some of the messages appeared a little schizophrenic, as did some of the messengers. Luckily, this period didn't last long. From 1977, LM Ericsson was promoting AXE all over the world. And AXE was not only a new stored program control concept, it was a digital switching system.

The digital breakthrough

At last, Australia

The fourth order for AXE came from the Australian Post Office.

It was the culmination of the dogfight with ITT that had begun in 1969, when Ericsson lost the contract for the large Pitt Street transit exchange to ITT and its Metaconta system. For Ericsson this had been an important input to the decision to form Ellemtel and to develop a totally new system.

While licking its Pitt Street wounds, Ericsson continued to supply crossbar, and the APO became interested in ARE. In 1972, the APO made a decision that seemed to indicate that the Pitt Street order would not automatically lead to further Metaconta installations – for the City North exchange in Sydney it chose Ericsson crossbar; and by 1973, pilot installations of ARE were being ordered. ITT's Pitt Street Metaconta exchange was due to go into service in January 1974 – but didn't make it. Ericsson felt that honour was restored, at least to some degree.

It was known that the APO was now preparing to make a long-term system choice for local exchanges, and that the invitation to tender would be issued in 1975. Ericsson realised that to match the APO requirements – and the competition – it must offer the new AXE system. But the APO was also insisting that any system offered must be proven, and that there should be exchanges of the proposed type in service.

It took some high-powered arguing, and detailed presentations, to convince the Australians that the AXE system should be included in the tenders, but a proposal was finally submitted in mid-1975.

By May that year, the APO had decided to instal ARE as a standard. In September, it issued a press release announcing that the remaining

contenders for the new system had been whittled down to ITT, with Metaconta 10C, and Ericsson, with AXE. And the APO was prepared to wait, for a couple of years, with its final decision – it still insisted that an AXE exchange should be in service and open for inspection before its final verdict.

And so it was arranged that a delegation from the APO would visit and inspect the first AXE installation in service, at Södertälje, on 2 March 1977, the day after the cut-over. It was a thorough exercise, with Australian engineers crawling all over the place. But the exchange performed well, and the Australians were satisfied that AXE was a working system.

On 13 September, 1977, the APO announced that Australia would standardise on AXE for local exchanges. After eight years the dogfight was over.

Coming just seven months after the cut-over at Södertälje, the Australian commitment was a source of great excitement. But in those seven months, an even more exciting opportunity had appeared.

OPPOSITE:
Testing new AXE-applications at Ericsson Broadmeadows laboratory, Australia, 1976.

The biggest contract in the history of telecommunications

In June 1977, the Ministry of Telecommunications in Saudi Arabia issued an invitation to tender for the largest telecommunications project ever – the entire job of extending the Saudi network with nearly half-a-million lines, and modernising the existing network with stored program control. The project included new SPC exchanges and the updating of crossbar exchanges, telephone sets and transmission systems, plus the installation of all equipment, the building of the cable networks and exchange buildings, and a five-year contract for operation and maintenance.

The Saudi Ministry refused to consider Ericsson's crossbar systems: it must be AXE or nothing at all – at a time when the entire world list of installed AXE systems consisted of the nursery exchange in Södertälje and the small analogue Turku system, still under test.

Ericsson had supplied and installed the existing 200,000-line crossbar network in Saudi Arabia, but in the years after 1972, when Ericsson had nothing new to offer, Philips (with its PRX system) had come very close to getting the huge extension contract unopposed. The size of the contract, however, meant that the Ministry came under pressure to go to public tender, and the task of preparing a tender specification was assigned to the Arthur D. Little consulting company.

The Ministry was recommending that partnerships should be formed by suppliers, to reduce the risk to both sides. Ericsson and Philips agreed to join forces, and Bell Canada International joined the partnership to look after the network operation commitment. The competition was severe, including two consortia led by the world's foremost switching giants: ITT;

and Western Electric, the equipment arm of AT&T (which a year before had landed the contract for the Saudi long-distance microwave network). Ericsson and Philips agreed to share the content of the proposal as follows:

- The supply of switching equipment would be divided strictly 50/50. Ericsson would propose AXE for the largest local exchanges and the transits, and Philips would offer PRX for the remaining exchanges.

- Ericsson would offer new, electronic telephone sets. Philips would take care of most of the PCM transmission systems and cables.

- The exchange buildings would be designed by a Philips subsidiary and built by an outside contractor who would also handle cable network construction.

- In addition, LM Ericsson would offer equipment for updating the existing crossbar network to SPC status, by converting the ARF and ARM exchanges to ARE.

An important feature of digital exchanges was the opportunities they offered to reduce costs in the network (how, is discussed in the next section). Since this was very much a whole-network contract, Ericsson decided to offer exchanges with digital group switches.

Dialog telephone set for Saudi Arabia.

OPPOSITE: *Cable network construction in Riyadh.*

Saudi Arabia:

HM King Khaled and the Minister of Communications, HE Dr Kayal with Björn Svedberg and W. Dekker of Philips, 1978.

The huge proposal was delivered on 27 September 1977. On 13 December 1977, the Ministry announced that it had decided for the Ericsson-Philips-Bell Canada offer, and the contract was signed on 25 January 1978.

The importance to LM Ericsson of the Saudi contract was immense. As we have indicated, the mid-1970s were difficult times. If 1976 had been a hellish year, 1977 was, if anything, more so. The effects of the oil crisis were still being felt. Shipments of crossbar systems were down. The most serious problem was the negative cash flow, and there were again discussions at Board meetings about reducing staff and closing plants. There was even speculation that the company might come under the threat of being taken over.

The contract for Saudi Arabia was huge. The tender conditions specified that the offers be made in Saudi rials. The total contract value was around SEK 10 bn, but, with the rial tied to the US dollar, which rose during the project time, the contract value for LM Ericsson also rose. And 20 per cent of the contract sum was paid up front – which overnight meant a major improvement in LM Ericsson's cash-flow. LM Ericsson was out of the red.

There have been, as this chronicle should have shown, several critical periods in the history of LM Ericsson – World War I, the Russian revolution, the Kreuger crisis, World War II. 1975–77 was another such period, although most people did not realise it at the time. The Saudi Arabia contract was timely, to say the least.

Then came 1978, the year when AXE sales took off. Crossbar systems still made up the bulk of shipments and would continue to be sold for another ten years or more – as late as 1987, over 350,000 lines of local and some 25,000 lines of transit crossbar were shipped and installed, though all these were for extending existing exchanges – but the writing was on the wall. (And, incidentally, the old AGF 500-point system was still being manufactured and sold: it was not until 1982 that the last 'pancake' selector left the factory.)

Why digital?

For a full, easily-comprehensible description of digital telecommunications we have to refer the reader to the bibliography. Here, we can only look at the benefits digital technology was seen to offer in 1977.

Stored Program Control, or computer control, we've met. Its advantages had by now become universally accepted and understood in the telecommunications community. The concept of working with software, as opposed to screwdriver and soldering iron, in the telephone network had become well established.

But we haven't heard much about digital transmission – the transmission of a digital bit stream instead of a continuous analogue signal. Yet by the end of the '60s, digital transmission was arousing a lot of interest: using the techniques of Pulse Code Modulation, PCM, and Time Division Multiplexing, TDM, digital transmission systems had become widely deployed in the long- and medium-distance networks. Digital transmission was also attractive in the local networks, of course – in cities with growing numbers of dense cable routes, for example.

The potential reduction in the cost of cabling (which at that time represented most of the cost of a network) was obvious. But when digital transmission was switched by analogue switches, the transmission had to be converted from digital to analogue and back again wherever it entered or left a switch – and the devices for conversion, codecs (coder/decoder), were an added cost. Now, if a switch could be designed that would switch digital speech channels, the codecs could be eliminated and total network cost could be reduced …

And that, of course, is the facility that digital switching was designed to

Network planning

In the old days the planning of cable networks was largely a manual discipline. In a town or city the exchange, or exchanges were tentatively positioned on the map, the expected numbers and locations of subscribers were marked in and the different parts of the cable network and distribution points were sited and calculated. As the telephone networks grew in density it became a matter of growing economic importance to find methods of optimising networks.

Dr Yngve Rapp had worked with network construction in, among other countries, Turkey, Greece and Italy. In the 1950s he began a series of studies to formulate models for network planning, and brought out several reports presenting solutions for economical planning of local and trunk networks, economical locating of exchanges and determination of the most favourable expansion stages for cable networks and exchanges. His methods were computerized in the 1960s and became recognised in most parts of the world. They also became an important tool in Ericsson's customer relations and marketing of crossbar, and especially so when the digital network became the key to marketing the AXE system.

offer at every level, from small local exchanges to huge international transits. We should remember, too, the modular architecture of the AXE switch, which allowed the network planner to locate the access switches of a local exchange remote from the exchange and close to the subscribers, connected over digital lines.

With SPC to look after the handling costs, integrated digital switching and transmission transformed the economics of the network. Eventually it would lead to its complete re-structuring.

And for the first time, the network was becoming the key concept. Before digital technology entered the picture, switching was switching and transmission was transmission – different technologies, different disciplines, different departments within an administration. With digital technology, the network began to take the central position it still occupies within telecommunications.

Developing the digital network

The most visible and dramatic events of the years 1978–1988 were in the field of marketing, and we'll look at those in the next section.

But those ten years also saw the development of the digital network systems and solutions that would carry the basic structure of the world's networks into the new millennium.

IDN

The first concept was called just IDN, the Integrated Digital Network. It was strictly a network definition, for networks where switching and transmission were integrated.

But soon, a new concept emerged, based largely on the needs of the private networks – the businesses and other customers who were increasingly dependent on data services. ISDN, the Integrated Services Digital Network, aroused much interest and, at the time, seemed to have great potential.

ISDN

The ISDN standard specification was developed within the CCITT, and was given some initial push by the PTTs and other public network operators. It had many merits, but above all it was seen by network operators as a means of attracting data traffic. ISDN was part of a long-term strategy to ensure that future data traffic and services stayed in the realm of the public networks.

ISDN installation at Jydsk Telefon in Aarhus, Denmark. By this time, 1989, practical testing was being carried out in many parts of the world with simultaneous transmission of voice and data.

With the ISDN concept, operators would offer subscribers 144 kb/s facilities over the local loop, initially to give two 64 kb/s voice channels and a 16 kb/s data channel – the 2B + D configuration; or for business customers, 16B + D. Ericsson was the first company to demonstrate ISDN, at the International Switching Symposium in Florence in 1983, and installed the world's first nation-wide ISDN in Australia.

But ISDN was expensive to develop and expensive to instal. In real network life, operators were for many years more concerned simply to digitalise their core IDNs, and were not very adept at marketing ISDN to their customers. It was only in the '90s, as operators were looking for new services, and becoming aware of the Internet expansion, that ISDN took off.

IN – the Intelligent Network

Services provided by the Intelligent Network, on the other hand, were immediately popular, and developed rapidly. The key technology for the Intelligent Network is Common Channel Signalling, most notably the Number 7 standard developed by the CCITT (CCITT No 7). In the traditional analogue network, speech and signalling occupied the same circuits and travelled at the same speed, and the time taken for signalling significantly tied up the network. With CCS, signalling is separated from the speech or data traffic paths. It travels as high-speed data to any network node, along whichever routes are available, and massively reduces the 'signalling overhead'.

Before the Intelligent Network concept was introduced, any service required in the network had to be wired in, or programmed into and resident at every network node involved. With the Intelligent Network, services are defined in software, and can be introduced at one or a few IN nodes in the network, and activated by signalling. Many of these services depend on number translation at a network node, a Service Control Point (SCP), which is a computer with database capability. So, for example, when a subscriber dials an 0800 (called party pays) number, a signal goes to an SCP, which compares the number with the instructions in its database and says, 'Ah, this number means that the call should go to the Gothenburg office of the XYZ company, not the Stockholm Head Office, and should be charged to the XYZ company, not the caller.' It then instructs another node, the Service Switching Point (SSP), to set up the call in the most economical way. The whole transaction is virtually instantaneous, and the subscriber is unaware of it.

Today, very sophisticated and elaborate services – premium rate offering, account calling, universal access number, virtual private network, virtual leased lines, universal personal telecommunication – are available through the Intelligent Network. Standards are not truly global, and the

European version, in the development of which Ericsson was a very active partner, differs from the US version. But Ericsson supplies IN equipment worldwide.

In its first implementation of the Intelligent Network, in 1986, Ericsson combined the SCP and the SSP in a single AXE unit. In 1993, separate SCPs and SSPs were introduced, and today a UNIX-based alternative is on offer. The third node element in an Intelligent Network configuration is the STP, the Signal Transfer Point. The STP is a switch that connects common channel signalling circuits from the exchanges to the SCP and the SSP. Implemented in AXE, it became quite popular, even with the Regional Bell Operators in the US. Ericsson has become one of the leading suppliers of IN, with systems installed in a large number of networks, including multi-national operators and cellular operators.

Network management

In an earlier section we have seen how the LM Ericsson Defence Division developed a computer system for production-control applications, the UAC 1610. In production control, this computer had a limited life, but as early as 1976 the international crossbar exchanges in London, Mollison and Thames, were equipped with international accounting systems using the UAC 1610.

At around the same time, the AXE proposal for Australia was being prepared, in which an important item, strongly emphasised by the APO, was a system for centralised operation and maintenance of the AXE exchanges. In the proposal, LME specified PDP computers from DEC. But by the time the contract was signed, in 1977, it had been decided to upgrade the UAC 1610 for applications as a network management system. The product was named the AOM 101. The AOM 101 came out in 1978–79 and went into AXE networks in, among other countries, Australia, Saudi Arabia and Finland. A total of some 250 systems were sold.

In some ways, the introduction of centralised O&M (Operation and Maintenance) was even more dramatic. Certainly, the APO decision to implement AOM was a factor in a long battle with the union over staff reductions in the exchanges. With centralised operation and maintenance, the staff could be taken out completely.

By the mid-'80s, however, it had become clear that Ericsson needed a more modern and powerful system for operation and maintenance.

It is in the nature of the application that O&M computers are not sold in large quantities – basically, only one is needed per maintenance area. On the other hand, O&M systems require a very wide variety of software applications to run on these computers. So for the next generation of centralised operation and maintenance systems, it was decided to source the computer from outside Ericsson, instead of developing it in-house. There was a period when computers were bought from SUN Micro-systems, but Ericsson's systems people were not completely happy, since they considered the UNIX programming language a constraint. When development costs continued to soar, it was decided to seek a partnering solution instead.

In March 1992 (we're getting ahead, but we may as well complete the story) agreement was reached with Hewlett Packard to form a joint venture company, Ericsson-Hewlett Packard Telecommunications, EHPT, in which Ericsson has a 60 per cent share.

The TMOS, Telecommunications Management and Operations System, that EHPT supplies is now well established. TMOS is a platform on which are built many different operation and management applications. One example is CMAS, Cellular Management System, for cellular networks, which includes cell-planning facilities; another is BMAS, Business Group Management System, for business networks and Centrex applications.

In the old days, top management in telephone companies often tended to regard operation and management systems as something of a necessary evil. Not so today. They are the main tools for assuring operators that the network is performing efficiently and to high quality standards, on a continuous basis. They are also important planning tools for growth and change in the network. A well-planned and well-run network management system has become a key competitive tool for the operator.

Many other developments, which were in the pipeline in the '80s, began to make a contribution only in the '90s, and will be considered there.

But one development of the digital network (if you like to see it as that) is so important that it must have a section to itself later: mobile telephony, which had an effect on Ericsson's global status and success even more dramatic than that of AXE.

Dog bites man bites dog

An old chestnut: What staff is required for an AXE exchange?

- A man and a dog.
- ?
- The dog is there to see the man doesn't touch the equipment.
- ?
- The man? Oh, he's there to feed the dog.

Telecommunications control centre in Riyadh, Saudi Arabia.

CHAPTER 15

Opening up the digital market place

A s the '80s began, it was clear not only that AXE was a great success, but that the whole world of information management and movement had wakened to new ways – digital ways – of doing things.

It was still early days for digital telephony, but IBM was about to introduce the personal computer. Nearly twenty years later, the seismic shocks that followed its introduction are still being felt.

There were structural shocks to absorb as well. Though the break-up of AT&T and the privatisation of British Telecom were not to happen until 1984, even the discussions on the way led to an all-pervasive restlessness. Like several other industry leaders, Ericsson also foresaw the convergence of the telecoms and computer worlds, and was eager to be in at the beginning – prematurely, as it turned out.

'Change' began to appear as a factor in every industrial analysis, every report from management consultants, every strategy and every mission statement. (It has never disappeared.)

On 1 January 1983, just seven years after its 100-year anniversary, a transformed LM Ericsson demonstrated its response to this changing world.

The world according to LM Ericsson.

OPPOSITE:
Installing aerial cable, Thailand.

A new company

ERICSSON

Though the official name remained Telefonaktiebolaget LM Ericsson, the Group began to project itself simply as 'Ericsson', with a new symbol (a stylised E), and a completely new organisational structure. Ericsson was organised into 'Business Areas', as follows:

BX, Public Telecommunications: telephone, telex and data exchanges; transmission equipment.

BI, Information Systems: systems and products for office automation and telecommunications in business and industry – 'private' systems.

BC, Cable: power and telecommunications cable; optical fibre cable.

BD, Defence Systems: defence electronics; military telecommunications for strategic and tactical networks.

BR, Radio Communications: microwave systems; mobile radio; cellular systems; paging systems.

BN, Network Engineering and Construction: planning and construction of networks for public and industrial telecommunications; network material; traffic signalling systems.

BK, Components: electronic components and power equipment.

The many local companies in different countries were allocated to the business areas representing their major business activities. And as we know, Ericsson had already bought Marconi out of SRA, which was now ERA, Ericsson Radio Systems.

What sort of telecoms market place was emerging, which this structure was designed to address?

Transportable container-housed AXE exchange in Thailand.

The digital market place: early 1980s

Let's start by looking at who had what digital technology to offer.

It's possible to make a rather fine distinction between a digital switch and a digital switching system. By 1978, the AXE system had a digital group switch, while the subscriber switches were still analogue.

But by the early 1980s, CIT-Alcatel's E10 was a digital switching system. So were Ericsson's AXE, and Northern Telecom's DMS 100. And for a while, these three had the market to themselves. E10 was a special case, designed originally for rural France but now enhanced and beginning to be marketed internationally. Northern Telecom confined its attentions to Canada and the USA. Ericsson had the rest of the world to play with – theoretically, at least, though many of the old restrictive practices died hard.

The oil crisis of the early '70s had held up the plans of many administrations to modernise and expand their networks. When stability returned, they were eager to get back on course. With its digital advantage – an advantage it could exploit throughout most of the '80s – AXE began to do very well indeed.

Of course, the competition was racing to catch up. The list of manufacturers and systems from about 1980 looks formidable. But Ericsson had a working system and a growing installed base, carrying dramatically-increasing volumes of real traffic. In their efforts to stay in the race, the

Oh, all right, then ...

At times it's convenient to be a little selective in historical recording. Ericsson has paid its respects to CIT-Alcatel and the work that company did in developing the world's first digital switch in the early 1970s. This became the E10 system, which, to begin with, was installed in rural areas in France. What Ericsson has sometimes chosen to forget is that Alcatel also got the first export order for a digital switch, with the E10.

This was a contract for the city of Valetta, on Malta, for a local exchange (with a digital group switch) of some 4,000 lines that went into service in 1976.

The Turku installation in 1978 was the first all-digital system – but it was a tandem exchange.

This commemorative replica of the 1892 desk telephone was brought out in 1981. The handset had modern components and the phone circuitry and key-set were incorporated in the wooden base.

The Swiss PTT used this phone for celebrating its 100-year anniversary, and in the US it became the darling of the interior decorators.

competitors were, at times, somewhat optimistic in their delivery under-takings. And a couple of the digital systems listed below never left the drawing board, or later sank without trace.

TABLE 13. THE DIGITAL MARKETPLACE 1980

Company	Earlier analogue SPC systems	Later digital systems	Main markets
Western Electric (US)	No 1 ESS	No 5 ESS	USA
ITT (US, Belgium, Germany)	Metaconta	System 1240	Belgium, France, Germany, Spain, Mexico, etc.
GTE (US)	1EAX, 2EAX	5EAX	USA, Belgium, Italy
Northern Telecom (Canada)	SP1 (digital)	DMS100	Canada, USA
Siemens (Germany)	ESK, EWS-A	EWS-D	Germany, S. Africa, Denmark, Finland, etc.
Philips (Netherlands)	PRX	PRX-D	Netherlands, S. Arabia
Thomson-CSF (France)	AXE (analogue)	MT 20/25	France
Nippon Electric (Japan)	D-10	NEAX 61	Japan, Asia L. America
Fujitsu (Japan)	D-10	Fetex	Japan, Singapore
Hitachi (Japan)	D-10	HDX 10	Japan
OKI (Japan)	D-10	KB270	Japan
Plessey, GEC (UK)	TXE2	System X	UK
STC (ITT,UK)	TXE4	-	UK
CIT-Alcatel (France)	E10 (digital)	E10	France, Africa, L. America, New Zealand
Nokia (Finland)	-	DX200	Finland, USSR
Stromberg-Carlson (US)	-	Century	US
Ericsson (Sweden)	AKE, ARE	AXE	Sweden, Denmark, France, Mexico, Finland, Italy, Australia, S. Arabia Netherlands, etc.

It is also only fair to point out that many of these manufacturers depend-ed heavily or entirely on sales to their respective home markets, or through manufacturing subsidiaries in various countries. Ericsson had sold an initial number of AXE systems to Televerket, but as Teli (Televerket's factory) started up its own production Ericsson had a very small home market for its switching systems.

Still, at a period when the time lag between a system choice and the acceptance of the first working exchange could easily exceed a couple of years, even offering a paper system could block a market for a long time while an administration waited to see how the system shaped up. An example is Mexico, which issued a tender for a digital SPC system, to be manufactured in Mexico, and received seven bids. ITT and Ericsson were the finalists, and the contract was split between them – ITT won a 75 per cent share of the market. Contracts were subject to each manufacturer's cutting in a pilot exchange in Mexico City by June 1981. Ericsson cut its pilot over on schedule. ITT put its System 12 pilot next door in the same building … and never did manage to cut it into service. Yet ITT received the lion's share of the first Mexico contracts, and it took a few years to restore the balance.

At the beginning of the '80s, however, the world seemed restless, but still an orderly enough place. Digital switching technology would eventually lose its power to thrill. The usual suspects were performing to plan. The struggle with ITT was becoming a ritual dance. The excitements of mobile telephony, and particularly digital mobile, were still to come. Ericsson and its customers were making cosy, comfortable progress.

And then came the flash of lightning, and the thunderbolt that shattered the universe and meant the world would never be the same again …

Oman: sun-powered MiniLink installation.

The divestiture of AT&T

Until the '80s, just about everybody would have agreed that AT&T was providing America with the world's best telecommunications service – cheap, efficient, friendly. And that the Bell organisation had an outstanding record of technological innovation.

It should be pointed out here that AT&T, or the Bell System, owned and operated about 80 per cent of the local telephone networks in the US. The remaining 20 per cent were divided up among a number of operators, the independent phone companies, the largest of which was, and is, GTE. AT&T operated all the long-distance and international telephone services in the US through the AT&T Long Lines organisation. Western Electric was the manufacturing arm of AT&T, and Bell Laboratories the universally-respected research and development organisation.

Everybody thought that AT&T was a good thing. Everybody, that is, except its would-be competitors. AT&T was a monopoly – a benign monopoly, no doubt, but a monopoly none the less, and it had every intention of staying that way.

As we've seen, this wasn't unusual. Monopoly power was the price many countries chose to pay for the provision of universal service to all potential subscribers, no matter how small, remote or unprofitable to the operator. And even AT&T didn't have total monopoly power: its tariffs were approved by such federal and state agencies as the Federal Communications Commission. AT&T, however, was privately owned, and so very visibly different from the state-owned PTTs of most other countries.

Non-Americans usually saw the AT&T service as outstanding, and most of its customers were also very happy with it. But for much of AT&T's life, there was concern in Congress … about AT&T's size, the prices Western Electric was charging the Bell operating companies for equipment, possible cross-subsidising between services, and the balance between monopoly and tariffs.

Court actions against AT&T began after the Second World War, and continued through the '50s and '60s. Most of them AT&T managed to fight off; but in 1959, AT&T was forced to concede that the private line market, at least, should be opened up to competition. Bell responded with a special cheap private line package (TELPAK), but the FCC ruled that AT&T was involved in 'cross-subsidising' (the ultimate crime in fair traders' eyes) and the case dragged on.

The toughest challenge came in the late '60s, not from the politicians or the regulators, but from a commercial competitor, MCI (Microwave Communications, Inc.). MCI applied to the FCC for a licence to build a microwave link between St Louis and Chicago, and to sell capacity on the system as private lines. When the question arose how customers in

St Louis and Chicago should connect to the microwave link terminals, MCI argued that the local Bell telephone company should provide connections for the cost of a local call. AT&T resisted, but the FCC ruled for MCI, and in 1971 approved the applications of MCI's affiliates to build microwave systems all over the country. MCI was recognised as a new class of operator – the Specialized Common Carrier.

Following another FCC ruling, the supply of subscriber equipment was also opening up, and by the beginning of the '70s, the only parts of the Bell System still protected as a monopoly were the switched public networks, long-distance and local.

AT&T clung on for a last ten years, but in 1982 a final ruling against it came from Judge Harold H. Green of the Justice Department. On 1 January 1984 the 'divestiture' took place, and AT&T was broken up. Seven new autonomous Regional Bell Operating Companies (RBOCs) emerged, and AT&T became a long-distance operator and equipment manufacturer. It also began to develop strong international aspirations.

Optical fibre cable provided by Anaconda-Ericsson for linking the Statue of Liberty and Ellis Island to Manhattan, 1986.

The signal for a new world structure

The importance of the divestiture was not so much in what it did, as in what it stood for: the liberalisation, deregulation, privatisation, reregulation – all these terms were used in various contexts – of the telecoms industry.

AT&T hadn't done anything particularly sinister. Indeed, you could argue that the originator of the transistor and the cellular mobile principle (among so many other brilliant and fundamental discoveries and inventions) was a benefactor to mankind, not just to telecoms. But AT&T was both a victim and a symbol of a whole general feeling that telecommunications (and other public services) would benefit from the fresh air of straightforward commercial competition.

In the UK, Mrs Thatcher, Tory Prime Minister, was implementing a programme of privatisation that embraced gas, water, electricity, railways and other public transport – and telecoms.

To a greater or less degree, the rest of Europe was following Thatcher's lead, and open provision in telecoms was becoming the policy of the EEC (later the EU). As opening up the market seemed to produce almost immediate consumer benefits, the fashion spread, until today there are fewer and fewer official telecoms monopolies.

AT&T was the most powerful and successful telecoms company in the world. Its divestiture became the most spectacular symbol of the end of the habits of a hundred years.

Taking on the world

The importance to Ericsson of the growing trend towards deregulation and, in consequence, open procurement, cannot be over-stated.

For years, the big national monopolies bought first and foremost from the big national suppliers. Deutsche Telekom bought from Siemens and Standard Elektrik Lorenz. AT&T bought from Western Electric. Britain's GPO bought from a cartel of Plessey, GEC, AEI, STC and Ericsson (the UK company, which after 1949 no longer belonged to LM Ericsson). And so on and so on.

This gave the big suppliers substantial, assured, home markets, in which they could sell on a profitable cost-plus basis. The benefits of cost-plus invoicing, together, in some cases, with development funding, were an important factor in a company's competitiveness on the export markets. Even so, there were by now several long-standing telecoms companies

*A captive audience: cable work
in Thailand.*

that were withdrawing from international competition. There was no driving incentive to stay in it.

Ericsson's case was different. Though Televerket initially bought AXE from Ericsson, the Swedish market was much too small to support a world-scale business, and Ericsson had built its success on export.

Though preference went to national suppliers, most of the substantial operators saw quite clearly the danger of having all their eggs in one basket. They usually went to at least one additional supplier, and sometimes more, to guarantee security of supply and reasonable pricing.

In many markets, Ericsson was that second supplier – a comfortable, and often very profitable, if not very glorious, position. At the end of the '70s and the beginning of the '80s, the world's telecommunications press usually referred to 'little Ericsson' or, in a more generous spirit (and after the Saudi contract), 'Ericsson the giant-killer'.

In the early '80s, the time was right to change all that.

First, for those with eyes to see, Ericsson had a clear technological lead. The only exported system it encountered regularly as competition was ITT's System 12. System 12 was a fine system on paper, but the product suffered a series of introductory problems and delays.

Second, the surge of openness which was about to engulf the industry, was gathering force. In time, as more countries deregulated, it would dash the cosy operator-vendor relationships to pieces.

Third, as we'll see in the next chapter, Ericsson had found a new business – mobile systems – in which its digital switch gave it an edge, and this new business would help to give the company critical mass.

And fourth, as a result of abolishing the monopolies, a whole community of new telecommunications operators came into being. They were entrepreneurs, eager to challenge the erstwhile monopolies, with business concepts based on competition. And they were not encumbered by traditions and age-old relationships. For over a hundred years, Ericsson had served a customer community of fewer than 100 companies – the PTTs. Now there were new potential customers cropping up all over the place.

After the years with nothing to sell, Ericsson stormed into selling AXE.

We've seen the beginnings of success with Turku, France, Australia and Saudi Arabia. By the end of 1978, Ericsson could show orders from Finland, France, Kuwait, Spain, Sweden, Yugoslavia, and Denmark. The orders for Finland and Denmark were for fully-digital switches; and the order for Denmark was the first step on the road to becoming Denmark's dominant supplier in 1980.

By the end of 1982, there were over 2.3 million lines of AXE installed, and a further 4.1 million lines on the order books. AXE had been sold to 44 countries. And the financial results were certainly promising. AXE was now one of the main contributors to the results of the Ericsson Group.

The results were excellent, but the struggle was tough, and success was never certain. Ericsson failed to capture Egypt, failed to become the dominant supplier in Malaysia and Thailand, and, very disappointingly, hung for some years with no more than a 25 per cent share of Mexico. (ITT held on to its 75 per cent.)

Worst of all was the loss of Norway to ITT in 1982 – so near Ericsson's home, and lost to a system which Ericsson believed to be inferior to AXE. Even at the time of its success in Norway, ITT had no commercial System 1240 installations in service. Ericsson's comparative failure to penetrate central Europe, where the old monopoly relationships were at their most established, haunted it for a decade.

But the big successes far outweighed the disasters. Switzerland, home of the International Telecommunications Union, chose Ericsson for the first time. South Korea came into the fold – to become for several years in the mid-'80s the largest single AXE market.

Ericsson's competitors were of course not standing by quietly. In the early 1980s, AT&T set about strengthening its international presence by forming a European company together with the Philips public telecommunications division. AT&T Philips Telecommunications N.V., APT, a Dutch company, introduced a combined product, the PRX-5ESS system and invested heavily (though not very successfully) in marketing.

Meanwhile, in the mid-'80s in France, an extraordinary situation was developing. Thomson-CSF had installed about 70 analogue AXE exchanges, some 900,000 lines, and then began to instal its own MT20/25 system instead. Sales of AXE sank to nothing. Then, in the early 1980s, both Thomson and CGE, Alcatel's parent company, were nationalised. Telecoms activities were concentrated in Alcatel. Alcatel's sales declined as the modernisation of the French network neared completion, and CGE began to look for an acquisition. It found one in ITT, which in 1986, sank exhausted out of the telecoms market.

CGE acquired all ITT's telecoms activities and located them in a new company, Alcatel N.V., headquartered in the Netherlands. CGE's MT20/25 manufacturing activities were transferred by the French government to CGCT – another nationalised company, with a traditional allocation of 16 per cent of the French market (around 300,000 lines p.a.). But CGCT was too small to continue development of the MT20/25 systems, and too small to act as an effective alternative to Alcatel as a source of supply. The French government was in a difficult situation, particularly since AT&T-Philips and Siemens (each suppported by muscle from its respective government) were both making aggressive noises. To cut the political Gordian knot, the government turned to the politically-neutral Ericsson with its AXE, and asked it to join a joint venture with another French company, Matra – originally a defence electronics manufacturer. Matra Ericsson Telecommunications S. A., MET, became France's official, and flourishing, supplier of AXE.

Most dramatically of all, Ericsson became the second supplier to one of the biggest prestige operators: British Telecom, separated at last from the rest of the Post Office in 1983.

Ericsson had been a major supplier to the British, making Strowger exchanges at its Beeston factory, near Nottingham. By 1949, Ericsson wanted to concentrate on producing crossbar, while the GPO's strategy was to continue with electromechanical systems until it could go completely electronic. Since Ericsson also needed funds to support its entry into the US (the North Electric acquisition) and for the crossbar systems development effort, it decided to sell Beeston with a guarantee that it would not attempt to compete with public systems in the UK for 20 years. Some years later, the former Ericsson company was acquired by Plessey.

After the sale of the Beeston company, Ericsson maintained a sales company in the UK providing a range of phones, intercom, etc. for the private market. After 1968, it also supplied PBX and certain other equipment for connection to the public network. A joint venture was set up with Thorn-EMI, Thorn-Ericsson Telecommunications (Mfg) Ltd, in the early 1970s.

By 1971, Ericsson had returned to the public network market with the order for a large international crossbar exchange for the Post Office, in London. This was followed by several more international switching centres, first crossbar, then the AKE SPC system, and finally an AXE switching machine in London. But supplying a large piece of equipment every three years or so was not really enough to keep Ericsson happy. The goal was to sell AXE local exchanges into the British network.

The home of an international AXE exchange, London.

At the beginning of the '80s, British Telecom was working on its own digital SPC system, System X. Largely designed by BT, it was handed over for completion of development and manufacture to Plessey and GEC, as the core of a replacement programme for the British network. It was a good system, but BT was not happy to rely on a single source, or even a single system. Quietly, in 1983, it began to explore the other possibilities. The subject was dynamite – a foreign system for the British network! Union trouble was expected. Political trouble, too.

As Mrs Thatcher got into her liberalising and privatising stride, BT became bolder, and in 1984 it announced its intention to select a System Y and invited tenders for a pre-qualification round.

Ericsson, represented by Thorn-Ericsson, made it through to the final selection, along with AT&T, Northern Telecom, Alcatel, Siemens, and ITT's British subsidiary, STC (offering System 12). By October 1984, BT had whittled this list down to AT&T, Northern Telecom and Ericsson.

The final offer was submitted in November 1984. After a nerve-racking interval, BT privately announced its decision for Ericsson on 21 March 1985. The intention was to release the news gently, but that night a couple of Members of Parliament went public with their dissatisfaction with BT's intention to acquire a System Y from a non-British company. BT was forced to make a full public announcement on 22 March. The decision held.

Every customer is important to Ericsson – that goes without saying. But BT had a special standing in the industry, and its choice was clearly a major testimonial for AXE. Short of being asked to instal AXE to replace Western Electric's System 5 throughout the entire US Bell network, Ericsson could hardly have got a better validation for its system.

So what *about* replacing Western Electric in the Bell network? Ericsson tried …

In 1981, Ericsson set up a joint venture with the American oil company, Atlantic-Richfield, ARCO. The joint venture, Anaconda-Ericsson Inc., had sizeable operations in cable manufacture (through the former Anaconda

Some ups and downs in PBX

Sales of PBX systems in the UK developed positively. One contract should be mentioned here. The London County Council ordered a large switchboard for its offices in County Hall, London. Technically, the specifications were easily fulfilled with the AKD 790 code switch system, but there were several specific requirements. One of these caused some merriment in the LM Ericsson offices: union regulations stated that telecom equipment must be installed with a minimum height off the floor of some two feet (the exact number has been lost now). This meant that all the PBX racks, in County Hall or elsewhere, had to be set on wooden blocks – for the convenience of the maintenance staff who otherwise had difficulty bending over to inspect the nether parts of the switch equipment.

copper mining and cable company, owned now by Atlantic-Richfield) and sold PBXs and transmission systems. In its labs, it was also working on fibre-optics. Ericsson's American operations included sales of PBX and other equipment for the private market, plus transmission systems. These operations were consolidated into the Anaconda-Ericsson venture.

The strategy over-all was to exploit the looming liberalisation of the US market, and Anaconda-Ericsson had a heavy programme. It was intended to milk the cash cow of the cable business. It was to act as a conduit into the USA for AXE, PBX and transmission systems. And it was to sell the data terminal and computer products of a new Ericsson division, Ericsson Information Systems (another story, told later in this chapter).

One part of Anaconda-Ericsson got off to a flying start – transmission. The new long distance carriers, such as MCI, needed microwave and transmission equipment, and they were in a hurry. LME's transmission systems were not designed to the traditional US standards, defined by AT&T from the beginning of time. But MCI did not see any point in acquiring systems to US standards, especially as they could not buy them from Western Electric, their main competitor. A deep and fruitful relationship had developed between LM Ericsson and MCI, which became an important springboard for the new Anaconda-Ericsson Inc.

Other areas had a less promising start.

Anaconda-Ericsson was pushing AXE (alongside other products) against Northern Telecom and AT&T's Western Electric, who between them supplied virtually the whole public switching market in the US. (AT&T's involvement in the divestiture drama might, it was felt, at least distract them a little, and provide an opportunity.) New competition – Alcatel, Siemens, the Japanese NEC and the American Stromberg-Carlson – was also emerging, as other companies eyed the vast US potential. AXE was an unknown system, and adapting AXE to meet US standards would be a long and costly business, with an uncertain return.

Early progress was unspectacular. The cable business cash cow began to dry up, affected by an economic downturn. To develop the MD110 PBX for the specific requirements of the US market a joint venture company was set up, Honeywell-Ericsson. The target market was the large-scale and network installations. MD110 eventually sold quite well, but limited funding limited success. The other Ericsson Information Systems products got off the ground, but they didn't exactly fly.

One of the difficulties was lack of awareness of Ericsson in the US. Anaconda-Ericsson began the long process of raising this awareness through promotions and road shows, and Ericsson's major stock issue in the US market (a huge $ 240 m) gave the programme a boost.

But the target market was extremely tough. At its heart were the RBOCs, and although they were severed from AT&T, they relied heavily

As others see us   *A snippet from the memoirs of Bob Morris, retired from BT as head of Contract Administration in 1990*

Looking ahead to the degree of release from controls when privatised, BT at last put the home manufacturers into partial competition by placing a contract for AXE10 digital switching equipment with LM Ericsson of Stockholm, through its British subsidiary Thorn Ericsson Ltd.

The strategy for this contract was worked out by the Directors concerned at the Strand Palace, London, in 1985. I and my Section had to finalise the detail of the Contract and operate it. I remember the historic occasion when the first delegation of Swedish engineers and managers visited BT headquarters. They and we were taken to lunch in our Director's dining room, where (horror of horrors) diced swede was on the menu. Fortunately, there was no international incident, as their limited command of English made the whole menu an unknown quantity to them. Later some friendly arguments arose on contract clause interpretation because the Swedish equivalent of the 300,000 words in the Shorter Oxford Dictionary is only 100,000. Soon after, the Ericsson board decided that their company could use only English in all its dealings, internal and external.

It would be asking too much to expect my usual 'good weather' luck to hold on all my contract visits to Stockholm. I seemed fated to visit Sweden in the winter rather than the summer, and on several occasions

the DC8 SAS aircraft taking me there had to land completely 'blind' at Arlanda Airport, with the wingtip lights showing up solid cones of falling snow. Indeed, we often had to 'stack' while the snow was removed from the runway since the previous aircraft landed. Later, at the hotel, the two thermometers, one inside the double glazing and one outside, showed +25 degrees C and -25 degrees C respectively. These trips were quite arduous, especially as I was the only BT commercial manager present, although several Engineers attended. The normal sequence of events was to suffer the 'normal' indignities of British Rail and the Central Line, like any other morning,

doing a full day's work running my Section and then, after an incredibly tightly-timed afternoon usually culminating in the Director or his Deputy 'wanting a word' (unscheduled) on this or that, scrambling down the Holborn escalators with 10,000 homegoing folk on to the Piccadilly Line to Heathrow. I soon learned to travel as light as possible with my pyjamas and razor interleaved with the contract papers in my briefcase which I carried as hand baggage. Not only did this make life tolerable on the tube, it also cut out the intolerable baggage reclaim delay at Heathrow on the way back. Ericssons usually sent a limousine to Stockholm (Arlanda) Airport, and I normally arrived at the Stockholm Sheraton around 10.00 pm their time. There, fresh and bushy-tailed, was the whole Ericsson Commercial Department, regaling me with gins and tonics (I could not stand their rubbery aperitif called Punch) and hoping that, in my supposed worn-out state I would divulge some vital commercially sensitive fact prior to the next day's meeting. I rather enjoyed the challenge of these cat-and-mouse sessions, and (so far as I know) gave nothing away. It was the same in the formal meeting next day at Ericssons' office at Telefonplan, except that the gins were replaced by an endless supply of over-strong black coffee and ridiculously sticky Swedish (or Danish?) pastries.

An AXE exchange in Guangzhou, China.

King Carl Gustaf and Queen Silvia on a visit to the Ericsson facilities in Dallas, Texas. Gunnar Eriksson is the guide.

on a surviving portion of the old Bell Labs: Bell Communications Research, or BellCore. BellCore was owned and funded by the RBOCs, and among its tasks was the on-demand validation of any new systems an RBOC might think of adopting. The validation process was severe, professional and costly for the supplier. Long before Ericsson could think of any volume sales of AXE to the RBOCs, it would have to persuade one of them to enter AXE for validation. And until the system was validated, Ericsson was reluctant to commit fully to the heavy investment needed to adapt AXE to the US culture and the stringent US telecoms standards – significantly different from those of Europe and most of the rest of the world.

In January 1984, a seminar was arranged in New York for people from Ericsson's US organisation and from Stockholm. Invited speakers came from Nynex (the New York RBOC), consulting firms, the specialised press, BellCore and the FCC. Ericsson began to acquire an understanding of the new game and its rules.

In the spring, Ericsson took a dedicated AXE roadshow round all the RBOCs. The object was to introduce Ericsson, explain the company, its organisation and strengths, and present AXE and Ericsson's network philosophy.

The reception was mixed. The RBOCs were uneasy about the depth of Ericsson's understanding of the US requirements and specifications. But the interest shown was enough to persuade Ericsson that it was worth starting the adaptation process. The facility in Richardson, outside Dallas in Texas, was inaugurated in August 1984 to handle this work and act as headquarters for the drive with AXE. Discussions with the RBOCs continued.

In the spring of 1985, three of the RBOCs combined to ask BellCore to perform a Phase A evaluation of AXE. Though this was only a paper evaluation, it was an important first step, and Ericsson was proud to announce that it was the first of the new competitors – Ericsson, Siemens, Nippon Electric and Stromberg-Carlson – to have a system evaluated.

The outcome of a successful Phase A evaluation would be what was called a 'hunting licence' – a go-ahead to try and do business with the RBOCs. And the Phase A evaluation would have to be followed by a Phase B evaluation, performed on a trial AXE switch. And that, of course, meant finding an RBOC prepared to instal a switch and ask for an evaluation.

In the spring of 1986, US West ordered an AXE switch for a Phase B field trial in Canyon City in Colorado, and Ericsson began to make progress.

Phase B approval came in August 1986, and was followed by an order from US West for an AXE STP for its Intelligent Network.

At the beginning of 1987, Bell South ordered its first AXE STPs, and Nynex ordered a trial installation. In the second quarter, South Western Bell ordered a trial exchange for Sedalia, Missouri, and – at last – Ericsson

Main distribution frame wiring in Malaysia.

received a bulk order from US West for 30 AXE switching systems for Idaho.

There were other small orders in that year from US West and Nynex, and Canyon City and the Idaho exchanges were cut into service before the end of the year.

AXE was on the US map.

But being on the map didn't necessarily mean it was very easy to find. Though the Idaho contract meant AXE was approved, this was at a time when the RBOCs were busily upgrading their entire networks to digital technology. The bigger cities had largely been upgraded, and what Ericsson and its competitors were getting was predominantly the switching for rural areas. More adaptation was needed to bring AXE up to the stiffer standards typical of the demanding city networks.

Then the blow fell. Western Electric and Northern Telecom were obviously worried about the risk of having to divide the market with the newcomers. But by now, late 1980s, they had in place a huge installed base with the Bell operating companies. A large portion of their telephone exchange business thus consisted of the supply of extensions to existing installations, equipment which on a per-line basis costs less to manufacture than complete new systems. So they were able to choose the least painful solution – they lowered their prices. In just a short period, the price per line of digital switching equipment in the US came down from over $ 200 to below $ 100.

For Ericsson, and the other newcomers, the RBOC market had become much less alluring, not to say impossible. The AXE sales efforts were toned down and, as far as the RBOCs were concerned, focused on supplying Intelligent Network systems and certain other special switching equipment.

Today, Ericsson can claim, with every justification, that AXE is the world's most popular switching system. A few numbers (see table 14) will illustrate the continued strong sales in the 1989–1999 period.

The aggressive drive in Europe has been exceedingly successful; and hundreds of switches have gone into the Far East, including China and Japan, and to Australia. AXE is the system of choice in Latin America.

And in the USA?

For the last dozen years, Ericsson has continued to receive orders from the RBOCs, though never in any really significant volume. Its competitors have fared very similarly. The stranglehold of Western Electric and Northern Telecom has been too tight to break. The other, non-Bell, networks, like MCI and MFS (Metropolitan Fiber Systems), have been much more open in their approach, and the overall volume of direct orders for AXE-based systems and solutions for fixed networks has been, and continues to be, well worth having.

But the real success story of AXE in the US lies in its role as an 'embedded' system. Embedded in what? Why, in the mobile networks with which Ericsson has made such a strong impact in North America.

And that's a story that will be told in the next chapter.

TABLE 14. AXE SYSTEM
Installed total capacity (lines) in fixed networks

Jan 1989

Installed	18,950,284
On order	9,049,017
Total*	27,989,301

Jan 1999

Installed	136,836,358
On order	10,153,435
Total*	146,989,793

Excludes subscribers in mobile networks.

From Ericsson AXE reference lists.

Upmarket alternative: the Dialog telephone built in hardwood.

Completing the picture

In the preceding sections within this chapter, we have walked a narrative path which started with the development of a world-beating switch, and continued with systems sales to operators in a digital market still dominated largely by the PTTs, or administrations.

But operators were by no means Ericsson's only customers. Two major product lines were targeted directly at users, business users. One failed; the other is a major and successful business in its own right.

PBX: the unsung hero

Along with the AX project assigned to Ellemtel in 1970 were two other main development programs: AY, the development of an electronic PBX system; and AZ, the building of a data network.

The data network, AZ, was eventually implemented as The Nordic Data Network, serving Denmark, Finland, Norway and Sweden. Many of us in those countries have used it often: the automatic cash dispensing machines that grew up all over the country in the 1980s, were connected to this data network. But it was a circuit-switched system, introduced at a time when packet switching was gaining rapid acceptance, and the data network never made it outside the Nordic countries.

The PBX development project was another matter – eventually.

The first PBX project, AY, finally resulted in the ASD 551, using reed relay switch configurations and electronic control, and aimed at installations with up to about 300 extensions. The project suffered various delays, and the product was not introduced until 1977.

A second design, ASB 100, for up to 100 extensions, was by then well under way. Preliminary studies for yet another, more future-orientated system, provisionally called IPR 110, had also started up. But one can discern a certain amount of indecision at LM Ericsson at this time over the future direction of the PBX business.

Televerket found that something radical had to be done about its PBX supply situation, and late in 1976 it concluded a licensing agreement with Northern Telecom for the SL-1 digital PBX. The SL-1 was successfully re-engineered for Swedish network requirements, and production at Teli started up. LM Ericsson, of course, lost an appreciable portion of its Swedish PBX market.

The ASB 100 used a thyristor solid state switch and was introduced in late 1977. It turned out to be a success in the international market, and became a very stable product, both in production and in operation. These results inspired LME to start development of a technically similar product, the ASB 900, to replace the not so successful ASD 551. ASB 900 was developed internally at LME, and the ASB 551 system was discontinued.

With the appearance of the Northern Telecom PBX switch at Televerket, and an incomplete range of its own modern PBX products, LME had to think hard and make some decisions. As the IPR 110 study intensified, it was realised that it would be a major development effort, and would need time. With ASB 100 and ASB 900, Ericsson felt it could hold its position in the markets well enough, and the IPR 110 development was assigned to Ellemtel. It emerged in 1983 as the MDS 110, soon shortened to MD 110.

MD 110 has become another Ericsson success story. In most countries, the PBX market had become, or was in the process of becoming, deregulated, which meant significant new market opportunities.

Testing MD 110 PBX switchboards.

After a typical initial period of perfecting the design, the MD110 turned out to be a very versatile and stable product. It is a distributed system, made up of self-contained modules, each serving up to about 200 extensions. One or more modules may be installed as a single PBX system, but the strength of MD110 has above all been demonstrated in its applications for building PBX networks.

MD110 has contributed strongly to Ericsson's business volume in the US, with a particular focus on, among others, the so-called campus market. A campus network links all the various buildings, labs, etc of a university – often including far-away locations. Among the customers we find the University of Massachusetts, with 34,000 extensions! But of the total US PBX market, Ericsson's market share is small, while companies such as Lucent (formerly Western Electric), Nortel (Northern Telecom) and Rolm (now belonging to Siemens after a period in the IBM fold) and a swarm of smaller suppliers dominate the scene.

The largest MD110 network is that supplied to the People's Army of China with about 400,000 lines: the network covers the whole country. In China, MD110 systems are manufactured by a joint-venture company. A special Chinese version of the MD110 has been developed for applications in the Chinese public network as a rural exchange.

Today, the MD110 digital PBX system is finding its place in enterprise networks. This means that the PBX switches are integrated into comprehensive network systems, handling voice and data, and supporting and interconnecting to a wide range of other systems, such as local area networks (LAN), databases, Intranet configurations and – Internet. We shall return to these matters in later chapters.

What's in a name?

In the UK, Thorn-Ericsson was having difficulties maintaining its PBX market share. There were considerable delays in completing the development of the MDS 110. The board even discussed making arrangements for buying PBXs from a US company. Luckily, such extreme measures were not needed and the UK became an early market for the new system.

Anyone who asked what the name stood for got the answer: 'The McDougal System, £110 per extension.' (Duncan McDougal was at that time Managing Director of Thorn-Ericsson, and £110 was a very competitive price.)

Soon after, in Stockholm, a letter arrived from Mohawk Data Systems Inc in the US, claiming that Ericsson's use of the MDS acronym constituted infringement on a protected name. It threatened to sue, so Ericsson decided to shorten the name to MD 110. Incidentally, MDS stood for Modular Digital System.

Ericsson Information Systems: an idea ahead of its time

In the first half of the '80s, alongside the development and marketing of AXE and the ventures into the USA and the UK, Ericsson undertook yet another 'enterprise of great pith and moment': Ericsson Information Systems.

Like so many other companies at the same time (IBM and AT&T among them), Ericsson was seduced by the apparently imminent convergence between the markets and the technologies of computing and telecommunications. Both depended on digital techniques. Both were driven and financed primarily by business customers. Both dealt with the raw material of what is now called the information revolution.

It was natural to look for synergy, and try to exploit it.

In 1981, Ericsson acquired Datasaab, a Swedish company making computers, terminals and air traffic control systems; and in 1982, Facit, another Swedish company, manufacturing typewriters and office furniture. These operations, together with Ericsson's PBX, telephone instrument and various office systems were brought together in a new company, Ericsson Information Systems, EIS.

Ericsson Information Systems: terminals and PCs.

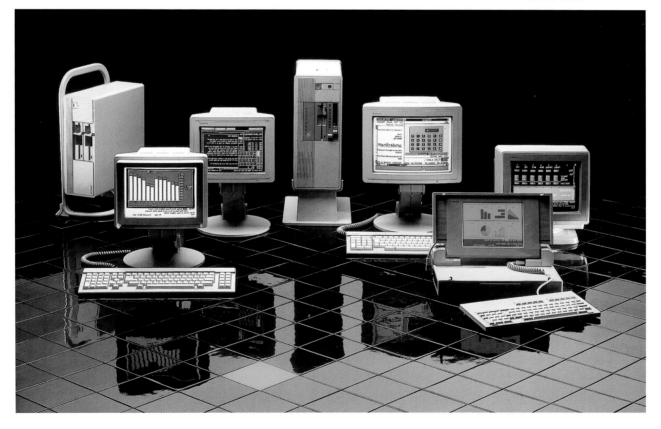

EIS launched its campaign, based on the concept of 'the office of the future', and including a strong emphasis on ergonomics. A new product was added, an Ericsson personal computer, and the sales drive began in Europe. In the US, Anaconda-Ericsson took over the former Facit and Datasaab sales networks.

With hindsight, it's easy to criticise the EIS venture. Probably Ericsson underestimated the funding necessary for a foray into data-processing – particularly as the revenues expected from Anaconda-Ericsson's cable business dried up as a result of a down-turn in the US economy. Perhaps it overestimated the degree of technological convergence. Almost certainly it overestimated the degree of market convergence: in the early '80s, most enterprises had different people and different departments handling communications and data-processing. Perhaps it failed to appreciate the very different culture involved in selling office systems. Perhaps, at least in the US, with the drive towards cellular mobile systems sales in full swing and the beginnings of a concentrated attack on the RBOCs with AXE, Ericsson was simply over-extended.

Whatever the reason, as with other companies which followed the same route, the performance of EIS was unconvincing. By 1984, it was in trouble. In the third quarter of that year, Ericsson announced to a startled financial community that there were problems in the design and manufacture of EIS products, and there was a general shortage of components on the market. The introduction of the Ericsson PC, in particular, looked like a mistake. Earnings expectations would not be achieved.

Corrective action was inevitable. New management was brought in and the operations were drastically restructured, including pulling out the PC

In confidence

In the early 1970s there were technological strategists who had begun speculating about the convergence of data processing and telecommunications. On a few occasions, LM Ericsson was approached by would-be allies. One was IBM.

Very discreetly, in 1974, IBM got in contact with LM Ericsson's top management with a proposal to join up the two companies, naturally with IBM as the dominant partner. LM Ericsson was politely interested, various aspects were studied

and plans tested. There were, naturally, certain potential obstacles: one was LM Ericsson's close relationship with Televerket, and another the position of the several manufacturing facilities in Sweden. Televerket and the Government were kept privately informed about the ongoing discussions. The talks went on for several weeks, in secluded chambers, but the whole concept was eventually abandoned.

Information about this episode is scanty today. What does seem clear is that IBM's

primary interest was to bring PBX technology and a PTT customer base into its fold – after all, offices and organisations were the main IBM customers. A few years later IBM did acquire a PBX company, ROLM, although that acquisition never became a great success.

The incident can be seen as an early and somewhat curious attempt to do what so many companies are doing today, in the new telecoms world.

from the markets. After three years of tough conditions, EIS was out of the red, but the experience had been costly, and Ericsson was formulating a new corporate strategy with a renewed focus on telecommunications. In 1988, the Data Systems and Office Equipment Divisions of EIS were sold to Nokia. (Nokia later sold most of its computer operations to ICL of the UK, which company, in turn, was acquired by Fujitsu.)

The technology of the technology

Components for digital systems:
from RIFA to Ericsson Components

Large Scale Integration – a key to success

Digital systems hugely increased the importance of the work RIFA was doing with system components. With integrated circuits, more and more of the design work was carried out 'on silicon', until complete systems were crammed onto one or a very few chips. The first Large Scale Integration, LSI, circuit in 1978, was a dual tone generator for telephone instruments, developed for GNT in Denmark.

Yet while RIFA was playing a greater and greater role as a source for development of key micro-electronic circuits for Ericsson's telecommunications systems – AXE, MD110, optical-fibre transmission, and others – the capacitor business had declined, and was no longer of strategic importance. It was clear that RIFA should focus on micro-electronics, power supply and distribution, but it was also clear that RIFA, on its own, would not be able to carry the substantial investments that continued development and manufacture in micro-electronics would necessitate. In 1980, LM Ericsson concluded a long-term know-how agreement with Advanced Micro Devices, AMD, of the US concerning MOS technology. As a result of this agreement, RIFA set up pilot production of NMOS integrated circuits at Kista. The first product was a 4 kb static memory.

By an extension of the AMD agreement, in 1983 RIFA obtained access to technology for developing its own CMOS technology through the CS-2 process – very advanced and fast for its time. The primary objective was to allow design engineers within Ericsson to define Application Specific Integrated Circuits, ASICs, and have them manufactured by RIFA. A central LSI Design centre was established in Kista.

Further development of the CMOS process was effected within the

National Microelectronics Programme, NMP, a partly government-sponsored programme aimed at raising the level of technology in Swedish industry. The work has to a great extent focused on line circuits for new generations of the AXE switching system.

In 1987, a long-term cooperation agreement was concluded with Texas Instruments. The agreement ensured that the company had access to key CMOS technology, in which the 0.5 micron BiMOS process was paramount at the time, including development systems. Extensions of the agreement have gradually led to new technologies well into the sub-micron (line width under 1 millionth of a metre) region.

The following year, 1988, the capacitor business was sold off to the Finnish company Finvest OY, including the RIFA trade mark and the capacitor plants in Gränna and Kalmar. The remaining activities of the company were renamed Ericsson Components AB.

Opto and microwave components

In the early 1980s, Ericsson Telecom started development of transmission systems for optical fibre. Dr Takashi Ishii was hired away from Japan to lead the work with the new semi-conductor technology.

The first products, in 1982, were a GaAs-FET (Gallium Arsenide Field Effect Transistor) and the first Ericsson laser diode. The following year saw the introduction of, among other products, the first Lithium Niobate modulator, which was a sensation at the time. Transmitter and receiver modules for optical fibre communication in 1984 set new industry standards.

The technology was further improved, and by 1988 the first Wavelength Division Multiplex, WDM, modules were introduced, for transmission and reception on a common fibre. The first 2.4 Gbit/s laser appeared the following year.

In 1990, a group of high-frequency experts were hired and an R&D centre was set up at Morgan Hill on the outskirts of Silicon Valley in California. Ericsson had also become a leading producer of power transistors for microwave.

Development in the field of optical telecoms transmission continues at a high pace. The second generation of WDM modules is represented by BISAM, or Bi-Directional Subscriber Access Module, which is intended for applications of Fibre To The Home, FTTH. Together with Toshiba, Ericsson has developed transmission and reception modules for the SDH/Sonet standard. These are produced at Kista for transmission speeds up to 2.5 Gbits/s.

Lastly, we should note the work going on in so-called photonic switching, for which an optical switch based on indium phosphide technology has been brought out.

OPPOSITE:
SunWind installation.
MiniLink systems powered by
wind generator and solar cells.

330

King Carl Gustaf (third from left) visiting Ericsson Components at Kista.

Power equipment

At the same time as Lars Magnus Ericsson started making telephones, in 1878, he also started to manufacture the batteries that were required. When central battery networks came in, the individual 'phone batteries' were no longer needed, but the exchange batteries became larger. Eventually, several industries specialising in battery manufacture grew up.

In the early days, motor generators were used for charging the batteries. In the 1930s, LM Ericsson became the first company in Sweden to manufacture rectifiers. The rectifiers could replace the motor generators and were used to convert AC mains power to DC for the charging of batteries in telephone exchanges.

Selenium rectifier valves came into use in the 1940s, to be replaced from 1964 by thyristors. The thyristor rectifiers were a world first.

With the introduction of electronic switching systems, new concepts for power distribution were needed. In 1977, the first Power MOSFETs came on the market. This technology eventually led to a new type of miniaturised power converters for mounting on circuit boards, which in turn led to today's power modules, the PKAs, which were first introduced in 1983.

In this same year, the power department was transferred from the telephone exchange division and incorporated as a division within RIFA.

1985 saw the introduction of the control and supervision system called Ericsson Energy Master, signalling a breakthrough for microprocessor technology in power supply equipment. Continued development led to Integrated System Power, ISP, in 1992. Power supply now became integrated into the telecoms equipment, its modules sharing the cabinets with the rest of the equipment.

Ericsson Components – core business

The role of RIFA, and later Ericsson Components, within the Ericsson Group has changed over the years. It started as a means of securing the availability of certain key components for switching and transmission systems. RIFA was for many years basically a subcontractor. But with the advent of computer-controlled and digital switching and transmission, to an ever-increasing extent system design takes place at the micro-electronic level, and the functionality of a system is defined in silicon. This development has meant that today the design know-how and manufacturing resources of Ericsson Components are a key element for the success of Ericsson – Ericsson Components is a development partner in the creation of all the systems and products which at an increasing rate are brought to the market by Ericsson. Ericsson Components is a core activity and core business.

Subscriber Line Interface Circuit, SLIC. Early 1990s.

CHAPTER 16

1977–1990

The move to mobile

An idea ahead of its time

In 1901 Lars Magnus Ericsson had already left the company he had built. He devoted much of his energy to farming and introduced several modern concepts using electric power. He was also a pioneer in the use of reinforced concrete. In 1908 his successor and friend, Axel Boström, had been killed in an automobile accident and for this reason, we are told, he was for some time against the idea of acquiring a car. However, his wife Hilda, who for years had also been his close associate in things technical, eventually persuaded him, and the Ericssons were soon to be seen touring the countryside around Stockholm in a large open automobile.

One of the reasons for Lars Magnus' change of mind was that he found a way to use a telephone while on the road. It was not of course an early application of radio – instead he had prepared two long fishing rods with contact hooks at the ends. Hilda handled the rods and would select a pair of wires. When a free pair was found, Lars Magnus would crank the handle of the phone which would alert the operator at the nearest exchange, who in turn would set up the connection to the desired party. Naturally Lars Magnus would be careful to use lines belonging to the SAT company – around 1912, Televerket was not yet ready to handle this early form of personal communications service.

Mobile systems: Nordic analogue

Establishing the principles

When we talk about mobile telephone systems today, we're nearly always talking about cellular mobile telephony, with its facilities for hand-off (or hand-over) from cell to cell, and its economical use of frequency.

But there were other, earlier, approaches to mobility – single-cell systems, operator-assisted ('manual') systems, and the land mobile radio approach still in use today in 'private' networks. In one way or another, Ericsson was involved with all of them, but its first tender for modern, cellular, mobile telephony was less than 25 years ago.

Yet as early as 1946, AT&T got permission from the FCC in the US to build and operate the first commercial portable, or mobile, telephone service, in St Louis, Missouri. It was successful, and other US companies joined the game until there were similar networks in 25 cities, serving a couple of thousand subscribers.

These systems bore little resemblance to the cellular systems of today. Typically, they involved one base station, as high up as possible, with a powerful transmitter and six channels. The 'telephones' were mounted in cars or trucks, and were large transceivers with big batteries attached. Their mobility depended on the mobility of the vehicles they were in.

The systems met a need, but were severely restricted. The need to transmit a strong signal from the vehicles meant heavy batteries and frequent recharging. Furthermore, the systems made very inefficient use of spectrum. A system with six channels could handle around 200 subscribers. More subscribers meant using more frequency, and the carrier frequencies had to be widely spaced to avoid interfering with each other.

The MTA system in Sweden, a photograph from the late 1960s.

SRA built the first mobile telephones in Sweden, for the MTA system, 1956.

Frequency is limited, and demand for it nearly always exceeds supply. The service provided by the mobile networks was available only to a comparatively small number of people, and it was competing for frequency with television, with its audience of millions and vociferous lobby. It was up to the companies involved – AT&T, Motorola, GE and the rest – to find a better way to use spectrum, if they were to convince the FCC to allocate them some more.

By 1947, AT&T had solved the problem. The solution was the cellular concept, which allows the re-use of frequencies. The cellular concept divides the whole area to be covered into a number of cells. Each cell has its own base station, with the number of carrier frequencies allocated which corresponds to the estimated number of customers to be served in the cell area. Adjacent cells have different carrier frequencies to avoid interference, but cells further away can use the same carrier frequencies as the first cell – the spectrum is being re-used. The smaller cells also reduce the transmitting power required.

All that was needed was a system to hand the call over from one cell to the next while it was in progress ('hand-over'). AT&T had a theoretical solution, but it depended on a high level of 'intelligence' in the system, and such intelligence could not be built into a workable system in the days before transistors, microelectronics and computer technology were available.

It was over 30 years before the system principles could be implemented.

From principles to strategy

The work by AT&T was too high-profile to go unnoticed, and was paralleled in any case in other countries. The '50s and '60s saw several early, non-cellular, systems start up and run profitably.

Televerket was an early starter. Late in 1950, a trial system was installed in Stockholm, with a single base station antenna placed on top of the Lidingö water tower. The system had two, duplex, radio channels and served five mobile stations. The results were encouraging, and led to the setting up of two systems, in Stockholm and Gothenburg, fully equipped for commercial operation, though it was not until 1956 that these mobile networks went into operation. It was named the MTA system, and it remained in service until the late 1960s, with a total of some 125 subscribers.

Televerket's work with the MTA system was closely monitored by the radio industry, including Ivar Ahlgren, the Managing Director of SRA. SRA built the first mobile station for MTA, in 1956.

The next generation, the MTB system, was set up on a trial basis in 1961, and came into service from 1965 onwards. MTB went into operation in Stockholm, Gothenburg and Malmö, with around 2,000 subscribers. SRA became one of the manufacturers of the mobile stations for MTB as well. Customer response to the new service was favourable, even though, for obvious reasons, the costs for equipment and tariffs were high. But to expand coverage would be costly, and would require tremendous chunks of radio spectrum. Televerket realised that available technology would lead to a dead end.

But Televerket had already decided that these difficulties must be tackled, and in 1964 set up a study group under Carl-Gösta Åsdal (later head of Televerket's mobile telephone operations) which was given the task of investigating 'all aspects' of mobile telephony. The group reported in 1967, recommending the development of a nationwide cellular mobile telephone service, alongside a national paging system and a new land mobile radio system.

Both the paging system and the land mobile radio system were successfully implemented as recommended, and the Televerket labs started work on the cellular telephony system.

But in 1969, Åsdal also presented the report to the full Nordic Telecommunications Conference, suggesting that mobile telephony might be a worthwhile subject for Pan-Nordic cooperation. The proposal was accepted enthusiastically, and a joint Nordic working party, with representatives of the Nordic PTTs, was set up. This working party became the NMT, the Nordic Mobile Telephone group, and its first report came out in 1970.

This 1970 report recommended that a new, pan-Nordic, mobile telephone system should be developed. But it also concluded that such a programme would take about ten years to complete, since it would depend on new technology – especially microelectronics – that was not yet available. It therefore also recommended the setting up of an interim, manual mobile telephone system to a common Scandinavian standard, to take care of the growing demand, and to develop the market. MTD was introduced in 1971 and lasted until 1987.

The report also contained one of the first cracks in the monopolistic armour of the Nordic telecoms administrations: it argued strongly that the future mobile stations, the terminals installed in the vehicles, should be owned by the subscribers, who would buy them from manufacturers competing in an open market. This would help to drive down prices and fuel growth.

The NMT Group kept relevant manufacturers, including SRA, abreast of progress from 1971 onwards, and in 1973 invited comments and suggestions on the system specification and design proposals, and preliminary costing. SRA's main contribution focused on the air interface, the method of handling the exchange of information between the mobile station and the base station. The prevailing solutions were based on using tone signalling, but SRA argued, successfully, that to handle the necessary amounts of information at sufficient speed the system should employ data technology – digital signalling.

It is interesting to reflect that only thirty years ago, it was possible for operators, admittedly with exclusive rights to the market, to spend ten years in planning and developing a new mobile network!

Progress was good, and a field trial performed satisfactorily in Stockholm in 1977–78. Due credit should be given to Televerket's Thomas Haug, who was Chairman of the NMT Group at the time, and to Östen Mäkitalo, who was largely responsible for the design, construction and running of the trial.

In 1977, manufacturers were invited to tender for the supply of base stations and MTX switches to be installed in the different countries.

The first NMT tender

When the NMT Group invited tenders, both Ericsson's X Division and SRA were somewhat out of harmony with the market.

The NMT Group wanted AXE, which had shown its paces at Södertälje, and was beginning to be ordered – but the X Division was nervous about proposing an immature system, and wanted to offer AKE. The NMT Group insisted on AXE: even in a generally analogue environment, the speed of digital switching would add considerable value when it came to performing hand-over, roaming and many other specific functions.

SRA was in an even more difficult position.

It had been doing good business for some time, but largely as a supplier of land mobile radio – though by the '60s it was also supplying a range of radio systems (radar and troop radio) for the Swedish armed forces, and had entered the business of local area paging.

Asked to supply base stations for the NMT system, it simply had no designs ready, and was actually more interested in producing the terminals, the mobile phones. Initially, SRA's contribution was limited to the Control Units, CU, it developed for the base stations of another Swedish company, Magnetic; and Magnetic and Mitsubishi were the two original suppliers of base stations for NMT. However, SRA's experience meant that it could make intelligent noises, and in 1977 it acquired some major parts of the Swedish SONAB company – which did have an existing base station business. Bringing all its resources to bear, SRA eventually produced its own base-station product.

So it was a pair of rather reluctant heroes, LME and SRA, which got the job of implementing what Televerket and the other Nordic telecoms administrations planned as the world's first commercial cellular mobile telephone system, NMT, to be inaugurated on 1 October 1981.

From strategy to the world's first NMT system

Only as it happens, Televerket didn't cut over the world's first commercial cellular system, or even the world's first NMT system. That was inaugurated on 1 September 1981. In Saudi Arabia!

The Ericsson-Philips joint venture was active in Saudi Arabia, implementing the original gigantic contract of 1978. In 1979, the joint venture received a second contract to expand the network with outside plant and some additional switching and transmission. Ericsson persuaded the Saudi Minister of Telecommunications to allocate some money for a mobile telephone network. Philips approved – it was already designing a mobile telephone system (not cellular) in its German subsidiary. Sadly, it emerged that the Philips system was built to operate in the 160 MHz band of spectrum, and this band was already full in Saudi Arabia. Philips turned back to Ericsson for help.

By now, Ericsson was starting to supply MTX (Mobile Telephone Switches) to NMT, and making progress with base stations, and it suggested that the most straightforward solution would be to supply the Saudis with an NMT system. Happily, the 450 MHz band, the NMT band, was free! In the end, when its own German company was in any case swamped with system orders for Germany, Philips reluctantly agreed.

With a tremendous effort, SRA and LM Ericsson managed to complete the Saudi network on time. The Saudis were pleased. Philips was less so. And the NMT Group was a bit sad at being scooped – but it had consciously and purposely (and wisely) made the NMT standard an open specification, and could hardly complain too loudly.

And anyway, for Televerket, the Saudi first was a minor irritant compared to its first competitor at home, Comvik. Sweden was to have competition in mobile telephone service right from the start. Jan Stenbeck, Comvik's head, had acquired a couple of land mobile radio operators and with them the right to use certain frequencies. Comvik's first cellular network was cut over in September 1981, just one week before Televerket's NMT system was opened for commercial service.

1978 was the cross-over year for AXE. 1981 was the cross-over year for NMT. At the end of the year, SRA was given full business responsibility for the development and sale of mobile systems, and shortly afterwards, when Marconi had sold what remained of its interests in SRA back to Ericsson, SRA became ERA, Ericsson Radio Systems AB.

NMT system in Saudi Arabia, 1981.

A new business for Ericsson

In cellular mobile telephony, Ericsson had found a new business, based on digital switching, but with an equally starring role for radio, and with its own, different, dynamics. SRA, soon to become ERA, had the business responsibility. The MD of SRA was Åke Lundqvist, who had been the prime mover in bringing out NMT and in defining the business idea around mobile telephony. He was to play a key role in the next several stages of the company´s new business. Progress was rapid, and by the end of 1981, things looked encouraging.

In Saudi Arabia, three mobile networks were in operation, in Riyadh, Jeddah and Damman. They were small, but the coverage was extended a couple of years later to handle 20,000 subscribers in total.

In Sweden, there were two MTXs, one in Stockholm, one in Gothenburg. Each had the capacity to connect 10,000 subscribers initially, and each could be expanded to handle up to 50,000 subscribers. 53 base stations, spread round the country, were connected to the Stockholm MTX, with a total of 236 traffic channels, plus calling, data and reserve channels. Gothenburg had 51 base stations and 238 traffic channels, plus the extras. Similar systems were being installed in Norway, Denmark and Finland.

Both Saudi Arabia and the Nordic countries had substantial, capable, systems supplied by Ericsson. But in 1981, it was by no means a foregone conclusion that Ericsson should be the world's natural supplier of NMT networks, and it took a battle in the Netherlands to clinch the case. In 1980, talks began on the construction of a cellular system in the Netherlands. The Dutch PTT specified NMT. Ericsson's major competitor was Motorola, who put forward a strong bid, but the Dutch held out for AXE switches – because of the capacity of AXE and because AXE was familiar, since it was being installed in the fixed network at the time.

Motorola suggested the Dutch should consider AXE switches combined with Motorola base stations, and the Dutch found this proposal attractive. There was even some support for this arrangement within Ericsson, from people who felt that ERA hadn't quite got a grip on base stations, and who could see a lot of switch business coming from a link with Motorola.

In fact, a cellular system proposal consists of a great deal more than switches and base stations. Cell-planning capability, for example, is important, and Motorola could (and did) argue with some justification that Ericsson had no great experience or capability in this discipline.

SRA decided not to compromise. It hired the services of a couple of world-class cell-planning experts, made a few changes to the original pro-posal, and asked for one more meeting with the Dutch PTT. In a fairly fiery meeting, SRA (with Åke Lundqvist resolutely driving home every argument) demonstrated its new-found cell-planning capability, pointed out that the Motorola specification lacked some key equipment (such as antennas), and found a way to cut some of its prices. At the same meeting, the X Division stated that if the Dutch wanted AXE switches, they had to have SRA base stations as well: Ericsson was selling a mobile system, not separate packages of switches and base stations.

The Dutch agreed, but even more important, Ericsson had found a new selling proposition: a system package, made up of the AXE switch for the MTXs, SRA's own radio base stations, and a highly advanced cell-planning service.

All, of course, to conform with the NMT 450 analogue Nordic standard.

A brief note on standards

A large part of Ericsson's success, especially in the mobile telephone business, has been its ability to conform to different standards. What does this mean? Why are standards so important?

A closed system can work exclusively according to its own rules and protocols. But if two systems are to work together, interwork, they have to have common rules for what happens at the point of interconnection, the interface. Such issues arose very early in telecommunications – at the point where telegraph systems met at national, geographic and language borders, for example.

Throughout the twentieth century the need for creating standards has grown in importance, and telecommunications, which increasingly involves the handling of data, has become a key area of attention.

In the period after World War II, the International Telecommunications Union, ITU, which is a United Nations agency, became very active in developing transmission and signalling standards for international telephony. The national telephone networks were rapidly being converted to automatic long-distance (trunk) dialling, and soon, through bilateral agreements, ways were established to set up calls, automatically or using operator dialling, across boundaries to neighbouring countries.

The task that the ITU set itself was to establish common international procedures and technical specifications so that a subscriber in any country could dial directly to a subscriber in any other country. Over time, a number of international signalling standards emerged. Named after the CCITT (the telecoms committee within the ITU), they were CCITT No 5 for operator dialling; CCITT No 6 for subscriber dialling; and CCITT No 7, common channel signalling, which is dominant today. International signalling systems are only one example of the many areas in which the ITU successfully worked to make international telecommunications possible.

Today, the role of standard-setting, particularly in technology standards, has to some extent been taken over by other, often regional, international bodies. These include ETSI, the European Telecommunications Standards Institute, in Europe, and a number of national institutions, user groups and industry associations. There is some further development of the standards theme in the next chapter.

With deregulation and the rise of open multi-vendor procurement, standard-setting and conformity with standards have taken on a new critical dimension. A network operator must be able to purchase his different network elements from different, competing, vendors. This is an absolute prerequisite to ensure competition, and avoid the risk of a vendor, or a group of vendors, creating a protected market.

In mobile telephony, as we shall see, two different analogue standards emerged in Europe – NMT; and TACS, which later evolved into ETACS. NMT did actually provide roaming between the Nordic countries and some others, such as Switzerland. But it was CEPT, the Conference of European Post and Telecommunications administrations, preparing for the important step into digital mobile telephony, that first realised the need to create a single pan-European standard – the standard that became GSM (initially named from Groupe Spéciale Mobile, the CEPT working party). This European standard was created to ensure on the one hand that any subscriber can use his mobile telephone in any European country, and on the other hand that operators and subscribers may purchase equipment and mobile telephones in an open market.

In the US, things have gone a bit differently. The first mobile standard, analogue, was AMPS, Advanced Mobile Phone System, originally developed by Bell Labs. The big difference compared with Europe was that the country was divided up into many – literally hundreds – of markets, with two mobile operators licensed in each. This ensured competition between operators, and indeed vendors, but led to some serious limitations in roaming. And, as we shall see in a later section of this story, progress into digital mobile was not as smooth as in Europe – in the US today, there are no fewer than three different digital cellular standards (or, to be more precise, three 'digital cellular specifications').

Manufacturers are naturally involved in the work of the standard-creating bodies. But they must also do a balancing act to protect their own developments and designs, and patents offer such protection. The handling of a company's patents and IPR is more than ever a strategic function today.

Playing by the standards: expanding the new mobile business

The USA: an early success

As we've seen in Chapter 15, it was not until the Spring of 1985 that any of the RBOCs in the USA even requested an evaluation of AXE for use in fixed 'wireline' networks.

Yet by then, AXE had been successfully handling commercial traffic for a year in the USA – not, however, for an RBOC, and not in the fixed network. Ericsson had broken into the USA with its cellular mobile system.

A number of factors contributed to this early success.

In 1981, the RBOCs and the established independent operators, as well as a number of entrepreneurial companies, were getting ready to file applications for licences to operate mobile services. Though the FCC had not announced the date for filing, it was clear that each area, or market, would have two mobile operators – an RBOC or independent, and a non-RBOC entrepreneur.

Still Ericsson might not have considered entering the States at this early stage if it had not been for the urging of the American consultants hired to provide cell-planning capability at the time of the Netherlands bid. They were convinced that the US represented a real opportunity for Ericsson's new system, and a report by one of them, *The US Cellular Mobile Telephone System Marketplace*, outlined the potential and the dynamics of the market. It was a fairly aggressive estimate of how the US cellular market would develop, but after only a few years even this view of strong growth turned out to be far below the actual numbers. This under-estimation of the market potential was typical of the cautious approach of the times all over the world, and was to continue well into the 1990s.

Åke Lundqvist was convinced that an attempt on the USA would be relatively low-risk and high-potential. He persuaded the X Division to agree to the software development needed to adapt AXE in the mobile exchanges to match the standards in the American market. By 1982, a brochure was available describing the CMS 8800 system, the system Ericsson was offering for the American market and the American AMPS standard.

Ericsson realised that the RBOCs would go for equipment from their traditional manufacturer, Western Electric, and would not be open to discussions on cellular equipment from a foreign upstart. Accordingly, SRA targeted the non-wireline entrepreneurs. These applicants for licences had to put forward to the FCC extremely detailed proposals, containing legal and financial qualifications, a business plan, and a complete area cell layout, identifying all the base stations and their transmission data and frequencies. They also had to name the systems they proposed to use and their system suppliers. Throughout 1982, SRA presented to as many of the entrepreneurs as possible, describing the CMS system and offering to help prepare the licence applications. In March 1982, the FCC announced that the filing date for the first 30 markets would be in June.

Of 130 or so non-wireline applications handed in, Ericsson was specified in 40. There was, of course, no guarantee that any applicant specifying Ericsson equipment would win, or that if it did win it would go ahead with Ericsson as specified, and there were some early disappointments. But by May 1983, Ericsson (or to be correct Anaconda-Ericsson, the US joint venture with ARCO described in Chapter 15) had its first contract. It was for Buffalo, NY, cut over in April 1984, and other contracts followed fairly rapidly. At the time of the Buffalo contract, Ericsson had no base station product of its own for the US, but a crash development programme meant that it was able to meet the cut-over date with its own products.

As further tranches of applications were heard by the FCC (the second round in November 1982, the third in March 1983) the selection system was gradually simplified – though it took eight years for the FCC to complete the process. Long before then, it was clear that Ericsson had a success on its hands, and had become a major player in the US. By 1988, it was one of the three top cellular infrastructure suppliers, with about 30 per cent of the US market.

The cut-over at Buffalo

Both the Buffalo operator and the Ericsson people were nervous. Some of the testing had not been conclusively successful, indicating that the system, too, was still a bit nervous. It was decided to have a plan B for the cut-over so as not to embarrass the Mayor of Buffalo, who had agreed to do the opening honours. Plan B was the 'manhole method'. A little man would be concealed down a manhole conveniently situated in the street along which the cortège would roll. At the crucial moment, the limo would stop, right on top of the manhole, and, if necessary, the manhole man would emerge furtively and plug a telephone line into the limo. Barring severe problems in the fixed network, there would then be no difficulty making the inaugural call to Sweden.

However, at the moment of truth the new mobile system did perform perfectly. The Mayor made his call, and talked to Carl-Gösta Åsdal about – we know not what. It was a success, and the first non wire-line network in the US was in operation.

Cementing success: the UK follows the USA

In the USA, Buffalo was cut over in April 1984. Nine months later, the first Ericsson mobile network was cut into service for Vodafone, in the UK.

Though it followed so rapidly, the UK situation was different from that of the USA, and presented some interesting features of its own.

As Ericsson was preparing its sales programme in the US, the UK was deciding on its own mobile telephone arrangements. In the winter of 1981–82, the UK government set up a panel to advise on the liberalisation of value-added services, and the duopoly concept was born. In the UK duopoly, BT (soon to be separated from the postal division of the GPO) was to be one of the mobile operators through a subsidiary called Cellnet, which it would share with a minority co-owner. Applications for the second licence were invited.

Among the applicants was Racal, which could bring to the party a long history in radio and a joint venture with a US company called Millicom, already engaged in a mobile telephone trial in the US. Racal was chosen, and set up as Vodafone.

There followed a long wrangle between BT and Vodafone over standards. BT favoured a Siemens system; Vodafone wanted a variation of the US AMPS standard, with 25 kHz spacing between channels instead of the American 30 kHz. Vodafone realised that for the subscriber, cost of entry – of which the cost of the telephone formed a large part – would be critical. It reasoned that the cost of the phone would be lower if it could share its shell and a major part of its electronic componentry with any phones to be produced in bulk for the USA.

BT suggested an alternative French idea, but was again blocked by Vodafone. BT suggested the Nordic NMT 450 standard, but Vodafone stood firm, believing (quite rightly) that NMT volumes would never match AMPS volumes, and that volume would reduce the cost of the infrastructure as well as the phones. It also harboured some doubts about the security of the NMT system. Eventually BT gave in, and a British version of AMPS, called TACS (Total Access Communications System), was adopted. Today, Cellnet agrees that it was the right decision.

Vodafone then turned to finding its infrastructure provider. It whittled the contenders down to AT&T, Motorola and Ericsson, and chose Ericsson because of the large capacity of the AXE switch. It believed that the larger British cities needed a large switch, which would cut down on inter-switch hand-overs and signalling. The AT&T and Motorola switches at the time were relatively small.

Vodafone, which had been awarded its licence a year later than Cellnet, put Ericsson under heavy time pressure, and commercial operation began on 1 January 1985.

*When in Rome, do as
the Romans do.*

An interesting outcome of the duopoly approach in the UK was the emergence of the independent service-provider: neither Cellnet nor Vodafone was initially allowed direct access to customers, and instead a number of companies were created to take care of the connections, sales and service of mobile telephones.

The Italian way

The introduction of mobile telephony services in Italy had some interesting twists and turns and is worth relating.

In Italy, too, there were various early experimental systems. Then, in 1973, SIP, the Government-owned telecoms administration, opened the first public mobile telephone network, a semi-automatic system.

In 1983, the first fully-automatic system, designed by Italtel, was introduced. Italtel and Telettra supplied the terminals, which were leased to subscribers. The system had hand-over functions and excellent transmission quality, but had an upper limit of some 70,000 subscribers and – most serious – it could be fraudulently misused.

Around 1985, FATME, Ericsson's Italian company, made attempts to interest SIP in a new, high-capacity, system – NMT or TACS – but was unsuccessful. SIP had decided to make do with what it had until the new GSM standard was a reality (scheduled at the time for around 1990). An interim analogue system was considered an unnecessary luxury.

But SIP was suffering from a bad press as a result of an aborted attempt to merge Italtel and Telettra, and was being accused of offering poor-quality service. This was the more serious as Italy was attracting international attention as the host for the upcoming 1990 World Cup football games, an event of global interest. The World Cup would draw large numbers of fans to Italy, along with participants, press, radio and television.

It came as a surprise when SIP announced to the press a change of priorities: it had been decided that a new mobile telephone system would be constructed, working to the TACS standard in the 900 MHz band. The new system would cover all the World Cup cities and the major highways between these cities. This decision turned out to be a very intelligent and profitable move for SIP.

By now it was clear that the GSM system, the 'next generation' of mobile telephony, would be a year, or even two years, late: certainly there was no chance that GSM would be in time for the World Cup. The decision meant that SIP's status and image improved overnight – SIP was recognised as a proactive, forward-looking organisation.

SIP chose to have a single system design, but to generate some degree of competition, and eventually supply reponsibilities were allocated in this way: FATME would supply the switches (AXE) and the network management system; Ericsson would license to Italtel the TACS radio base stations; Telettra would be sub-licensed, by Italtel, to share the manufacture of the base stations.

FATME and Italtel formed a consortium, CORAM, to take the responsibility for installations and system integration – a guarantee that Italy would not land in a situation of national embarrassment due to any delays in implementation.

The Italian TACS network was opened for service on 2 April 1990, three months before the opening of the World Cup games. The service quickly became an outstanding success. The Swedish soccer team performed miserably, and the Germans won the Cup.

The beginning of the mobile years

Taking responsibility

Many people have argued that mobile telephony is 'simply' an extension of telephony in the fixed network, and that radio just happens to be a way of access.

In this view, all the really clever stuff goes on in the switch – the MTX – which is the heart and soul of the system, and there's nothing particularly special about mobile telephony.

This view really isn't tenable. The radio portion of the network – the radio base stations and the mobile telephones – is, of course, an integrated part of the cellular system, based on technology as advanced as that of switching. The use of spectrum, the interchange of data over the common air interface, the science of cell-planning and the politics of antenna-siting – these and other matters are critical to the success of a mobile network, and quite outside the constituency of terrestrial systems. For a deeper discussion of some of these things, and of the technology at a comprehensible level for non-specialists, try the reference list at the end of the book.

There is, of course, the opposing view as well. This maintains that all the clever stuff goes on in the radio portion of the network, and that the switch can be quite small and simple. This isn't right, either: the switch in a mobile system has vast amounts of functionality, most of it unique to mobile networks. In the early days, the market was, if anything, clearer than Ericsson about this: it insisted on having AXE, when even Ericsson (or at least some of the ERA people) felt it might be over-specified and expensive and a bit on the large side …

Today, most people agree that both switching and radio expertise at the highest level are essential for successful mobile networks, and that mobile telephony is a business all of its own. In the late '70s and early '80s, Ericsson was probably the only systems manufacturer in the world with real strength in both areas, and sufficient marketing experience to get across that this was the case.

But the strongest argument for the uniqueness of this new business came in the early '80s. Mobile telephony became the spearhead of liberalisation: many authorities insisted on licensing at least two mobile service providers from the very beginning, one of which was usually the fixed-network incumbent. Third and fourth operators often followed when digital mobile was introduced. Though the driving force behind this development was political, the facilitator was technological.

One view that does have a certain apparent respectability is that mobile networks are primarily overlay networks, in that much of the traffic spends most of its life in the fixed network – already in place in most countries. The entry cost is lower, which makes it easy for new start-up mobile service providers. But even this view isn't very tenable: mobile telephony really is every bit as much its own business as terrestrial telephony, and, as the business has shown, mobile telephony has in many areas become an attractive alternative to fixed networks, and so a competitor.

In 1981, Ericsson installed the world's first NMT system. Just over four years later, it was installing large-scale networks for all three of the mobile world's standards: NMT, America's Advanced Mobile Phone System, AMPS, and the UK's Total Access Communications System, TACS. It was the only supplier that could claim such capability.

It went on to absorb the several standards which followed, and to become the world leader in mobile systems.

And all this meant that before the end of the '80s, the centre of gravity within Ericsson was shifting. For over 50 years, public telephone exchanges had been the dominating product area. Now, things were changing: the mobile systems business was growing at an exciting rate and would, in a few more years, definitely take the lead. The stage was set for the mobile years.

Change and response

These last two chapters cover a period of just over ten years. At the time, no doubt, any decade in a company's history seems turbulent and exciting. But these ten years began in one generation of telecommunications and ended in a completely new one.

Everything changed.

In the pivotal years in the beginning of the 1980s, Ericsson was leading the field with its digital AXE switch. By 1983, it had sold 2.3 million lines, with a further 4.1 million lines on order.

As a leader in digital switching, Ericsson next established itself as a leader in cellular mobile telecommunications – again, not just a new product, but a whole new business. Digital switching invisibly revolutionised fixed networks. Mobile telephony very visibly revolutionised the market's expectations of what networks can provide.

Meanwhile, the telecoms market was changing even faster than telecoms systems. In the wave of new political thinking that swept the world in the early '80s, just a few short years saw the creation of British Telecom, the introduction of competition in public and mobile networks in the UK, and the divestiture of AT&T in the US. Mobile telephony, with its duopoly licensing, was replacing monopoly by competition, and the demand for

Björn Svedberg

Dr Björn Svedberg, Managing Director 1977–1990 and Chairman of the Board 1990–1998, is an engineer, and held positions as Technical Manager of the switching division and, from 1976, Technical Director of LM Ericsson. His first task as MD was to start the conversion of the production facilities from electromechanical systems to electronic, a process which had to be speeded up as the result of the large supply contract to Saudi Arabia. This contract was, over the next several years, followed by many more as the AXE system and the digital network captured old and new markets.

These years also saw the acquisitions by LM Ericsson of Datasaab and Facit and the forming of Anaconda-Ericsson Inc., a joint venture with Atlantic Richfield of the US. The failure of Ericsson Information Systems, chiefly in the US market, was a setback which earned a lot of comment. In Svedberg's words, when he looks back today, 'there were many reasons'.

He agrees that the Facit acquisition, based on a concept, popular at the time, of integrating electronic typewriters and text-processing equipment into a comprehensive telecoms and data-processing system, soon proved to be a mistake. The Alfaskop terminal system was, on the whole, a success, but the introduction of the Ericsson PC was

bedevilled by delays in development and production and contributed to a decline in profits. And, thinking back, Svedberg adds that the difference of company cultures between Ericsson and Datasaab certainly contributed to the difficulties.

Other market leaders, including AT&T, Siemens and IBM, tried unsuccessfully to follow similar paths.

Björn Svedberg's team introduced a re-organisation of the company on 1 January 1983, initially with eight Business Areas. The biggest outside factor affecting the shape of the new organisation was the start of deregulation in the operating industry – a factor which was to change

the conditions of the telecoms industry forever.

Today, Björn Svedberg identifies the expansion of Ericsson's market in Central Europe during the 1980s as the most exciting, and gratifying, experience of his time. The AXE system, the MD 110 PBX, defence systems, optical fibre cable and other products achieved very good market penetration. But the highlight of these years was provided by mobile telephone systems, in which Ericsson, in just a few years, established itself as the leading supplier globally – including a remarkable, and durable, 30 per cent or greater share of the US market for mobile systems.

open standards (and open procurement) was becoming insistent. Real competition was sharpening marketing skills everywhere – and the associated techniques of design, costing, pricing, service and delivery. The telecoms world and the telecoms business were changing.

Brave new world

So by 1984, with a new identity and a new structure, Ericsson had entered a radically new telecoms environment.

How was Ericsson placed?

By now, Ericsson could begin to regard itself as a world-class company, one of the top half-dozen equipment manufacturers. It could be mentioned in the same breath as AT&T, ITT, Northern Telecom, Siemens, Alcatel and NEC. It had been propelled to that position by AXE, and was being pushed into an even higher orbit by cellular mobile systems.

By the end of 1985, the AXE system had reached 7.5 million lines installed, and another 6 million on order. Not all these lines were digital, but it

The new business tool. Malaysia, NMT system.

was Ericsson's digital technology that was fuelling the growth. As 'P86', the first major upgrade, AXE was entering its second digital generation, and Ericsson still reckoned itself a couple of years ahead of the competition.

Since its start in Saudi Arabia in 1981, NMT 450 had captured the new cellular mobile markets in the Nordic countries, the Netherlands and Switzerland, and countries in the Far East such as Malaysia and Thailand. Since 1983, Ericsson had become one of the major suppliers of infrastructure for the AMPS cellular networks in the USA. In 1985, Vodafone had pushed Ericsson into a TACS system for the UK. The mobile gold rush had started, and everywhere Ericsson was establishing itself as the key supplier of cellular infrastructure systems – often the only supplier to meet all the emerging standards.

And most of Ericsson's other businesses (the significant exception was EIS) were making progress.

Geographically, Ericsson's traditional strength as an exporter was serving it well. It was quick to introduce new technologies and concepts into its export markets, and to turn presentations into orders. On every continent, and in every area of telecoms, Ericsson was becoming an expected presence.

In the market as a whole, liberalisation was beginning to encourage the emergence of prospective new customers, as – spearheaded in the mobile business in the US, the UK and the Nordic countries – monopolies began to crumble.

There were setbacks, of course. A growth in the number of customers meant a growth in the number of competitors, all now competent with digital systems; and that, in turn, was beginning to mean pressure on margins. Ericsson Information Systems was a worry. AXE was not yet well established in Central Europe – where many PTTs and their national suppliers were muffling themselves against the bracing breezes of liberalisation – and had received embarrassing rebuffs in Mexico and Norway. AXE was also just beginning on its long and frustrating journey through the RBOCs in the US. Motorola was still providing very serious opposition in mobile systems, and was far ahead of Ericsson's fledgling development of mobile telephones.

Most important, customers committed to open procurement were realising the power they had, using competition to beat down prices and shorten deliveries. The traditional total cost for building a telephone network had for years been accepted as around $ 2,000 per line, of which, typically, the local switching equipment accounted for upwards of $ 200. Competition, and digitalisation, was now driving it down towards today's $ 1,000, or less – and switching equipment to below the $ 100 mark.

But there was no lack of enterprise or energy. In fact, it began to look as though there was too much ...

The 1983 organisation, described in the last chapter, shows that Ericsson

Hans Werthén

After the death of Björn Lundvall in 1980, Hans Werthén was elected Chairman of the Board, a position he held until 1990. Werthén was a doctor of technology and had been one of the drivers in the early work to introduce television in Sweden, and thereafter worked for the Swedish Philips company with electronics production. He then spent several years with LM Ericsson as Director of Production, a post he left to become head of Electrolux. Hans Werthén died in early 2000.

was very broadly extended. It was time to refocus strategies and strengthen external partnerships.

Ericsson was no stranger to partnerships. AXE was born in a joint venture with Televerket. The world's biggest telecommunications contract had been given to a joint venture between Ericsson and Philips in Saudi Arabia. Ericsson was in partnership with Thorn-EMI in the UK, Atlantic-Richfield in the US, Matra in France, OPC in Korea, Telefónica in Spain, Ascom in Switzerland … Sometimes, as in its 1987 cooperation agreement with Texas Instruments, a long-term partnership was formed to add technological strength. Often, a partnership would be formed to satisfy a requirement for 'local content', and to boost financial resources and reduce financial risk. For whatever reason, partnering became a significant element in Ericsson's development strategy for the '80s and '90s. Other suppliers have followed the same route – as have most of the significant customers, whose constantly shifting alliances have become so bewildering.

This drive for partnerships was a part of the strategic refocusing carried out from 1986 onwards by Dr Lars Ramqvist, who (significantly) became Managing Director of Ericsson Radio Systems in 1988, and CEO of Ericsson in 1990. It was balanced by the concept of Core Businesses. Core technologies, core products and systems and core businesses were defined. In non-core areas, partnering was welcome. In core businesses, and core technologies, partnerships would be treated with caution, to safeguard proprietary Ericsson know-how.

The core business concept became central to Ericsson's way of thinking in the late '80s. Certain systems and solutions were identified as key to the future strength and growth of the company. AXE was still the flagship. Cellular mobile systems were clearly crucial. The MD 110 was the key to building a greater presence in the 'private', or enterprise, market. The TMOS platform for network operation and management systems was identified as a core product, as were digital transmission and products in microelectronics, defence, and optical fibre. The most significant, though natural, omission at the time was mobile telephones. Most of these core businesses have maintained their importance and have succeeded.

For a company like Ericsson, accustomed to thinking and acting in a rather monolithic way, the new pluralism was not easy to accept at first. Where every business had been part of one business, and all of that business had been equally important, staff were now asked to accept the Animal Farm-ish concept that all businesses were equal, but some were somehow more equal than others.

To help staff maintain their personal balance, in 1989 the company adopted as its official shared corporate values the concepts of professionalism, respect and perseverance, applicable in any sort of business, core or otherwise.

OPPOSITE:
Bringing the telephone to a Malaysian village. Solar-powered coin-box as an extension of the NMT network.

CHAPTER 17

1990–2000

Taking the lead in the mobile revolution

GSM emerges

I
n 1981, as we've seen, the world's first commercial cellular mobile telephony service was inaugurated. It was analogue. In 1990, Ericsson received its first order for a network for the new standard, GSM. It was digital. In the new, de-regulated world, there was strong demand for the new technology.

And once again, Ericsson was in the lead.

What did GSM offer that the analogue systems didn't?

There were a variety of benefits, from greater clarity of speech (so it was claimed) and freedom from eavesdropping to better use of frequency; but the main benefit was that the GSM specification had been developed as an international standard, originally pan-European, but soon spreading to most parts of the world.

International roaming was built into the GSM technical specification, but far more important was the effort made by various bodies to get at least all the European operators on board.

The first necessity was a common frequency band. As early as 1978, CEPT had set aside two blocks of 25 MHz in the 900 MHz band. In 1982, CEPT set up a standardisation working group for second-generation mobile, the Groupe Spéciale Mobile, GSM, with representatives of 11 European PTTs. The numbers of participants and contributions grew, and in 1985, the Group was split into five working parties to deal with specific aspects of the system. In 1986, a secretariat, the 'Permanent Nucleus', was formed.

In 1988, all the CEPT Group's activities on GSM were transferred to a new organisation, the European Telecommunications Standards Institute (ETSI). ETSI participation is not restricted to PTTs, but includes members from other operators, user groups – and manufacturers. As it happens, the

OPPOSITE: *Two ways to go mobile. Hanoi, Vietnam.*

GSM group had already invited a similar range of representatives to participate from 1987 onwards.

Open interfaces for open procurement

A key characteristic of GSM is the open interface principle.

With 'open' interfaces between the components of a system, any manufacturer's components can be integrated into the system provided their interfaces match the published specifications. What goes on within the component doesn't matter, which allows a manufacturer to incorporate proprietary technology and functionality, provided the interfaces still conform.

The aim of GSM was to create conditions for a seamless international mobile telephone network, and to set the stage for competition and open procurement – to prevent any one manufacturer, or operator, from imposing one proprietary solution across a market, thereby creating a monopoly.

It was official European Community policy to build open interfaces into the structure of the GSM system: it was designed to encourage competition among system suppliers and operators – and, it may be noticed, to allow smaller manufacturers to go for the GSM market as well.

For Ericsson, the competition began early.

TDMA/FDMA? Broadband/narrowband?

From the first introduction of cellular mobile telephony into Europe, Ericsson had taken a leading role. It was the only manufacturer making both NMT and TACS systems, and it was the only manufacturer with equal strengths in switching and radio technologies. Ericsson was in a dominating position.

With the advent of GSM, the French and German suppliers saw an opportunity of breaking that dominance. Both governments announced that they would place orders for systems incorporating new technology within the GSM specification, and they funded four Franco-German consortia to develop experimental systems.

Various combinations of four different technologies were being considered: Time Division Multiple Access, TDMA, Frequency Division Multiple Access, FDMA, broadband and narrowband.

In Sweden, a lot of work had been carried out by an R&D Group jointly set up in 1977 by Televerket, Ericsson, and the four principal Swedish technical universities.

From 1981 to 1986, this R&D Group occupied itself designing and building demonstrators for FDMA and TDMA. In the course of this work, the Group members convinced themselves that narrowband TDMA offered the greatest advantages in terms of capacity (spectrum efficiency), and they recommended the use of microcells; frequency-hopping to combat fading; and a hand-over function controlled from the mobile base station. Even the economics looked right – broadband had advantages in dense urban areas, but was too expensive elsewhere.

The Franco-German consortia proposed competitive evaluation tests, and these were set up at CNET, the laboratories of the French PTT, in 1986. The consortia fielded four systems, mostly wideband TDMA, with a 2 MHz channel width. Ericsson, Televerket, Nokia and Elab of Norway fielded narrowband TDMA systems, with 300 kHz channel width.

The tests persuaded all the European countries except France and Germany to choose narrowband TDMA. Germany set up a day of technical hearings and exhaustive analysis of the technologies, and finally Germany, too, came down for the narrowband TDMA.

Which left the French …

In 1986, ERA had set up an agreement with LCT, an independent French telecoms company, formerly part of the French ITT. LCT was working on narrowband TDMA and exchanging technology with Ericsson, and through LCT the French PTT was also supporting narrowband TDMA. When the French finally remembered that broadband had never been their idea in the first place, the battle was over.

A Memorandum of Understanding, the GSM MoU, was signed by the European operators at Copenhagen in 1987. The GSM MoU was an answer to the need for cooperation on commercial and operational matters, such as time schedules for procurement and deployment of networks; compatibility of numbering and routing plans; harmonisation of service introduction; and tariff and accounting procedures. When the specifications for GSM were completed in 1988, operators began to send out requests for proposals. Both Ericsson and Nokia were well placed to hit the ground running.

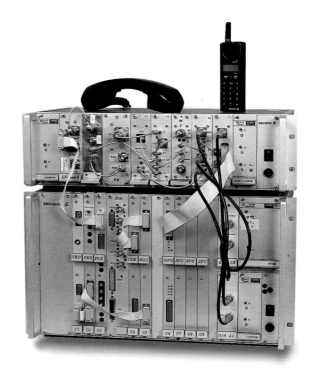

1986: The Ericsson GSM demonstrator that went to the Paris evaluation trials. The mobile telephone standing on top is the model into which the first GSM phone was eventually designed.

A patchy start

GSM has achieved worldwide penetration, and is the most widely instal-led cellular mobile system in operation. Though there are, of course, other suppliers of GSM systems, it became almost an Ericsson proprietary pro-duct, at least for several years. It came on stream as some of the steam was going out of AXE in fixed networks, which were becoming more concerned with accesses, overlays and the Internet than with the big network en-gines, and it fuelled the company's dramatic growth through the '90s. Even on Ericsson's 125th anniversary, GSM has plenty of life ahead of it, though the specifications for its successor are now agreed and implemen-tation of the third generation has begun.

But GSM was primarily designed for Europe, and it found its feet there. Though there was never any doubt that it would succeed, it had a sticky start in some territories.

Germany

Traditionally, the Deutsche Bundespost was a very hard-line monopoly. It bought from German manufacturers, chiefly Siemens and ITT's Standard Elektrik Lorenz (now part of Alcatel). To sell to the Bundespost, Ericsson went into partnership with Siemens, which had not been involved in the earlier Franco-German consortia.

The idea was to develop a common base station controller, BSC, and it was over the BSC that the partnership came to grief. By now, Ericsson was committed to using AXE for both the BSC and the mobile switching centre, MSC. Siemens found it hard to adopt a system which would con-tain one of its own switches (EWSD) as the MSC and one of its direct competitor's (AXE) as the BSC. And there was also strong doubt whether the Bundespost would accept such a solution. Added to all that, Siemens was under pressure to work with the German Philips company, and in the end, it broke off its relationship with Ericsson.

The German authorities, at long last, had decided to license two com-peting operators. Deutsche Bundespost, now becoming known as Deutsche Telekom, would have GSM network D1. GSM network D2 was up for allocation. During 1988, ten different consortia were formed to pitch for it. Ericsson's strategy was, of course, to be as helpful as possible to any of the consortia which would accept help, and hope to be included in the winning bid.

In December 1989, the winning bid was that of the Mannesmann group, which immediately went out to invite tenders from the manufacturers. Out of a feeding frenzy that included Motorola (with Siemens switches), a Siemens-Philips combination, Alcatel, and Nokia (which was starting to move to the front of the stage), Ericsson emerged as the victor.

PacTel, the California RBOC, was a partner in the Mannesmann consortium, and well acquainted with Ericsson's high-profile activities in the US. PacTel also understood the need for big, powerful switches (like AXE) at a time when some people still felt a smaller, cheaper switch could handle what they perceived as the limited number of customers and basic functionality foreseen.

The problem that now faced Mannesmann was where to source its mobile phones. We shall see the answer in the next chapter.

France

Ericsson, which, as we've seen, had left France by 1976, returned in the mid-'80s as a minority partner in a new French company, Matra Ericsson Telecommunications S.A., MET. MET was encouraged into existence by the French government as part of an inordinately complex restructuring of the whole French telecoms industry. It became the successful supplier of AXE switches in France.

It was natural for Ericsson to introduce GSM into France in conjunction with MATRA, its AXE partner. In 1987, MATRA and Ericsson reached a cooperation agreement, covering the development and marketing of a GSM system integrating Matra base stations and Ericsson mobile switches (AXE, of course). But Ericsson and MATRA were pursuing two different base-station controller concepts, one suitable for large urban areas (Ericsson), the other for less populated and rural areas (MATRA). The agreement allowed the joint venture to sell internationally, as well as in France.

The delays endemic in every large technological development were more damaging to MATRA than to Ericsson, and sales of GSM inevitably led off in the large cities and metropolitan areas – just the areas for which Ericsson's version was more suitable.

MATRA achieved sales in France, and in the UK Vodafone bought some MATRA systems involving BSCs from Orbitel (with whom MATRA had a separate agreement). There were also sales to Italy and Spain. But overall, the venture was out of balance in sales terms and a source of friction between the engineers internally. In 1992, the MATRA-Ericsson GSM partnership was closed. GSM systems in France are now sold direct by Ericsson.

Italy

When the time came for Italy to go digital with GSM, SIP again played an active pioneering role, just as it had with TACS. After the normal Request for Proposals procedure, in which it asked for an Italian GSM network, designed for national coverage, its decisions clearly show the effect of Government industrial policy on procurement.

SIP decided that its mobile phone switches should be supplied by Ericsson and FATME, while its radio base stations would come from Italtel, Telettra, Marconi, Siemens and OTE.

There was some disagreement between ERA and FATME over pricing. It was ERA's policy to price uniformly in every market. FATME, on the other hand, argued that it felt the need to be flexible, to be able to 'modulate' pricing principles, functionality concepts, and so on, to match variations in national outlooks. Eventually, ERA concurred, and FATME went

MiniLink terminals and mobile system antennas, northern Italy.

on to introduce into its proposals such concepts as the right to use pro-prietary software, licence fees, and IPR. SIP was a tougher prospect than ERA, and in Italy (as in other markets) these approaches are still subject to some discussion.

FATME had hopes of forming a partnership with Italtel, as it had in the CORAM consortium for the TACS system, but this time Italtel formed a partnership with Alcatel. FATME was proposing the AXE switch in its GSM product programme, while Alcatel was offering its 8300 processor system. The 8300 could be used as a GSM switch in combination with Italtel's own Linea UT switching system – itself the result of a cooperation between Italtel and GTE. The principle had been demonstrated within Alcatel, where the 8300 was used with both of Alcatel's own switches! With this reasoning, Alcatel, which had not been selected in the tender competition, got its foot in the door. But not content with this, it also announced to SIP that it had lowered its prices. Reluctantly, SIP put FATME and Alcatel through a second tender process, but the result was the same: the contract went to FATME.

The contract asked for an experimental installation in 1990, but the base stations were delayed, and the MoU in-service target date of 1990 had in any case been abandoned.

In 1990, Alcatel acquired Telettra. This pushed Italtel back into the arms of FATME to discuss the base station question, and the original partner-ship was reinstated. The partnership would supply switching systems from FATME, and base stations from Italtel (supplied at first by ERA).

The Italian GSM network went into service in 1992 – with a number of subscribers who paid no subscriptions and no call charges. They were employees of SIP and STET, the Italian long-distance operator. The reason? Under pressure from the European Union, the Government had decided to postpone the opening of the GSM services until a second, competing, GSM network had been set up. This came about in 1994, when Omnitel, a consortium led by Olivetti (and with Sweden's Telia as one of the smaller partners), opened up Italy's second GSM network.

The UK

In the UK, the start was anything but sticky.

Vodafone became the first operator in the world to place a firm order with Ericsson for GSM infrastructure equipment. It was for one switch and eight base stations, to be delivered in mid-1990 and to be upgraded to an operational system with 93 base stations by 1993. The complete system was to handle 60,000 subscribers.

Vodafone specified precisely what it wanted, as a turnkey requirement, and it was up to Ericsson to deliver to spec. and on time. Vodafone was in a hurry, determined to take an early lead over British Telecom's Cellnet. It believed the Ericsson system had a lot of sophistication relevant to GSM operation, in activity-supervision and mobility-management, for example.

The UK also saw the first introduction of a variant of GSM, called Personal Communications Network, PCN. This system used technology identical to GSM – in fact, it is a GSM system – but in the 1.8 GigaHertz frequency band, instead of the usual 900 MHz GSM band. The higher frequency means a shorter signal range, and therefore smaller cells. This is no disadvantage in densely-populated urban areas, and the extra cost for rural or more scattered populations can be averaged against the high urban income. The high frequency also allows greater penetration of buildings. But the key value of PCN is the fact that it allows the use of another band of that scarce commodity: spectrum.

PCN as a system had a difficult birth in the UK. There were intended to be three operators, and three licences were awarded to three consortia. As some of the members of the consortia got cold feet, they sold out, and eventually only two networks opened: Mercury Personal Communications (One-to-One), owned by Cable & Wireless and US West; and Orange, owned by Hong Kong's Hutchison.

The infrastructure for Mercury's One-to-One network was largely supplied by Ericsson. It opened in September 1993, and was followed by Orange in 1994. Both networks have had a somewhat rocky road in terms of numbers of subscribers and coverage, but are today well established.

The US

In America, the situation was sticky indeed.

As we've seen, the US and Canada began with the AMPS standard – analogue, and often without roaming, and initially at least with a multitude of different cellular operators.

As GSM emerged, Ericsson discussed at the US Cellular Telecommunications Industry Association, CTIA, the possibility of its introduction into the US. It became clear that the US would not accept GSM, and that the 900 MHz standard did not, in any case, fit the spectrum very well.

A fundamental related question concerned the access standard: Time Division Multiple Access, TDMA, or Frequency Division Multiple Access, FDMA? AT&T and Motorola were promoting FDMA, on the grounds that it made better use of spectrum. Ericsson was promoting TDMA, as being more advanced in development, but was prepared to go in either direction.

By 1988, Ericsson was one of the three top cellular infrastructure suppliers in the US, with about 30 per cent of the market. As such, it was invited, alongside Motorola and AT&T to present its case. Each company set up a test version of its system, but Ericsson was the only company to

get its test system to work well, and the decision went in favour of TDMA.
The new standard was a digital version of AMPS, D-AMPS, with the official
denomination IS-54 (Interim Standard 54).

The strength of Ericsson's TDMA based D-AMPS system proposal was
that it could be 'grafted on' to the existing analogue networks, using the
same base stations. It was, in other words, designed as a digital upgrade
of the existing analogue networks. In the existing base stations the 30 kHz
channels were used, with a number of analogue transceivers replaced by
digital transceivers, each providing three channels instead of one. For the
operators, it was a comparatively simple matter to change out transceivers and gradually upgrade their networks, instead of investing in new
cell sites and complete new base station equipment. But this approach
meant that the customers of any such operator might need dual-mode
(analogue/digital) handsets, to ensure connection at all times.

As part of its test system, Ericsson had developed dual-mode telephone
prototypes. Some competitors claimed that these prototypes could never

*Solving a problem at the
Lynchburg plant, US.*

be turned into commercial terminals small enough to go into handheld mobiles. Ericsson decided to design and produce its own D-AMPS phone – a diversion of effort that combined with a recessionary economy to slow the progress of D-AMPS for a while.

Nor was D-AMPS having things all its own way. Though it had seen off FDMA, yet another standard came on the scene: Code Division Multiple Access, CDMA. CDMA was introduced by Qualcomm and accepted as a standard. The system based on it became IS 95. Motorola and Lucent seized on it as a way to keep the Europeans out, and the operators were forced to make a choice.

It was 1993 before the first D-AMPS network was cut over. In 1997, the first IS 95, CDMA, networks came into operation.

Meanwhile, promoted particularly by Nokia and Ericsson, and with the success of GSM in Europe and elsewhere as a strong argument in its favour, a US version of GSM called the PCS1900/GSM was introduced. The first commercial PCS1900/GSM network went into service in New York in late 1995.

Ericsson is now offering D-AMPS under its new name, TDMA, in an improved version of the IS-54 called IS-136.

This story continues in chapter 18.

The technological excitement of the US cellular system manufacturing industry has been more than matched on the operator side. The original market-by-market duopoly set up by the FCC in the early 1980s is no longer there. Through mergers and acquisitions, the larger operators, both the RBOCs and the non wire-line companies, have enlarged their networks. AT&T entered the field through the acquisition of McCaw Cellular. New licences for the digital standards have been awarded through auctions.

And cellular penetration in the US is spectacular.

Japan

With Europe focused on GSM, and the US pursuing its several digital standards and solutions, one more significant bloc emerged.

From the mid-'80s, Japan was identified as a strategic market for Ericsson. It was due to liberalise, the US was pressuring the Japanese government to reduce the trade gap, and Ericsson had good contacts as a customer for Japanese micro-electronic components.

At the time when FDMA looked like winning the TDMA/FDMA debate in the US, a similar debate was going on in Japan. NTT, the Japanese PTT, was under pressure to introduce the US standard, and was backing FDMA. It's recorded that at a dinner attended by an ERA team and NTT management, ERA presented the case for TDMA in the US, and said it thought it would win. The Japanese laughed politely, and said, 'If

OPPOSITE:
Mount Fuji, serene above the complexities of modern Japan.

367

you win in the US, we will give you a contract.' It was a joke, of course, and by no means an official commitment – but when the US decided for TDMA, NTT followed suit, and in 1989 asked Ericsson to participate in the specification work, and to develop part of the radio system. (It must be added that Motorola and AT&T also received contracts.) This was a foot in the door.

Japan's digital standard is known as PDC, Personal Digital Cellular. PDC was originally set in the 800 MHz band, but soon thereafter new regional operators were licensed to introduce a Japanese PCN service in the 1.5 GHz to 1.6 GHz band. The Japanese Digital Phone Group, with Japan Telecom and PacTel as partners, had an interest in several regional operating companies offering PCN and chose Ericsson as a supplier. On 1 March 1994, ahead of the contractual time, the first network was handed over to the customer and inaugurated on 15 April.

Along with the supply of international AXE exchanges, the cellular systems business has led to Japan's becoming a major market for Ericsson.

Summary

By 1998 the total of subscribers served by analogue networks had peaked at some 91 million worldwide. Table 15 estimates the development of the different standards of the world in the period 1994–2000:

TABLE 15. MOBILE SYSTEMS AND USERS 1994–2000

Digital systems	Phones in service (millions)	
	1994	2000
GSM 900 & 1800	5	291
GSM 1900	0	13
TDMA *(Formerly D-AMPS)*	1	60
CDMA	0	70
PDC	1	56
Analogue systems		
NMT, TACS, ETACS, AMPS	49	68
Other		6
Total	**56**	**564**

Source: Ericsson statistics.

Few businesses have enjoyed growth figures of this sort.

Testing at the Ericsson-Toshiba joint venture, Tokyo.

The digital mobile drive

Ericsson's success in driving the specification efforts and the development of the three digital standards of mobile systems was the remarkable outcome of dedicated commitment. Ericsson came to the party with years of know-how in digital radio, and with proven experience of the advantages of narrow-band time division multiple access, TDMA.

Preparatory work with the GSM concept after the standard was finally issued by ETSI led into the main system development program, which was completed in only about two years. Yet at around the same time, Ericsson was also completing the development programmes for the American D-AMPS and the Japanese PDC systems.

It was a tremendous effort, of heroic proportions.

First, the projects needed funding, which meant increased development costs. Lars Ramqvist, initially as head of Ericsson Radio Systems, and from 1990 as Managing Director of Ericsson, had to convince the Board and the financial markets.

Second came marketing: the systems had to be sold, and we've seen the first crucial contracts with important customers. Kurt Hellström, first as Marketing Director, and then from 1990 as Managing Director of ERA, knew how to nose out prospective customers and saw to it that the order books were replenished in the key markets. Jan Uddenfeldt was the Technical Director at ERA, and it was his task to organise the development projects and ensure that manpower, basic technology and drive were available, and to maintain a close working relationship with the key customers.

For each of the three standards, system development was divided into AXE switch development, largely software, under Gunnar Eriksson, and base station development under Ulf Mimer. Staffing was built up by recruiting new engineers from the universities and other companies; by the transfer of AXE engineers from the AXE units within Ericsson Telecom; and by closing down and transferring the staff of several ERA departments that had been engaged in developing military radio and encryption systems.

Each of the three system developments started up with around a thousand people, and each grew during the project. GSM work was mainly located in Sweden and Germany, but also in the UK and Spain; D-AMPS in Stockholm and Canada; and PDC mainly in Sweden and Finland. Development centres were set up where the right people could be found.

The GSM system was completed in 1991, D-AMPS (admittedly with a few lingering bugs) in 1992, and PDC in 1993 – at which point, Ericsson had taken the world lead in digital mobile systems.

Ericsson's leading role in the industry was now very clear – as market leader in both analogue and digital cellular systems. This was recognised when Ericsson received the American 'IEEE Corporate Recognition Award' in 1992, an award reserved for companies that have created a new business.

Several aspects of the organisation, management and execution of these digital development projects have become part of Ericsson's present strategy. We know that development objectives must be clearly defined and limited, so that the target is always clearly in view. We know that the platform concept provides for the introduction of additional features and new technology in later stages. We know that every development project must be limited in time – two years is probably a maximum. And we know that development projects must be carried out in close cooperation with one or more customers, a theme that will be picked up again in later chapters.

The cordless concept

So far, the story of wireless telecommunications at Ericsson has primarily been concerned with what is usually called mobile, or cellular, telephony. But during the '80s and '90s a second application of radio technology emerged in parallel – cordless, which targets a different community of users and has different applications. At Ericsson, the roots of cordless were in the paging business.

Paging

The first paging systems were acoustic. As early as 1928, LM Ericsson marketed such systems, with single-strike bells set up in different parts of offices and other premises. A person was alerted by means of coded signals. Such arrangements were disturbing, and were soon replaced by the use of visual systems with lamp panels. Typically, each lamp panel would have five lamps, which would be flashed in different combinations. An alerted person would go to the nearest telephone and dial the operator, or, in later systems, dial a code and directly answer a call.

With the advent of the transistor it became possible to build small radio pocket receivers to act as individual alerting devices – pagers. LM Ericsson introduced its first wireless paging system, ERICALL, in 1961. The system worked with a tone code allowing 150 code combinations, using reed relays as receiver elements. Later the tone code units were further developed and the number of code signals increased to 810. Another refinement was to include a small transmitter in the paging unit to enable the called party to speak, over short distances.

Police radio, Mexico.

The next development was the introduction of digital code signalling, instead of using tones. With this, it became possible to transmit different messages to a display on the pager. This system was marketed from 1974 under the name ERICALL CONTACTOR.

The head of the group designing paging systems was Dag Åkerberg, and for some years he was joined by Nils Rydbeck – of whom we shall hear much more in the next chapter. The paging business can be seen as an early example of building consumer products, even though, from a marketing point of view, pagers were also sold as systems, often together with PBX installations. The challenge was to cram as many features as possible into the confined shell of a pager. Dag Åkerberg and Nils Rydbeck started making their own ASICs around 1980.

In 1981, SRA acquired the Dutch NIRA company, and LM Ericsson became the leading supplier in Europe of on-site paging systems. Paging business headquarters were transferred to the Netherlands, with a dynamic Brit, Colin Buckingham, as MD. Colin set up branding agreements with several major distributors and they sold as much as SRA could produce. Paging quickly became a major and profitable business. Outside Europe, Taiwan in particular became a thriving market for paging.

Cordless telephones

At about this time, the first cordless telephones turned up in Europe from Japan and Taiwan. The phones were sold surreptitiously for use as home telephones. The PTT monopolies were not too keen on allowing the connection of 'foreign devices' to the public telephone networks, since they were a threat to the PTTs' leasing business. With their regular telephone suppliers, they checked the possibilities for extending the business to include cordless sets. At LM Ericsson, these enquiries ended up with SRA and the paging group – cordless phones were seen as a possible extension of the paging business.

Dag Åkerberg and Colin Buckingham were doubtful about cordless phones in the public networks, but they did see a potential future in the PBX market – the wireless office switchboard. Cordless phones could be seen as an extension of the paging concept: indeed, cordless phones might well become a threat to the future of the on-site paging business. The technical group brought out a report proposing the development of cordless technology based on TDMA radio access.

But, alas, this was 1982! LM Ericsson was heavily committed to spending development money in several other major projects, and the proposal was put in the bottom drawer.

Meanwhile, ESPA, the European Selective Paging Association, a manufacturers' group, had begun to promote the allocation of common European frequency bands for paging, looking after their interests at a time when increasing bandwidth was being reserved for mobile telephony. And now, around 1982, ESPA also began work to create some sort of standard for wireless PBX.

The cordless phones from the East, working at 25 MHz or 40 MHz, were never accepted by the European PTTs. Their organisation, CEPT, brought out its own standard, CT1, in 1981. An analogue FDMA system in the 900 MHz band with 40 channels, CT1 was also used for defining a standard for connecting cordless phones to the public networks, but it provided only limited functionality.

For a time, the British and the French had accepted the Japanese systems, but then the UK started work on a digital FDMA system with 40 channels, called CT2. The concept was Telepoint, a service with base stations set up at shopping centres, airports and other places with high throughput of people. It was a one-way service: you could make calls from your pocket phone, but not receive them.

Freeset, a DECT phone for the office.

Freedom in the workplace with DECT office cordless.

CT2 was duly registered as a CEPT standard, though most other countries had accepted the analogue 40-channel CT1. ESPA, however, had by now become heavily involved, and was aiming to standardise a cordless access that could also be applied in office systems, with additional services such as higher data speeds.

Meanwhile in CEPT, British Telecom now added certain new requirements – that a new system must serve not only Telepoint and office services, but also as access in the local network, at that time referred to as Radio in the Local Loop, RLL, an alternative to cable connection. ECTEL, too, the European Association of the Telecommunications Industry, got itself into the game and set up working parties to define a next-generation cordless system. The industry was awake to the fact that the time was coming when the European Union would be involved in telecommunications, and absolute conformity to standards would be enforced, instead of the rather loosely applied recommendations of CEPT.

It became a long drawn-out argument. British Telecom and the British industry fought bravely for their CT2 to become a standard. They also jumped the gun, and began to develop CT2 products.

It was now 1985, and at ERA they dusted off the digital TDMA proposal from three years earlier. It was clear that to have a chance to beat CT2, Ericsson must develop a product. Funds were made available and Televerket reserved space in the 900 MHz band for future cordless applications.

Cordless was a new area for Ericsson, but it was natural to assign the development to the Dutch paging unit. However, what expertise existed was found in the labs at Lund in Sweden, so a period of training was arranged for Dutch engineers there.

The company first demonstrated successful 'seamless handover' at a CEPT meeting in Lund in the autumn of 1987.

Early the following year, CEPT decided that the next-generation CT would be based on TDMA. The system was later to be given the name DECT – Digital European Cordless Telecommunications. But progress in CEPT was slow. The acceptance of a new standard was based on consensus and the British, with their digital FDMA, might go on blocking the TDMA proposal forever. The best argument would be a working system – so Televerket and Ericsson decided to take development a step further, using the 900 MHz proposal. The risk otherwise was that DECT would never materialise at all.

A smart move was made when Colin Buckingham christened the new system CT3 and as such it was accepted by CEPT as an interim standard.

ETSI, the European Telecommunications Standards Institute, a much more decisive body than CEPT, was set up in 1988, and work with the new DECT standard was transferred to ETSI. But it was realised that the work would take several more years to come to fruition. Ericsson decided to continue developing CT3, the proprietary system designated DCT900.

The first-generation DECT standard specification was issued by ETSI in 1992. It is what is termed a base standard, in the 1.9 GHz band, a sort of cupboard from which may be brought out the respective processes, procedures and messages for creating access technology. It should be stressed that DECT is neither a network nor a terminal. It is strictly an access system, which does not provide any particular services beyond mobility. Or, if you like, DECT is a transparent access system, and the various services are defined in the main network.

Starting with the DCT900 (proprietary) system, and then bringing out its DECT standard product, Ericsson has focused its sales efforts primarily on two market segments: the large wireless PBX office system; and Radio in the Local Loop.

The attraction of RLL, which was later called Wireless in the Local Loop, WLL, and is now Fixed Wireless Access, FWA, is of course that no cable network is necessary. This means that a system can be installed and up and running with new subscribers, in a matter of days. This may be a significant competitive advantage to an operator. Ericsson has supplied such systems to, among other countries, Sri Lanka and Uruguay, but due to the economic downturn affecting developing countries the market has remained limited.

For office applications, especially in the upper range, Ericsson offers the MD110 digital PBX with either fixed or wireless extensions, or a mixture

New styling of DECT for the home or office.

of both. Within Ericsson today there are large offices with no fixed telephone installations – every employee has a DECT phone (Freeset) which follows him or her around. This also means that staff do not necessarily have a permanently assigned place of work – DECT supports a flexible working mode.

DECT has, slowly, become accepted in the US. Naturally, the interpretation of the acromym has had to be modified, and DECT now stands for Digital Enhanced Cordless Telecommunications.

Today, there is a certain amount of debate over the longer-term future of DECT. The original idea, at Ericsson, was that DECT would come into the market as a forerunner to GSM in the second half of the '80s, to be followed by GSM in 1991. As it dragged its way through the standardisation bodies, DECT was severely delayed and GSM came first, which meant that DECT did not have a clear role to play.

DECT serves well as an office system, but increasingly office staff will want to be in contact outside the office as well. At the present time, it is foreseen that in UMTS, the Universal Mobile Telephone Service, the office wireless system will be defined as a subset of the public system and a DECT mode will be built into UMTS. For home phone applications, on the other hand, DECT may develop strongly.

The end of CT2

At this point we may finish the CT2 story – or at least its Telepoint applications. In January 1989, four operators in the UK were licensed. The first two came into operation in 1989. But it was a one-way system – and it never caught on. Maybe the marketing was weak, perhaps the competition from the cellular mobile networks was too strong – with competition and high volumes combining to drive down costs of both the phones and the service. In any event, by the end of 1993 the last of the Telepoint networks had closed down.

In France the service, called Bi-Bop, was marketed much better and became popular, although eventually GSM was to take over.

Among other markets, Hong Kong and Singapore have had successful Telepoint operations, but there, too, the alternatives have taken over.

CHAPTER 18

1978–2000

The march of the mobiles

*I*n the 1980s, much of the world began to turn its back on the collectivist orthodoxies that in one form or another had marked the years after the Second World War. The wide-spread beliefs in planning, social engineering, state ownership and control, and the equal partnership of Government, business owners and Unions, came under question.

The change was marked at the beginning of the decade by the election of Mrs Thatcher as Prime Minister in the UK in 1979, and at the end of the decade by the collapse of the Soviet régime in 1991. (And as we've seen, it was the decade in which the liberalisation of telecommunications began.)

Monetarism, the beating back of organised Labour, privatisation, the allowing of lame-duck industries to die – Mrs Thatcher became the symbol of a whole new tough world.

But in the late '80s, a different symbol emerged of the world that Thatcherism had started to create. In place of the earnest social planners came the new rich – youngish individuals in the City or on the Bourse or on Wall Street, traders and market-makers, living lives of gigantic stress on gigantic salaries and bonuses: the Young, UPwardly-mobile Yuppy phenomenon.

And the symbol of the Yuppy was the 'Yuppy teddy bear': the mobile phone. (Or as the Yuppy called it, simply 'my mobile'.)

OPPOSITE:
Harry HotLine in action, at a time when Dirty Harry had become respectable.

377

Before the mobile: portables and luggables

There are actually several ways of looking at mobility in telephony, most of them hinging on the question of who (or what) is mobile. When a conscientious executive diverts calls from his office to his home at the end of a day, the call and the executive are both mobile, but the phones stay where they are. But if, when he gets home, the executive picks up his calls on a cordless telephone and walks round the house with his handset, then the executive, the call and the phone are all mobile.

Hand-held mobile phones are now so commonplace that it's hard to believe Ericsson's first model appeared only in 1987 – less than 15 years ago.

As we've seen, Ericsson supplied most of the early NMT infrastructure. But an infrastructure is of no use without terminals – and there, Ericsson was only one of several competing suppliers.

But Ericsson was not new to terminals. For years, SRA had been producing terminals for land mobile and defence systems. And for years, Ericsson had been designing and producing standard telephone sets for the fixed network, and, from 1956, phones (more correctly mobile stations) for the early MTA and MTB networks. This was a good background – technologically. But Ericsson's terminals and telephones had been sold to operators and other network owners, not the end users. With mobile telephones, Ericsson entered the consumer market.

As NMT started up, it just seemed natural to Åke Lundqvist, Managing Director of SRA since 1977, to broaden SRA's range and start producing NMT terminals for Ericsson's NMT systems. There seem to have been no deep discussions about marketing, distribution, or any change of business direction.

Sonab, an SRA acquisition in 1978, had a land mobile radio product which could be adapted to become an NMT mobile telephone station, and Ericsson also had one of its own. (The word 'station' was often used in those days to describe these relatively large, heavy boxes, designed to be carried about by vehicles, not people.)

But mass production was a remote concept, and when, in 1981, Ericsson had to cut over its Saudi NMT network, the supply of 8,000 mobile stations stretched Ericsson's resources to the limit – so far, in fact, that for a while there were no terminals for sale to the Scandinavian market – a gift to the competition.

It's easy to make fun of the primitive early mobile terminals. But … NMT450 was a huge success, even with the unwieldy machines of the time, and no company had anything like a hand-portable to offer. Gradually, the terminals were refined to become detachable from vehicles, and turned from the barely-liftable into briefcase-sized luggables. Many a travelling executive counted himself or herself privileged to have one.

From luggable to loveable

There had been, as we have seen, no very serious strategic discussions about the status of mobile terminals within Ericsson's overall business development. It was a future-orientated policy decision of the NMT Group that terminals should be bought directly by subscribers, not hired or leased from the operators. So they sat rather awkwardly in the portfolio of an advanced systems house – unintegrated, if not exactly unwanted; of very variable quality; and not part of any systematic development plan. In the market place, the Danish Storno range and a few others were beating Ericsson easily.

Some attempt to introduce and present a logic in the range was made over the years from 1979 to 1983, and from 1984 onwards a more determined sales drive pushed the terminals outside Europe, as they followed NMT penetration into the Far East.

But a real sense of direction began to be visible only from 1983 onwards. In that year, the Ericsson Mobile Telephone Laboratory opened at the Ideon technology park in Lund, in southern Sweden. The park was the brainchild of Nils Hörjel, a board member of ERA and County Governor of Scania in south Sweden. No longer overshadowed by the systems operations in Stockholm, the dedicated terminals laboratory began timidly

Roadcom C600M.

HotLine Combi.

379

Typical HotLine application.

to find its own feet. Then, when Nils Rydbeck, the father of mobile phone design in Ericsson, took over as manager of the laboratory in 1985, he put in place a five-year development programme. In April 1987, mobile telephones became a separate business unit within SRA, with its own evangelical manager, Flemming Örneholm. Under the benign overall management of Åke Lundqvist, mobile terminals were acquiring a little muscle of their own.

From supplying the Saudi market in 1981 to the establishment of the new business unit in 1987 is six years, a long time. They had not been years of dynamic progress.

By today's standards, the unit's products were primitive – car phones and portables for NMT 450. At the beginning of 1987, Ericsson still had no hand-held 'mobiles' (but neither had anybody else). The luggables were functional, but not beautiful. They were expensive to produce, and buy. And year after year, there were serious quality problems. Volumes were small – about 10,000 in 1986. Marketing was not dynamic: the terminals were merely exposed to the risk of being bought at specialist retailers. There was no strong advertising or publicity, and the competitors – notably Nokia, still branded as Mobira, and Motorola – were ahead on design, manufacture, marketing and share of the market's mind.

Mobile phones were not strategic within Ericsson. They were just a necessary component to give credibility to system sales. Even manufacturing attitudes were those of a systems house: time was not of the essence, and any problems could be solved in due course.

Under Flemming Örneholm, the new team tackled everything at once.

A vigorous advertising campaign began: it branded the machines as 'HotLine'; invented a buccaneering character, Harry HotLine, as a brand 'property'; and positioned the portables as prerequisites for a fast, free-wheeling, executive life.

Product design leaped in the consumer direction, with orange buttons and a smart 'military' styling.

As early as 1983, the long-range plans had focussed on building a hand-held, or truly portable, mobile telephone. But it was not until the end of 1987 that the required technology became available. Two years' work in the labs paid off and Ericsson's first real hand-held 'mobile' finally appeared. Large, by today's standards, but pocketable (just), smart in black and orange, and heavily branded HotLine, it was just in time for the yuppy market!

At last, Ericsson's yuppy teddy-bear was out of its cage.

From loveable to – well, even more loveable!

The look and feel of the new mobile was hugely important. Flemming Örneholm's early days had been spent in consumer marketing, and he and Rydbeck realised that mobiles were consumer products.

Yet that first pocketable model (code-named Curt) was never intended to be anything more than a demonstration that the complex technology of a telephone, radio and battery could be crammed into a real mobile.

Curt originally worked with the new NMT 900 standard, which was being introduced at the time when the NMT 450 was reaching full capacity. NMT 900 got off to a slow start, because its coverage was inevitably inferior to the established NMT 450, and Curt was never a big seller in Sweden.

Instead, he was rapidly followed by an NMT mobile that looked a bit like him, but was sleeker and slimmer – code-named Olivia. Olivia was followed by Sandra, who in turn was followed by Jane, who was superseded by Emma, and so on. Each new design was sexier than the last.

The phones became 'platforms', basic designs that could be configured to hold the components required for the growing range of mobile standards round the world.

And from rugged Curt through to Emma and beyond, Ericsson phones began to do more than just make and receive calls efficiently: they became desirable possessions, like cars, and different models had their own informal fan clubs among users.

Curt, 1987 HotLine Pocket.

Kick-off party for Curt, the first Ericsson hand-held mobile phone. Starring from left: Lars Jonsteg, Nils-Ingvar Lundin and CEO, Björn Svedberg in Harry HotLine attire.

Demand shifts the spotlight to production

The kiss of life for Curt

The production run for Curt, the prototype, was originally scheduled to be only 300. But in 1987, just as Curt was coming to life, Panasonic realised that it was not going to be able to bring out a mobile of its own in time to catch the new NMT 900 market.

Curt was ready and waiting, and Panasonic fell in love with him and gave him the kiss of life. Re-styled and re-branded, Curt became Panasonic's first-ever outsourced product.

But for the factory at Kumla, Panasonic was a very different customer from sleepy old Ericsson. Panasonic sent its own quality engineers over, and their standards were strict. An agreement had to be reached, for example, on quite literally how many specks of dust were permissible inside a display. The Kumla factory had never had to consider such standards.

On quality, on price, on productivity, the factory was increasingly exposed to the standards of the world outside. It became as important to upgrade production as it was to upgrade the product.

The first production line using laser soldering.
Base station manufacture, Gävle factory, 1989.

Leif Byhlin, factory
manager, Kumla.

Olivia.

The kiss of life for Kumla

In 1973, SRA moved its production of land mobile radio systems from an old shoe factory in Kumla, in central Sweden, to a brand-new, purpose-built facility in the same town. The factory had around 400 employees.

In 1981, Kumla was selected to manufacture the first mobile telephone stations for the new NMT 450 system.

When you remember that these were, at best, luggables, there does seem to be a synergy with land mobile stations. And this, in a sense, was the problem: there may have been synergy between the products, but there was no synergy between the markets, and the markets inevitably dictate what happens in a successful factory.

In 1986 there was a yellow line down the floor at Kumla. On one side of it was the highly-valued production of the successful land mobile radios. On the other side of it was the production of everything else, including

Sandra.

Ericsson's mobiles get slimmer and sexier day by day.

mobile stations. Though great efforts were being made to improve its operations, the factory facility that Flemming Örneholm inherited as his supplier in 1987 was still struggling to emerge from its systems production mindset.

Production was a separate, self-contained activity, with its own management and accounting. Its job was to make the things designed by product developers (at Lund, in the case of mobiles) using the drawings and specifications provided, and to work out what they cost to produce.

Meanwhile, volumes were rising, and outsourcing and sub-contracting routines were being introduced – in the teeth of the Ericsson tradition of vertical integration. In 1988, the factory was able to give Örneholm 37,000 phones (well below its target of 43,000). In 1992, production reached around 200,000 phones, including the new Sandra model.

Producing 200,000 phones is an achievement. But its value as an achievement is lessened if a quarter or so of them find their way back to the factory with faults. And the problem is merely exacerbated as volumes rise. The key to quality was a massive change of outlook.

In 1985, Nils Rydbeck had begun the task of breaking down some mental walls at the Lund end.

Similarly, at Kumla, Leif Byhlin, factory manager at the time, formed 'a troika for change' in 1984. A programme called PT 88, Product Technology 88, was initiated, and ran through from 1984 to 1988. Among other things, the troika recognised that quality was at least as much a function of design as it was of production, and that the two disciplines should have a deep understanding of each other's requirements. Each member of the troika visited Lund every week – sometimes separately, sometimes together.

Slowly, the mutual understanding that is the basis of quality was built up.

In 1988, there was a reshuffling of the different production lines at the ERA factories, and Kumla became a dedicated mobile telephone production facility. Equally important, the factory came under Flemming Örneholm's management. The process began to pick up speed, but it was 1991 – or even 1993, under pressure from GSM – before production could be regarded as able to handle the market's demands on it.

Marketing for volume

With consumer products, volume is everything.

Volume cuts costs and builds profits. Volume pays for research and design. Volume makes distribution viable. Volume builds brands and develops momentum.

And what builds volume is marketing.

With phones for NMT, developing volume was tough. NMT had wide penetration, but nothing like the penetration GSM was later to achieve. Without volume, it was difficult to build profitability. Without profitability, it was difficult to fund the marketing that would build volume. The costs story alone dramatises the difficulty: in 1997, 18 Ericsson sales people managed a turnover of SEK 1.5 billion in Sweden. Ten years earlier, it took 150 people to generate just 1 per cent of this turnover – at a time when unit prices were very much higher.

Ericsson did its best to get its home-market marketing under way.

It began by working through the land mobile dealers already in place. Technically, these dealers were outstandingly competent. Commercially, they were naïve. Many failed, some survived – with training from Ericsson at a specially-created business school.

The only alternative in existence was the more traditional dealers, the big general-purpose shops. In Stockholm, at least, these outlets were not receptive. Ericsson had been a little too arrogant in the past, a little too often. Now, its products were technically behind Nokia's, and its marketing and sales promotion were even further behind. It had a lot of catching up to do.

The sales manager for the Swedish market was Jan Ahrenbring. He went for the only option left – shops wholly-owned by Ericsson. Ericsson HotLine stores were opened in the larger cities, which provided an opportunity to demonstrate and promote the mobile phones – they were more of a statement than real stores with volume throughput. But they also

The USA: market build-up for mobile phones went on throughout the '90s.

Asia was quick to adopt the mobile way of life. Here, in India …

allowed Ahrenbring to stage events to a real audience, and some outstanding launch parties are recorded in private history books. These parties did as much good inside Ericsson as they did to the dealers – who would remember them for years as true consumer-type events, with all the traditional associated glamour, and quite unlike Ericsson's usual low-key approach.

The shops did their job, but survived only two or three years. What really turned the marketing tide was the HotLine campaign, the improved product range, the obvious change in Ericsson's attitude – and the fact that, for a while, Curt was the only hand-held NMT 900 mobile on the market.

Sorting out the States

From the Buffalo contract of 1983 onwards, Ericsson had done very well with mobile systems in the US. For the first time, it had a big, durable American success on its hands. By the end of the '80s, Ericsson had a steady 30 per cent of the mobile systems market in the USA and Canada.

But success with systems was not matched by success with phones. At the end of 1989, Ericsson had yet to sell a single mobile in the States.

And even the success with systems brought its own problems. Growth in demand was straining Ericsson's resources in logistics, production, marketing and money.

… and on a huge scale in China.

Sharing the load

So in 1989, Ericsson set up a major joint venture with America's General Electric company to handle mobile telephones, mobile data systems and radio based security systems, world wide. GE's stake in Ericsson GE Mobile Communications was 40 per cent. Åke Lundqvist moved over as President, and the JV – and Ericsson's global mobile telephone business – was headquartered at Paramus, New Jersey. GE's former plant at Lynchburg became the new company's production facility.

In Sweden, ERA had learned the value of separation (as well as cooperation) between R&D and production, so R&D was located at Research Triangle Park, RTP, near Raleigh in North Carolina. By 1990, Nils Rydbeck had been persuaded to move in as head of the laboratories at RTP.

Ericsson was taking mobile phones seriously. In 1991, it produced about 225,000 phones. More than half came from Lynchburg. But while Lynchburg was producing the 'CarPhone', a portable AMPS model, Lund and Kumla were feverishly developing the first GSM digital mobile

387

phone. It suffered many delays (but so did GSM). Over all, Ericsson had about 3 per cent of the world market for mobiles – way behind Motorola, Nokia and a couple of other competitors.

It was not that the US was ignoring digital cellular telephony.

As we've seen, there had been a great debate over which system to adopt, and Ericsson's TDMA D-AMPS system had won the day.

But Ericsson was a small player. The big players, above all Motorola, were dragging their feet. And in the early '90s, the world was moving into a deep recession. Take-up of digital was slow in the US, and it was on a quick start into digital that Ericsson had pinned its hopes. By 1992, as we shall see, this was beginning to happen in Europe, helped by the appearance of Curt and the mass production of Olivia – pocketable platforms, with digital technology inside. But at Lynchburg, there was a point-blank refusal to admit that the plant as it was could ever produce an Olivia.

Calling in the consultants

When, in 1992, Åke Lundqvist decided to move back to Stockholm and wind his career down, the situation at Ericsson-GE was starting to look serious. GE had begun to lose interest: it reduced its financial holding, and was soon to give up its representation on the Board.

Ronny Lejdeman took over as MD, and brought over Bengt Undén, who had turned round the Kumla factory, to run Lynchburg.

When Bengt Undén arrived, Lynchburg was making mobile base stations, land mobile radio systems, and around 800 rather primitive portable phones per day. Costs were high. Quality was not, particularly. Bengt did not feel that any piecemeal solution would be of much value, and he and Ronny Lejdeman persuaded top management to allow them to call in McKinsey. McKinsey found four main areas of shortcoming: a lack of strategic direction; huge complexity in operations – the factory was producing 90,000 different things, manual and automated, high-tech and low-tech, high-cost and low-cost, long-run, short-run; cultural differences between Ericsson (used to matrix reporting) and GE (hierarchic); and, as an outcome of the first three, a death wish.

It was time for action. Unofficial history (or folk memory) relates that at the end of 1993 a decision was actually taken to sell off Lynchburg (or, in some versions, the whole of Ericsson GE).

What we actually know rather contradicts the folk memory. Lars Ramqvist, who by now had taken over from Björn Svedberg as Managing Director of Ericsson, called Johan Siberg and asked him to take responsibility for the mobile phone business. He also told him to move the headquarters of the company back to Stockholm, re-name it Ericsson Mobile

Communications, ECS, and run it as a Swedish company. Supported by the most able survivors of the Group's mobile phone operations, and modelling operations very largely on those that had proved themselves in Kumla, Johan Siberg supervised the turn-round of Lynchburg within 18 months.

Ericsson had invented a transplantable model of an operation that specialised not in traditional mass production, but in highly-flexible low-cost production – a very different thing, and precisely what is necessary to produce mobile phones. After the turn-round at Lynchburg, for example, the factory produced around half-a-million of the phones code-named Jane. There were 43 variants of Jane, and over half of them were produced in quantities corresponding to less than one day's production.

Rounding off the story: Mannesmann and after

In 1989, mobile phones were a side-show – a product line kept in being by the need to support sales of mobile systems, and by the vision and faith of people like Jan Ahrenbring, Åke Lundqvist, Flemming Örneholm and Nils Rydbeck. On their own, the mobile telephones seemed to generate nothing but marketing and production headaches – certainly not money.

By 1994, mobile phones had become unquestionably a core Ericsson product. Today, they are made in their millions at Kumla, Linköping, Carlton-on-Trent (the former Orbitel factory in the UK), the Indelec plant in Bilbao in northern Spain, Beijing, Tallinn in Estonia, Lynchburg, São Paulo …

What happened?

Basically, GSM happened, just at the time when things were beginning to go right at Kumla. Suddenly, there was such a shortage of GSM phones that generating volume demand was no longer a problem. If you could make a decent phone, you could sell it – and provided you kept an eye on costs, you could sell it profitably.

GSM took the world by storm; and for GSM, Ericsson was from the start one of the world's major suppliers, and the first to supply pocket phones in volume.

It so nearly wasn't!

Late in 1989, as we've seen, the Mannesmann Group emerged as the winner of the D2 licence in Germany. Though it was partnered by the American RBOC PacTel, Mannesmann was a steel manufacturer and entrepreneur, with no telecoms tradition or experience. It chose Ericsson to supply its GSM systems infrastructure, and when the GSM MoU group

American acceptance for global credibility

'Of course, we never seriously considered – or certainly not for long – abandoning mobile phone production in the USA,' says Lars Ramqvist. 'Certainly, the situation needed attention urgently, but we knew from our GSM experience with Mannesmann that we had to offer phones to support system sales, and we had to maintain our very successful system sales in the USA. We needed American acceptance for global credibility – particularly with a view to extending into Japan – and mobile systems were to give us that acceptance for the very first time, and in a very big way.

'We'd made a success of phones at Kumla, and there was no earthly reason why we couldn't do the same in the States – as, of course, we did.'

Nils Rydbeck receives his medal from IVA, the Swedish Academy of Engineering Sciences.
FROM LEFT: *Jan Uddenfeldt, Nils Rydbeck, Lars Ramqvist, Åke Lundqvist and Johan Siberg, 1996.*

moved the launch of GSM from mid-1991 to mid-1992, Ericsson's infra-structure was duly installed and running on time. Only one small detail was missing from Mannesmann's plan to beat Deutsche Telekom's D1 operation to the punch and sign up customers: there were no GSM mobile phones on the market.

The MD of Mannesmann was George Schmitt, a notoriously tough customer, but now a desperate man. Again, he turned to Ericsson, and there were months of frantic negotiation with the management at Lund. At this time, Olivia (successor of Curt) was about to be phased out in favour of the smaller, more elegant (and somewhat more expensive) Sandra. Agreement to supply Mannesmann with GSM circuitry in a Sandra shell was almost reached, when Mannesmann decided that for Germany's first GSM customers, price would be more important than elegance. It was quickly agreed that Olivia should be used rather than Sandra: she was cheaper, since she was bigger than Sandra and it was easier to pack the GSM works, many times more complex than analogue works, inside the shell. 30,000 were ordered for delivery before the end of 1992.

Though Ericsson had accepted severe penalty clauses for any late delivery, George Schmitt kept up the pressure. He made visits to Lund, to Stockholm to see Lars Ramqvist (who hasn't forgotten), and to Kumla. He inspected the production lines, and he talked to the staff working on them and made them promise to deliver for him.

It was George Schmitt who coined the interpretation of GSM: God Send Mobiles.

30,000 seems derisory today. For Kumla in 1992, it was a baptism of fire. Ericsson learned so much … that the customer – and in this case a customer who didn't understand the complexities of telecoms, and so wasn't impressed by the difficulties – ultimately calls the tune; that mass consumer marketing really is different, and price and market preferences may matter more than elegance and technological subtlety; that where there's a marketing will, there almost has to be a technological way; and that sometimes deadlines are just that.

George Schmitt got his mobiles (three weeks late, but he never invoked the penalty clauses), and Mannesmann has been a dramatically successful mobile operator. Ericsson never looked back, and the core product status of mobile phones at Ericsson probably owes a good deal to George Schmitt's perseverance (to say nothing of his professionalism and respect).

The rest of the GSM mobile phones story is largely a numbers game.

Whatever happened to Harry?

During the last few years of the '80s, there were several advertising campaigns and other promotional activities built around the character Harry HotLine, and all the mobile telephones were heavily branded HotLine. But when deciding on the product name, HotLine, there had been a slip-up and eventually another company, Hotline Electronics, sued Ericsson for copyright infringement. In 1992 Hotline Electronics finally won its case. The HotLine name had by then already been dropped – one of the reasons for a change being the fact that the name meant nothing in most languages other than English. So Harry retired.

It was decided to use the company logo as the single brand name on all products. And with the tremendous growth in the consumer market, the Ericsson mobile phones have indeed contributed strongly to making the Ericsson name known and recognised. Today the building and protection of the Ericsson brand is an ongoing and most important part of worldwide marketing – involving advertising in all types of media, promotions in film and TV productions and sponsorship of many different activities.

10-year family photo, 1996.
FRONT: *The first family:* FROM LEFT: *Olivia, Curt, Sandra, Jane, Emma.*
BACK: *HotLine Combi.*

391

CHAPTER 19

1990–2000

Ericsson in the '90s

*I*n the last few chapters we've followed Ericsson's dedicated and successful drive into digital mobile telephone systems and terminals – a drive that lasted well into the '90s, and which was to be followed by an even stronger effort to create a global, third-generation wireless standard and to bring together voice and data.

That story will be picked up in the next chapter. Now it's time to see how the company and its business developed as a whole during the last decade of the millenium. We can examine in turn Ericsson's overall strategy, its markets, its customers, its competitors, and the way in which it is structured to face the future.

In spite of a widespread economic downturn during 1991 and 1992, the '90s was a decade of altogether exceptional growth for the company. Annual net sales increased from SEK 45.7 billion in 1990 to SEK 215.4 bn in 1999. Income before taxes grew from SEK 4.9 bn to SEK 16.4 bn during the same period. At the end of 1990, Ericsson was employing just over 70,000 people worldwide; by the end of 1999, this number had grown to over 103,000.

The area of strongest growth has been mobile telephone systems. In 1990, this business (including mobile telephones) accounted for about 25 per cent of the company's total sales: by 1999, this had risen to 40 per cent. Mobile telephones and terminals had grown from a couple of per cent to about 25 per cent of the total turnover in 1998. It suffered a decline during the first three quarters of 1999, but regained strength in the last quarter. The volumes of AXE systems and other wireline products continued to increase in absolute terms, but decreased as a proportion of the total, from 45 per cent to around 17 per cent. Business communications systems accounted for 11 per cent of total sales in 1990 and about 9 per cent in 1998.

OPPOSITE: *Advertising at Cross Harbour tunnel, Kowloon, Hong Kong.*

The company's strategic development has been heavily focused on the development of new products, on strategic partnering and, in the last few years of the decade, on acquisitions and outsourcing.

R&D and new products

R&D spending increased from 11 per cent of sales in 1990 to 17 per cent in 1993, but fell to 14 per cent in 1999. Including market adaptations and engineering, the latter figure rose to around 16 per cent in 1999, down from 23 per cent in 1990. Major development projects have included the digital mobile systems for the three standards, GSM, TDMA and PDC, and digital mobile telephones for GSM, TDMA in the US, PCN and PCS. The period has also seen dramatic updating and miniaturisation of the AXE system hardware, modernisation of the software, new open system interfaces, and applications development for new services and market requirements.

Development of the MD110 system has continued, and BusinessPhone, a PBX switch for small offices, has been introduced.

The Defence Systems operation has continued to develop ground-based and airborne radar systems for defence and civil uses, command-and-control systems and microwave.

And then there was AXE-N …

In the late 1980s, before the impact of the Internet was foreseen, Ericsson and Telia initiated at Ellemtel a major development project called AXE-N. AXE-N was a large packet-switching system based on ATM, Asynchronous Transfer Mode, technology. AXE-N was seen as a key system for building national and international information highways to carry voice, data and various broadband services in packetised form. Test prototypes were installed in Sweden and Germany.

AXE-N was an ambitious development project, but politics and the market were moving faster than technology. By 1995, Televerket had become Telia, one of several competing operators in Sweden, and hence no longer interested in co-funding major system development. And, as we shall see, technology and market development had taken a different direction with the Internet. The AXE-N project, which had lasted for several years and cost a great deal of money, was discontinued, together with a second development, broadband cross-connect. Ericsson's effort was redirected into access and carrier systems for TCP/IP.

AXE-N was probably the last manifestation within Ericsson of a dream which has haunted many telecoms companies and engineers. It's the dream of the single universal system for all telecoms, a dream which seems further and further from realisation as time goes by. For the dream to come true, telecoms would have to stand still long enough for technology to embrace it completely – and it never will. Telecoms is increasingly a multi-discipline, pluralist affair, and much of the cunning of the engineer is devoted to making its disparate elements cooperate.

Cooperation and acquisitions

In 1991, Ericsson acquired 33.5 per cent of the shares of the Austrian company, Schrack Telecom AG, a licensee, and six years later became the sole owner. The company was re-named Ericsson Austria AG. Incidentally, before the Second World War, the Schrack company was 'Ericsson Oesterreichische Elektrizitäts AG, vormals Deckert & Homolka'.

In 1992, the single remaining involvement in telephone operations, the Compañía Argentina de Teléfonos SA, was sold. For over thirty years, CAT had been something of an anachronism in the Ericsson Group.

In 1992, Ericsson increased its holding in Ericsson GE Mobile Communications to 80 per cent and in 1998 to 100 per cent. The company had already been renamed Ericsson Mobile Communications in 1993.

Sponsorship: The Ericsson Stadium, Charlotte, North Carolina, USA.

395

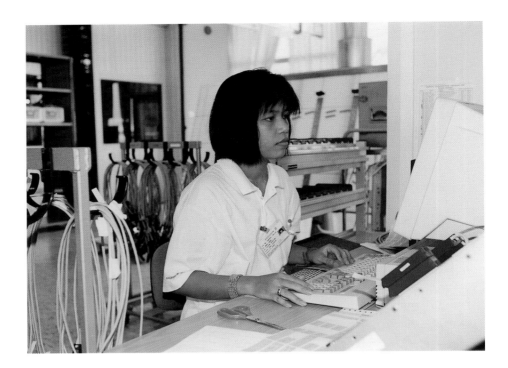

Rojan factory, Atthaya,
Thailand, 1994.

In 1993, Ericsson acquired Teli AB, the manufacturing facilities of Telia, and in 1995, at the full opening up of the Swedish telecoms market, Ericsson acquired all the shares of Ellemtel, the development company set up as a joint venture with Telia in 1970.

In 1993, Ericsson and the French company SAT took a half share each in a new joint venture company, Eritelcom, in France. In 1996, Eritelcom became a fully-owned Ericsson subsidiary.

And in 1998, agreement was reached for Ericsson to acquire the outstanding 50 per cent of the shares of MET S.A., originally the Matra-Ericsson joint venture.

Ericsson has a good record in building and developing joint ventures. Its early cooperative ventures with Texas Instruments in chip development and with Hewlett Packard in network-management systems, to say nothing of its partnership at a crucial time with General Electric in Ericsson GE Mobile Communications, have been hugely beneficial.

It's also learned to be good at the third art – the art of the break-up, when a cooperative effort has outlived its usefulness.

From 1998 onwards, Ericsson's acquisitions strategy has been given a new dimension and extra impetus through the explosive growth in data communications and the Internet. We'll see how this is working out in Chapter 20.

Outsourcing

Outsourcing is a natural complement to cooperation agreements and acquisitions.

In today's liberalised telecommunications world, manufacturing no longer has the key strategic importance that it did for over a hundred years. Outsourcing involves the transfer of manufacturing and certain other operations to outside suppliers, mainly as a means of obtaining benefits of scale in production, with flexibility and just-in-time delivery. Outsourcing will often involve the sale of a facility to an outside company in return for exclusive supply agreements. During 1997 the Ericsson plastics factory in Kristianstad was sold to Nolato AB; the circuit board assembly plant in Karlskrona was sold to Flextronics; and printed circuit board production in Norrköping was sold to SCI Systems Inc. and Solectron Corporation. In 1998 the Ericsson Distribution Centre in Huddinge, outside Stockholm, was sold to Caterpillar Logistics of the US.

Further steps were taken during 1999: IT support in the Nordic countries was outsourced to Compaq; more manufacturing operations in France and Sweden were outsourced to Solectron and Flextronics; and a software development unit in Östersund, Sweden was sold to AU-systems.

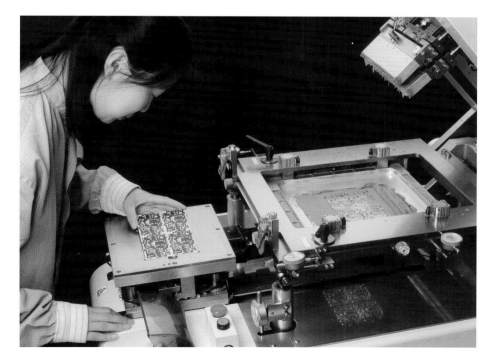

Ericsson Simtec Electronics Co. Ltd, Shanghai.

In 1999 it was further decided to divest the greater part of the company's real estate, and to transfer real estate management to outside companies, such as Skanska in the Stockholm area.

Outside Sweden, outsourcing arrangements have affected Ericsson factories in Australia, Brazil, Croatia, Italy, Malaysia, Mexico, Norway, Spain and the UK.

Initially, many people in Ericsson, accustomed to being self-supporting in just about every area, found the company's outsourcing strategy hard to digest. It seemed almost like giving up. And naturally, the plant closures and lay-offs that followed certain outsourcing decisions caused much public concern, some critical comment in the media, and political snubs.

Markets

As a result of the global move towards the liberalisation and deregulation of the telecommunications operating industry, Ericsson has been able to expand its market presence considerably.

With its strong product portfolio and marketing commitment, and often the additional strength contributed by some formal cooperation with national companies, we've seen how in the mid-'80s Ericsson penetrated such markets as the UK, France and the US.

Further penetration, spearheaded above all by the company's digital mobile systems, followed during the 1990s – most significantly in Germany, then in China, Japan, Taiwan, Vietnam and other Asian countries. Important new markets have also been developed in former Eastern Europe and Russia, although in the late '90s regional economic problems have forced some operations to slow down.

By 1999, the US and China were Ericsson's largest markets, accounting for 11 per cent and 9 percent of total sales respectively. These were followed by the UK (7 per cent), Brazil (7 per cent), Spain (6 per cent), Italy (6 per cent), Turkey (5 per cent), Japan (4 per cent), Sweden (4 per cent) and Germany (3 per cent).

By the late '80s, Ericsson was established in the US as one of the leading suppliers of mobile telephone systems, though the growth of AXE in the fixed networks was slow and difficult. Over time, however, the US has developed into a sizeable market for AXE even in fixed networks: both the regional operating companies and the new carriers (such as MFS, Metropolitan Fiber Systems, now acquired by WorldCom) are important customers. And in the PBX market, the MD110 is selling well, especially for large installations.

In China, Ericsson has supplied about half the installed capacity of the mobile telephone networks, or systems, serving some 20 million mobile subscribers. There are also well over 10 million lines of the AXE system installed in the fixed network. In the PBX field, some of the largest private networks in the world are found in China, based on the MD110 system; and, as we've seen, large volumes of the MD110 system are also serving as rural exchanges in the Chinese public network. Ericsson's operations in China are primarily based on a number of joint ventures with local partners covering development, production, sales and services. Ericsson employs about 5,000 people in China.

MOBITEX: Ericsson's pioneering system for the transmission of text and data on the move.

Victories and victims

Saddam Hussein's Iraqi forces invaded Kuwait on the morning of 2 August 1990. After a few days, Kuwait was completely overrun and under Iraqi control. The world was shocked, oil prices soared and stock markets fell.

In Sweden, however, concern was focused directly on a group of 90 Swedish residents in Kuwait caught up in the conflict, among them 33 Ericsson employees and their families. The group was transferred to Baghdad on 21 August. At the end of August, a first group of 32 women and children were released and were flown to Stockholm. They were followed on 2 September by a further group of women. On 2 November, the remaining Swedes were finally allowed to go.

We know what happened to the Swedes. Other nationalities did not fare so well as the conflict continued. Nor, later on, did other Ericsson employees …

'Desert Storm' took place in January/February of 1991. Kuwait was liberated, and quickly got going with rebuilding and repair. And Ericsson was soon back.

In the early morning of 3 September 1992, three Ericsson Radio engineers drove in a jeep along the border between Kuwait and Iraq, inspecting radio base stations for the cellular network under repair. Due to inadequate maps, or human error, they inadvertently crossed the border into Iraq territory, and were quickly picked up by a police patrol.

Christer Strömgren, Leif Westberg and Stefan Wihlborg were taken to Baghdad and detained in a military barracks. Two weeks later, they were sentenced to 7 years in prison.

Once the capture of the three Swedes was confirmed by the Iraqi authorities, a series of diplomatic activities got under way. Eventually, after much deliberation and a personal letter from the King of Sweden to Saddam Hussein (plus substantial gifts, defined as 'disaster relief', to the Iraqi nation from the Swedish government), the three were pardoned and set free – after 384 days in the Abu Ghraib prison.

Aerial cables still play important roles in all types of networks. Inca Pahacutec supervising. Cuzco, Peru.

The customers

Following liberalisation and the drive for new and improved services, the telecommunications market has shown consistent and dramatic growth.

In 1990, the fixed networks of the world served some 500 million subscribers. In 2000, this number has reached about 850 million, with an estimated continued growth of around 5 per cent per annum.

Much more explosive growth has occurred and is foreseen in cellular and Internet services. The world's cellular networks serve some 500 million subscribers in 2000, and are expected to reach 1 billion customers four years later. The Internet has around 300 million users at the millennium shift – and is forecast to reach the 900 million mark during 2004. Some 120 million subscribers are expected to be using third-generation cellular systems in that same year.

Overall, the market value of the telecommunications sector is expected to be over $ 200 billion per year during the next few years.

Ericsson is directing its efforts towards three main customer segments.

The operators

First, there are the operators, providing services to end users. Among these companies we find many of Ericsson's traditional PTT customers in their various new shapes. But the operating community has been, and continues to be, in constant flux. With deregulation, numbers of new operators have emerged – local, national and international. Alliances, mergers and acquisitions have already created a dominant group of around a hundred regional and global operators (among them AT&T, Vodafone Airtouch, British Telecom, Deutsche Telekom, Telefónica and France Telecom). There is a clear trend of continuing consolidation to a point where some 10–15 global operators are expected to dominate the entire market, along with a hundred or so regional and national operators.

Most of these operators, running fixed and/or mobile networks, are in the process of introducing IP, Internet services, and full multimedia standards by upgrading in various ways and adding new equipment.

Another class of operators, national and local, includes the cable companies, basing operations on their cable television distribution networks, and with ambitions and potential to expand into telecoms, data and multimedia services. Many cable companies have become the targets of take-over attempts by the large national and international operators.

Network construction in Thailand.

At the other end of the scale, we can already see a multitude of niche operators, with varying degrees of network ownership, offering specific services such as Internet access and call centres.

The former public networks, fixed and mobile, can be seen today as under fire from all directions. One trend is the takeover of customer groups by other businesses. These may be banks, chain stores, petrol selling companies, power companies – just about any company or organisation that has an active customer base is offering telephone subscriptions at lower rates than the telephone companies.

The satellite telecom operators, such as Iridium and GlobalStar, should also be mentioned here. So far, the future of satellite telecommunications is hazy, and the business has been slow to take off. Indeed, as this book is being written, Iridium has filed for bankruptcy. Unkind commentators refer to satellite-based mobile telecommunications as a CIA market: a typical user would be a CIA agent, or a CNN reporter – and their numbers are limited.

In fact, large or small, global or niche, all these operators share one current driver: they are desperate to expand into cyberspace and get their share of the Internet bonanza.

The enterprise market

This second segment of the market is represented by companies and 'private' organisations. It used to be called the private market, but is now usually referred to as the 'enterprise' market.

There, today's drive is largely towards the implementation of wireless voice and data services, and the integration of Intranet. Such concepts as UMTS, Universal Mobile Telephone Service, which will allow a person to use the same phone within the office and outside it, are becoming increasingly attractive. The segment also represents a major market for fixed and wireless terminals.

Consumers

Finally, there is the consumer products market segment, which includes wireless and fixed network terminals for voice and data.

In all three market segments, Ericsson is a major player. And the company's strategy clearly recognises that a leading market position in the respective businesses in which it operates is a prerequisite for continued success. The fight for market share must go on.

In the US Ericsson shares, in the form of ADRs (American Depository Receipts), are traded on the NASDAQ exchange.

The competitors – and Ericsson's position

From Ericsson's point of view, the main competitors are still the classic telecoms manufacturers, all of them restructured or being restructured to meet the changing conditions.

In mobile systems, or cellular infrastructure, the leaders are well-known – Ericsson, Lucent, Motorola, NEC of Japan, Nokia and Nortel. Ericsson is in the lead. In the market for mobile data networks, which will play a crucial role for the development of wireless Internet, Ericsson is also well placed.

As the major suppliers of switching systems and fixed network infrastructure, we find Alcatel, Lucent, Nortel, NEC and Siemens alongside

GSM antenna in Sarajevo, Bosnia, near the bombed railway station.

Ericsson. As a supplier of traditional fixed data transmission and transport network components, Ericsson is presently a second-line player.

The major competitor for packet data-communication systems is the US company, Cisco. From its original base as a supplier to private networks and enterprises, Cisco is successfully driving the explosion of Internet services in the public networks, but is increasingly being challenged by Ericsson and other traditionals.

Ericsson is one of the three leading suppliers of mobile telephones and terminals. The other two are currently Nokia and Motorola.

The largest suppliers of enterprise network systems are Alcatel, Lucent, Nortel, Siemens and Ericsson, now joined by Cisco, Newbridge and several more.

Lars Ramqvist

From 1990 to 1998, Ericsson was very much identified with the President, Dr Lars Ramqvist. He succeeded Dr Björn Svedberg, who took over the Chairmanship of the Board of Directors. Originally a technologist, Lars Ramqvist in his career at Ericsson was, for a couple of years, head of Ericsson Components. He then undertook the major task of defining the company's new corporate strategy in the mid-'80s – including the important technology cooperation agreement with Texas Instruments. From there, and at a crucial moment, he moved in as head of the mobile telephone system business, ERA.

Throughout his tenure as President, Lars Ramqvist was able to report continuous growth in earnings, and Ericsson's shares performed outstandingly on the stock market. The major achievements were the breakthrough in GSM systems, digital mobile systems in the US and the PDC system for Japan; and the long-awaited success with mobile telephones. Public systems (AXE) and enterprise systems continued to grow, but suffered from a weak market and pressure on price. Mobile systems became the strongest company sector.

Lars Ramqvist also became known for insisting on a high level of R&D spending. This was initially met with some scepticism by shareholders, but as the positive results kept coming in they cheerfully accepted the principle – and understood.

Lars Ramqvist identifies the challenges that Ericsson faced in the early '90s as 'being ourselves' – to grow the company while at the same time changing the company culture; and to understand and learn to operate in a global market. His eight years as MD became a period of fundamental changes in production, R&D,

marketing – indeed, throughout the company. For many people, this became a challenge to both the mind and the nervous system, and caused stress. Large numbers of employees changed jobs, and some had to leave.

There was closure of some production plants as the company took to outsourcing. This naturally caused much comment and criticism in the Swedish press, where Lars Ramqvist also became a critical voice on government industrial policy and taxation.

The decision in the late '80s to go all out for the terminal, mobile telephone, business to support mobile systems sales, was important, indeed crucial. We had to do it, says Ramqvist, even though we had been burned in the consumer sector before – most recently with the Ericsson Information Systems adventure. In the end, mobile telephones have become big business – and, yes, as a result of heavy brand exposure and mass marketing, Ericsson is now to some extent seen as primarily a mobile phone company. This isn't an accurate perception, but it's an inevitable consequence of exposure to some 100 million customers, compared with the 400 or so customers of the 'old days', and we ought to be able to live with it.

Nokia is a tough competitor and still ahead of us in mobile telephones. We have to admit that at times they do some things better than we do. But it does give us some satisfaction that the world's two leading suppliers of digital mobile phones and infrastructure are Nordic – Lars

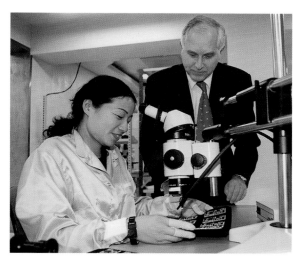

Dr Lars Ramqvist at the inauguration of Ericsson Simtec Electronics, Shanghai, November 1996. Simtec develops and manufactures energy components.

Ramqvist calls it a 'serendipitous situation'. The other 'traditional' competitors, chiefly Lucent, Alcatel, Nortel, and Siemens, have histories that are rather different from Ericsson's.

The conditions of business today mean a whole new set of responsibilities for the Managing Director. When asked to select the most important, Lars Ramqvist does not hesitate. 'You must benchmark yourself and your company's operations against the market and the competition – every single quarter. If you don't, one single quarter could change your destiny. And you must stay heavily involved in standardisation. The company must work very hard with and for the standardisation bodies in different parts of the world. This is not only a matter of working with leading-edge technology, it is also a political game going on behind the scenes all the time – and Ericsson must be part of it'.

In 1998 Lars Ramqvist took over as Chairman of Ericsson.

CHAPTER 20

On the verge of convergence

A change in the concept of 'a network'

From the '20s until the '90s, switching systems for fixed networks were the main drivers of Ericsson's operations.

But in the '90s, though switching systems remained crucially important, at least two other drivers in the industry can be identified – one of them, digital mobile telephony, largely generated by Ericsson; the other, the Internet, initially outside Ericsson's control. Between them, these drivers continue to set the pace in the new century, and for Ericsson, as for every other company in the business, they mean fundamental and irreversible change.

Not least in the concept of 'a network'. Throughout the book so far, it's been possible to talk of a variety of networks, in the plural, with no feeling of surprise or any lack of clarity. Without any definition of what a network is, it seems perfectly natural that the system carrying voice between people should somehow be different from a system carrying data, or pictures, or telemetry; and that these should be different 'networks'. The difference between a fixed network and a mobile network seems even more obvious.

At the same time, we're somehow also clear that the traffic in the networks doesn't go through completely different sets of cables or radio spectrum. We know that mobile traffic spends a lot of its time in the fixed network – just like every other sort of traffic. We realise, more or less, that all public networks these days are layered, and that traffic moves up and down between the layers. We know that bits of the network can be dedicated, for short or long periods, to one sort of traffic or another.

We also know that Ericsson has been making its money by devising systems which do an outstanding job in any one environment, yet as far as possible share their architecture with those in any other environment.

OPPOSITE:
The souk in Marrakesh, Morocco. A market for everything – spices, wood carvings, metalwork, carpets and now Ericsson mobile telephones.

And you may have noticed an increasing concentration on the systems for access – to what? A number of different networks? Or one network offering a variety of different services within it?

Until only a few years ago, the answer would have been 'a number of different networks'. Today, the fact that we can even ask the question shows how the concept of 'convergence' is taking hold. Indeed, convergence is rapidly becoming an installed reality.

Can one network efficiently handle voice and data? Can one network carry fixed and mobile traffic? Can one and the same network supply services required by a 16-year-old schoolboy and the President of the United States?

The answer is of course 'yes'.

And the network they're talking about is a Large Technical System: the Internet.

Large Technical Systems, LTS

A relatively new area for academic research is defined by the term 'Large Technical Systems'. Examples of such systems are many, and one common denominator is that they are created by man. An example is the road system: roads, bridges, viaducts – the whole infrastructure, and the vehicles that use it. LTS research is not only interested in how such a system is created and changes over time, but also tries to understand how such systems react to overloading and other forms of stress (in our road example, for instance, traffic accidents, gridlock, or bridge collapse).

An LTS is generally seen as a social construction, the result of interaction between man, society and technology. Consequently, there are also socio-political and economic aspects of any LTS to explore: what drives its creation, how it is controlled and financed, and what the social responses to it are.

One well-known LTS is the telephone network covering the globe, which today is still the largest and most advanced universal system in use in the world. It is often referred to as the world's largest man-made machine, including as it does the fixed and mobile networks, private networks and a host of facilities for a wide variety of services, all today based on sets of internationally agreed interface standards.

Another, probably better known LTS, is also the newest, the Internet, which appears in some ways to challenge the telecommunications machine. It is a challenge of many aspects, involving a multitude of interested parties and enormous financial resources. But the challenge, if indeed it is a challenge at all, will not necessarily end in the emergence of 'a winner'. In the longer term, we are poised for convergence, and the drivers of that convergence can be clearly identified..

Drivers for convergence. 1: the Internet

The Western world and the USA in particular suffered a bad surprise on October 4, 1957, when the first artificial satellite, the Soviet 'Sputnik', was successfully launched and started circling the world. It was a severe shock and was seen as a sizable setback in the ongoing Cold War. It caused a good deal of political hysteria, and US (and other) politicians started to talk about Russians travelling through space and dropping atom bombs at will on a defenceless United States.

This heated atmosphere saw the birth of NASA and in 1969 a man – an American – on the moon. Another outcome was the formation in the US of ARPA, the Advanced Research Projects Agency, in 1958. Generously funded, ARPA initiated a large number of research projects at universities and in industry. In an atmosphere of academic freedom and government financing, and in the young and dynamic disciplines of computer and systems science, the idea of fusing computers and telecommunications was born.

It was in 1962, the year of the Cuba missile crisis, that the Internet idea was conceived, at the Rand Corporation in California. Atomic attack was perceived as a real threat and the task was to create a communications system that could survive an atomic war between the super-powers. Traditional computer networks, centralised and star-shaped, could easily be knocked out by simply destroying the central computer – a ready-made target in case of conflict. The result could be that large parts of the US would become isolated after an attack, with social disintegration and general chaos to follow.

In a report entitled *On Distributed Communications Networks*, the researcher Paul Baran proposed a fully-distributed communications system without a vulnerable centre. Baran's idea was to divide up the information to be transmitted into pieces, or packets. Each packet would carry its individual address, and would seek its destination on its own. At the destination, the packets of information would be assembled to re-create the complete original message. The technology was called packet-switching.

There had been data networks and switches before, of course, but they were circuit-switched. The revolutionary points in Baran's concept were that no central control computer was needed, and that there were no pre-determined routes from sender to receiver. One packet might pass through four or five nodes on its way, the following packet maybe only one or two. If one or more nodes were knocked out, the flow of information would find its way through other nodes. The network would be able to survive even a substantial atomic attack.

It took seven years of work at Rand Corporation, the University of California and the Massachusetts Institute of Technology to turn the packet-switching idea into reality. In 1969, the Defense Department gave ARPA the job of building a packet-switched network. It was named ARPANET, and initially it had four nodes.

By now, the Cold War had been replaced by a period of relative détente, and other uses of ARPANET had been identified. At the universities, computer time was still a scarce commodity but it was found that by 'time-sharing' computer users could be provided with access to increased computer capacity. When the Interface Message Protocol, IMP, was introduced, different computers were made to interwork over ARPANET. In other words, as the universities took over the network, ARPANET was developed to tie together different computer environments, independent of manufacturers, hardware and operating systems.

By April 1972, ARPANET had 23 nodes, and in the following year the first international nodes were connected, in the UK and Norway. The atomic threat was now a thing of the past, and instead the researchers were focusing on how the network reacted in different stress situations, such as overload and faults.

At this stage – around 1972 – it was discovered that the network was an

A many-splendoured thing: The Ericsson A 2618 with a large variety of exchangeable snap-on covers. The A 2618 was the first Ericsson phone offering WAP services.

excellent means for supplying news and sending personal messages to colleagues at other universities. 'E-mail' happened as a 'spontaneous' application. Soon e-mail accounted for a major part of the data traffic – and ARPANET had taken on a social function that hardly suited a strictly military environment but was tailor-made for the free exchange of ideas and for the open milieu of the academic world. Still, the military continued to take a liberal (and generous) view and encouraged the academics to use the network. This was the beginning of the metamorphosis that was to transform ARPANET from a military command system into an academic tool.

Vinton Cerf – 'The Father of Internet' – led the work of creating a standard language, a protocol that could be used by computers to speak with one another over a packet-switched network. This was a combination of TCP, the Transmission Control Protocol, and IP, the Internet Protocol. A first version of TCP/IP was ready in 1974.

The US Defense Department chose TCP/IP as its standard, and other network owners followed. Thanks to its openness and wide distribution, TCP/IP came to play the same dominating role for the data networks as MS/DOS and UNIX do among computer systems. And the growing use of TCP/IP soon made it possible for private network operators to link up with ARPANET. Internet had become a 'network of networks'.

In the early 1970s, other networks were introduced using the new mini-computers. Research institutions, computer companies, telephone operators, postal agencies, all were building data networks – for their own use or for commercial purposes. IBM and Digital put their money on proprietary network technology as a complement to their hardware and software products, to bind buyers to their computer standards. But users soon began to see the possibility of interconnecting such networks. Internet-working offered a host of new and interesting possibilities – and encouraged competition.

The question of an international communications standard for computer networks, open or computer-dependent, became a fierce battle in the mid-'70s. The science community, particularly in the US, opted for TCP/IP, while public network operators outside the US, through the CCITT, adopted the similar X.25 standard. For a long time there were two distinct cultures and it was not until the late

1980s that the European Union dropped its Open Standard Interface, OSI, and TCP/IP was finally accepted as a de facto world standard.

In 1983, the military portion of ARPANET was spun off under the name MILNET. From 1986, ARPANET and other connected networks based on TCP/IP were formally named the Internet. It had become clear that the Internet had reached critical mass and that continued expansion would be self-powered. Since that time the Internet has doubled in size each year.

By 1996, the Internet consisted of nearly 140,000 interlinked networks connecting over 12 million host computers. Other non-TCP/IP networks, such as EARN/BIT-NET and DECnet exist, but intercommunication via e-mail is effected through gateways that translate information between protocols.

In its early days, the Internet was not part of the commercial sector, but it did not take long for people outside the academic world to see the advantages of the new communications method. Though some large companies built their own networks, over time they discovered cost advantages in using Internet for connecting their internal networks. Other companies, especially the telecoms operators, media concerns and a large range of banking and commercial organisations, have realised that the buying, selling and interchange of electronic information and entertainment via the Internet hold a large money-making potential. The Internet is now rapidly being developed for commercial exploitation.

Today, the Internet infrastructure is largely financed by private companies, above all the telecoms operators, along with a variety of Internet Access and Service Provider companies.

There is a clear trend towards Internet-focused technical integration, as an increasing number of telecommunications services – including radio broadcasting, TV, video conferencing and telephony – are becoming available over the Internet. Voice communication over the Internet, or Voice over IP, VoIP, which will mean international telephone calls at the cost of a local call, is becoming a strong competitor to the services of the traditional telephone operators.

It's not hard to pinpoint the drivers for the explosive growth of the Internet. It offers entertainment. If you're patient, it can provide you with an extraordinary amount of 'free' information. It will eventually cut the cost of phone calls. It may be a route to picture-telephony. It supports e-commerce. Access is often bundled with the programmes pre-loaded on a new PC. And, since the mid-'90s, it is becoming available as a mobile application, where a GSM phone acts as the access mechanism.

But the key driver has been the way the Internet cuts the cost and boosts the bandwidth of data transmission. In application terms, most of its addicts are particularly fond of e-mail, which is certainly as reliable as a modern Post Office, and much, much faster.

An 'Internet Bureau' in Pushkar, Rajasthan, India.

Today, Internet and the fixed telephone networks are converging. What the long-term result will be is not necessarily clear, but even today fixed and mobile network operators are busy implementing VoIP solutions, upgrading voice networks with packet-switching and transmission capability, and preparing for the third generation digital mobile (or first generation mobile Internet) networks. The problems of growth and the provision of 'real-time' voice quality ('carrier class') equal to circuit-switched connections over Internet connections have largely been solved.

To ensure data security there are now a number of systems based on encryption, and for many services, such as money transaction, certain common standards are being agreed. Some companies have bet their businesses on e-commerce over the Internet. But not all of them, even the high-profile ones, have yet made a profit.

The Internet has quickly become a most important asset to society. Most of its users have a sort of infuriated affection for it – just as people had with the early telephone services. It is adding immeasurable value to our networks of the 21st century.

Drivers for convergence. 2: digital mobile telephony

Winning the second-generation mobile war …

We've identified digital mobile telephony as the second major driver of the '90s, and a drive to a very large extent directed by Ericsson.

It's worth looking briefly again at the story of GSM and the other digital mobile systems. In the mid-'80s, when Germany and France were just starting to give Government support to their own national development of GSM, Ericsson was far ahead. Its unique know-how and experience, with support from Telia and certain other players, meant that its proposals for narrowband TDMA, Time Division Multiple Access, carried the day at the European evaluations, and Ericsson built up a valuable competitive lead in systems development.

The same ability to add value in response to change reappeared in the USA. When it became clear that frequency availability was a real problem, Ericsson rapidly adapted its familiar TDMA (in competition with FDMA) to provide the specific advantages of D-AMPS (now TDMA) in the American situation.

The story was repeated yet again in Japan, when the Japanese decided to shadow the American system choice. Ericsson's experience with TDMA and the development of the US standard, meant it was right on the spot to give active support to the creation of the Japanese TDMA-based PDC (Personal Digital Cellular) standard.

Meanwhile, GSM had rapidly spread far outside Europe, and when the US was preparing to license PCS, Personal Communications Services, a North American GSM version, the PCS 1900/GSM supported by Ericsson and Nokia was adopted as a standard. This was when a new competitor, Qualcomm, emerged with its CDMA, Code Division Multiple Access, technology, with the result that the US operators had no fewer than three different digital systems to choose from. Incidentally, the largest CDMA network is outside the US, in Korea.

This digital mobile system story appears direct and logical, but packed into just a few years, it was a period of struggle and great drama for Ericsson. The result was a resounding victory for the company – but even before the battles for second-generation mobile standards were over, preparations for the war for the third generation were beginning.

The battle for the third generation mobile standard

Ericsson stayed out of second-generation telephony systems based on Code Division Multiple Access, CDMA, but not because it was unfamiliar with CDMA technology. On the contrary, around 1980, Ericsson's SRA subsidiary built a CDMA demonstrator for military radio applications. It did not result in a systems product, but in a number of basic technology patents. An even earlier report exists that evaluates the use of CDMA in mobile telephony.

When the basic development of GSM was completed in the late 1980s, and it was time to consider the next generation of digital mobile systems, Ericsson was interested in exploring the properties of CDMA, especially the concept of 'soft handover'. The work resulted in several basic patents and a growing conviction that the next-generation mobile system should use CDMA technology.

Then, in the early '90s, the European Commission set up CODIT to consider standards for third-generation mobile. CODIT established two study groups – one to study the application of WCDMA, the other focusing on W-TDMA. Ericsson, and Philips initially, were active in the first group, while Siemens, Alcatel and Nokia were the heavies among the manufacturers in the second.

The goal in general terms was to find the best way to supply higher bandwidth, multi-media capability and new services. The early thinking was similar to the discussions which led to the ISDN concept in the fixed network some ten years earlier: that the new system should provide mobile ISDN access. But by around 1995, the Internet had gained a very

*The ER 207, for
NTT-DoCoMo in Japan.*

strong presence in Europe, and Internet became a prime consideration.

The WCDMA group made considerable progress, and so did the Siemens-Alcatel TDMA group, with a proposal called TDMA/TD-CDMA. Soon, it was time to try to bring the different parties together, and a new study group was set up for this task, named FRAMES. In 1996, Ericsson had preparatory discussions with Nokia, and the two parties agreed to continue support for WCDMA.

In Japan, meanwhile, the second-generation PDC system had been implemented and the Japanese manufacturers were eager to export it, especially to the Asian markets. The drive was not successful: GSM had already been established in a number of markets, while CDMA had been selected for Korea. There was no room for yet another digital system. So, when NTT-DoCoMo, the leading Japanese operator (and then the biggest in the world) began deliberations over a next-generation system, the starting-point was that any such system had to support a global standard.

Ericsson had excellent relations with the Japanese, having participated in and contributed to their work with PDC. The two parties stayed in close touch, and Ericsson kept the Japanese up to date with the European progress towards a third-generation standard – particularly the work with WCDMA. From 1995, DoCoMo became a cooperation partner in the WCDMA work. This was so successful that by 1996, Jan Uddenfeldt proposed in a meeting with Japan's Ministry of Posts and Telecoms, MPT, that Japan should choose WCDMA. Based as it was on GSM, it would find markets all over the world.

The MPT had been heavily lobbied by the Americans, especially Motorola, proposing first to build on TDMA and PDC, and then on IS95. Believing that Ericsson was stuck with TDMA, the MPT was at first incredulous of the Ericsson ideas, then began to see the advantages. NTT-DoCoMo had become deeply involved by now, and in 1997 ordered an experimental WCDMA system from Ericsson.

Ericsson could now start in earnest its worldwide campaign for WCDMA. Nokia, too, was now vigorously promoting WCDMA. Ericsson had invited Nokia into the DoCoMo discussions, and Nokia became an active supporting force – both in the continuing work with DoCoMo and in the European struggle towards a new standard.

By the summer of 1997, ETSI's third-generation thinking had crystallised around UMTS – Universal Mobile Telecommunications Service. Originally, as we've seen, UMTS was strongly flavoured by the old ISDN ideas: it was described as a concept for providing mobile ISDN access. Now the thinking had advanced – support of Internet access was the key requirement, and, furthermore, UMTS must 'rest on the global footprint of GSM'. Whether UMTS should use CDMA or TDMA was still an open question within ETSI.

The summer of 1997 was also the time when Siemens staged its insurrection. Siemens was joined by Alcatel, Nortel and eventually Motorola, and got going with a big PR drive for TD-CDMA. Ericsson and Nokia (now firm allies) had several meetings with Siemens, trying to show that its TD-CDMA concept would not work. The Ericsson/Nokia position was strengthened by the fact that DoCoMo had won acceptance of its decision in other countries in Asia, and had now also become active in Europe, where an early supporter was TIM, Telecom Italia Mobile. The Siemens gamble was aimed at creating an alliance between Europe and the US, which Japan would have to follow later, and which would eliminate Ericsson and Nokia as the driving force in the move towards the third-generation mobile system.

Ericsson and Nokia had assumed that eventually they would be able to bring Siemens round, and had not yet made much effort to bring their message to their customers, the operators. But by the autumn of 1997, with no signs of an end to the impasse and with Siemens estimated to hold 75 per cent in an upcoming vote in ETSI, Ericsson and Nokia got their market organisations going and set up meetings with each and every European operator to present their case. One by one the operators came over (even T-Mobil, the German operator). It was a time of many heated debates – and it was clear that the final outcome would really be decided by the operators.

The road to third generation mobile telecommunications – WCDMA demo centre at Kista, Sweden, 1999.

Nokia even managed to gain some high-level political support when Finnish President Martti Ahtisaari, on a visit to Britain in November 1997 for discussions on the extension of the European Union, had a word about WCDMA with the British Premier, Tony Blair. Two weeks later the UK operators announced their support of WCDMA.

Late in 1997, after a non-conclusive round of voting at an ETSI meeting in Rome, Ericsson and Nokia and their partners had quietly drawn up the outlines for a compromise solution. This, which added some features from the Siemens proposal to the WCDMA concept, was presented at a meeting in Paris in January 1998 and was accepted with a substantial majority. The European war had been won.

The ETSI decision was submitted to the ITU as a proposal for a world standard.

But there was to be further turbulence. In the summer of 1998, Qualcomm decided to act, and announced that the company was not prepared to release the IPR (Intellectual Property Rights) it held on several

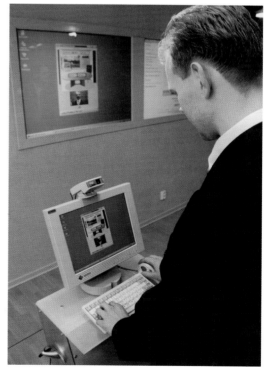

Qualcomm infrastructure division in San Diego, California. New members of the Ericsson team.

BELOW: *Loading test software for CDMA base stations.*

418

aspects of CDMA technology, unless WCDMA was 'harmonised' with its CDMA 2000 proposal. Qualcomm was effectively blocking the WCDMA standard which had been born in such turmoil.

On the other side of the fence was Airtouch, an important US operator with cellular systems in several countries: CDMA in the US, GSM in Europe, and PDC in Japan. Airtouch, naturally, was set on harmonisation of the development of all three systems into the global WCDMA. Airtouch took the initiative and arranged meetings, including an important one in San Francisco in April 1998.

A week after the San Francisco meeting, Lucent mobilised its CDMA customers, and even managed to bring in the State Department, which growled about quotas in Europe and Japan for American manufacturers. Airtouch took another initiative, and an international harmonisation body, the IHG group, was formed, with a gentleman from China as chairman.

The dispute over Qualcomm's IPR continued and the Ericsson/ Qualcomm relationship was further soured by Ericsson's initiation of legal action for patent infringement. Ericsson claimed that Qualcomm had exploited Ericsson patents from the late 1980s.

The battle raged through 1998 and into 1999. Qualcomm insisted on the harmonisation of CDMA 2000 with WCDMA. But, unbeknown to the debating telecoms community, Ericsson had started discussions with Qualcomm at which Qualcomm made it known that a sale of its infrastructure operations might be considered.

The war had taken on large proportions. In the US, the European Commission's decision to use common technology for third-generation mobile was regarded as a provocation. In December 1998, Washington sent a letter to the EU Commissioner, Martin Bangemann, in which Europe was accused of restricting competition in its choice of 3G technology. This was strong language, and a major added complication to the commercial problems between Europe and the US.

Mr Bangemann wrote a conciliatory reply, which somewhat soothed the US government. American industry also reacted against Qualcomm, and the Exports Council sent the President a letter in which it warned the government of the risks in acting in the interests of one single company.

On 17 February 1998, yet another gathering took place. The Trans-Atlantic Business Dialogue organisation had a meeting in Washington. In the TABD, companies were looking for a solution to the impasse that would satisfy the governments. T-Mobil, the German operator, presented a compromise in the form of an umbrella. The 3G technology umbrella would be based on CDMA and the technologies of the quarrelling parties would be gathered under the umbrella – thus each operator would be able to choose its preferred solution. In practice, this meant no major change but it did mean that the parties could stop quarrelling. This compromise was formally agreed upon at the ITU conference in Brazil at the end of 1998.

Soon after, Ericsson and Qualcomm were ready to announce their deal. Ericsson acquired the Qualcomm infrastructure business and the patents and IPR questions were settled. As one of the business papers put it: 'this is the best Christmas present the telecoms world could wish for'.

The 3GPP, Third Generation Partnership Project, was formed in late 1998, as a global joint venture of regional standardisation bodies to co-ordinate efforts and achieve quick results. In the autumn of 1999 3GPP released the final standard specifications for radio access in the third generation system. Later the same year the ITU approved the specifications, in preparation for the ITU recommendations for what this body terms IMT-2000.

In essence, the present four main digital standards will evolve, in harmony, towards the third generation. In the first stage, PDC will go directly to WCDMA, while GSM and TDMA will be developed to offer the Edge standard (see below). Later, GSM will evolve into WCDMA, now defined as IMT-2000 Direct Spread and corresponding to the ETSI UMTS. CDMA will be enhanced to what is named IMT-2000 Multi-carrier. IMT-2000 Direct Spread and IMT-2000 Multi-carrier will be the dominating broadband technologies, supported by some 90 per cent of the world's mobile operators at year end 1999.

No doubt there will be further evolution – new technologies, new networks and new services.

What does it all mean?

Ericsson's early participation in the work of setting the GSM standard gave it a flying start when the system was introduced. Its work on WCDMA is having the same effect.

It's not clear for how long voice services will dominate in the mobile networks, but it is estimated that when WCDMA is introduced there will be a total of some 500 million digital mobile subscribers, worldwide. These make up an important customer base and represent substantial investments by the operators. The critical feature of the third-generation cellular system is that it will be an *addition* in terms of new services and capacity to this customer base. WCDMA will expand and enhance the existing digital mobile networks, not replace them.

A key feature of WCDMA is also that it supports a step-wise evolution from today's systems, so that operators can make a gradual transition from second to third generation. The road to WCDMA is being taken in several stages. During 1998 a new solution, High Speed Circuit Switched Data, HSCSD, was launched, to provide higher transmission speeds in GSM systems – 57 kb/s circuit-switched. 1999 saw the introduction of the

*Attachments for the young yuppy: the 'chatboard',
for exchanging messages, and, below, GSM phone
with FM radio, mounted on bicycle.*

General Packet Radio Service, GPRS. GPRS offers packet data speeds up to 115 kb/s in GSM networks. GPRS is a user-friendly service that supports, for example, e-mail and other data communication over GSM.

'Edge' is a supplement to GPRS. During 1998, operators agreed to merge GSM and TDMA in a common packet data standard, Edge, which has been created chiefly for supporting multimedia services, with data transmission speeds of up to 384 kb/s. During 1999 Ericsson won a large proportion of the orders placed for GPRS and Edge. The first Edge system is scheduled for early 2001 and will be the first third generation mobile system in operation.

During 1998, Ericsson, Motorola, Nokia and Unwired Planet, a Silicon Valley company, also presented a licence-free Wireless Application Protocol, WAP. WAP makes it possible to create advanced mobile telephone services and to read Internet pages from a mobile telephone. The de facto WAP standard is now supported by a large number of manufacturers and operators. The first WAP mobile telephones were introduced to selected markets in early 2000.

As we have seen, Ericsson has been working with WCDMA technology since the late 1980s. Today's standardisation work is in part based on findings and patents made by Ericsson, and the company has become the recognised pioneer in next-generation mobile telephony.

The third-generation wireless mobile systems will offer a range of new services in the mobile networks. Among them we find high data-rate communication services and asymmetric data transmission; support of both circuit- and packet- switched services, such as the Internet and video conferencing; and support of the simultaneous use of two or more services (for example, the ability to receive a fax or a phone call while browsing on the Internet). The *Financial Times* in February 1999 identified 'wireless Internet' as 'a killer application that promises to turn the net into a true mass market product'.

From the network operators' and the future customers' point of view, the next-generation mobile system must also facilitate flexible new charging principles, based on data volumes, and radically-improved spectrum efficiency for increased network capacity.

Licensing of spectrum for WCDMA is under way in several countries. The first commercial system is expected to go into operation in the year 2001, in Japan. Ericsson received this contract in 1999. Early in 2000 a second contract for Japan was received and also one for a WCDMA network on the island of Åland in the Baltic.

Facilitating convergence. 1: the wireline networks

With the AXE digital switching system introduced in the late 1970s, Ericsson took the lead among the world's suppliers of fixed network infrastructure and switching machines. The AXE system is also at the heart of the different mobile telephone networks supplied by Ericsson. During 1999 more AXE lines were sold than in any earlier year.

The installed base of AXE in fixed networks totals some 150 million lines, which constitutes an important base for future revenues for Ericsson and for its customers. Several customers have now started different programmes for upgrading their wireline networks to next-generation architectures for handling data and multi-media services along with voice.

How has AXE developed to meet the challenge?

The AXE platform

The AXE of today has little in common with the early AXE switching system, except that it retains the original architecture. Today, AXE is defined as a network platform, on which are implemented a very wide range of network functions and services.

AXE has evolved into an open architecture, able to support interworking with other systems over standard interfaces, and dramatic improvements have been achieved in increased processing power and in reduced space requirements.

By continuously exploiting new hardware technology, space requirements have been reduced by around 50 per cent for local exchanges and by as much as 85 per cent for transit and international gateways. A typical gateway of 64,000 ports used to consist of over 100 bays: today the same capacity fits into about 10 cabinets – in 'footprint' terms, a reduction from 137.0 sq m to 13.5 sq m. And the new-generation hardware consumes 80 per cent less power.

At the same time, processing capacity has been vastly increased. A first step was taken in 1984 with a new processor called APZ212 with a call-handling capacity about 6 times that of the original APZ210. By 1990, the capacity had been raised to 12 times the original, and the processor was named APZ212 10. Just five years later, the new APZ212 20 offered about 50 times the original call-handling capacity, and the development of ever-stronger control systems continues.

The reasons for this continuous surge of processing power requirements are not primarily that exchanges are growing larger as the number of subscribers grows, but that switching systems no longer carry only telephone conversations. The character of the traffic is changing dramatically,

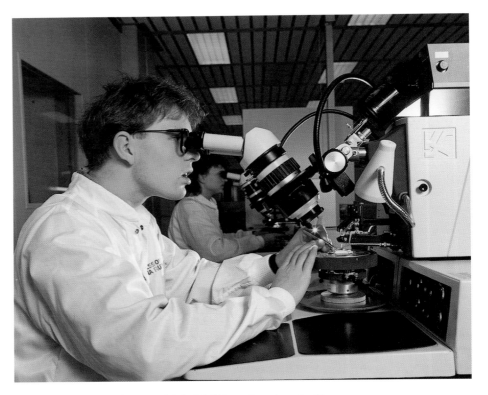

Ericsson Microwave Systems, Mölndal. 'Clean Room' production.

with ever-increasing volumes of data 'calls' for access to the Internet and information-retrieval. Alongside that, there is the huge expansion of network services implemented by the system processors, such as the Intelligent Network, with advanced Centrex and virtual private networks; universal access systems that integrate broadband and narrowband services; and ATM broadband facilities with high-speed data-transfer, video and multimedia. As all this traffic and all these facilities and services are converging in the 'new' network, it is of the outmost importance for Ericsson to be able to continue to offer its customers upgrading and growth based on the existing installed base.

Extraordinarily, the architecture of a switch designed for PSTN functions nearly 30 years ago is still acting as an engine in today's converging multimedia networks, as the following statistics show.

By early 1999, there were a total of nearly 5,800 fixed-network AXE exchanges in service, in 127 countries. Together, these served a total of over 135 million subscriber lines and trunks. On order at the same time was equipment for another 10 million lines, part of it designated for a further 400 new exchanges. To dramatise the rate of growth, we may compare these figures with the situation ten years earlier. In 1989, there were about 19 million lines of AXE in service, in a total of 75 countries.

In wireless systems (analogue and digital mobile telephone networks), at the end of 1999 there were a total of nearly 475 million mobile subscribers in the world, out of which some 190 million were connected to Ericsson systems, in more than 90 countries. This represents nearly 40 per cent of the world total. For comparison, the corresponding numbers for 1988 were approximately 2.2 million mobile subscribers served by Ericsson systems, when the world total was around 5.5 million mobile subscribers.

Starting up the ENGINE

Just as Ericsson's WCDMA provides technology for GSM customers to migrate to third-generation wireless services, a corresponding migration solution for fixed networks is provided by Ericsson's ENGINE, a platform accommodating both circuit- and packet-switched services. Existing AXE installations, for example, may be expanded with AXD 301, a scalable ATM switch, for handling growing volumes of data traffic. Several strategic orders for the ENGINE concept for migrating circuit-switched networks into multi-service status with IP and ATM capability were received during 1999 from customers including British Telecom, KNP of the Netherlands and Telefónica of Spain.

The AXD 301 is an ATM switch that was introduced in the late '90s and has attracted much positive attention. During 1999 the company further strengthened its position as a supplier of routers through several strategic partnerships. These include the extension of the partnership with Juniper, which gave Ericsson the rights to market Juniper's 40 Gb/s backbone router, AXI 520, and the acquisition in March 1999 of Torrent Networking Technologies (re-named Ericsson IP Infrastructure Inc.) in the US. The Torrent router is marketed as Ericsson's AXI 540. Ericsson's first access router, the Tigris, was obtained through the acquisition of the California-based company ACC in 1998.

With the acquisition of the Danish company, Telebit, Ericsson obtained leading-edge expertise in the development of IPv6, the next version of the Internet Protocol. Telebit already has the world's largest installed base of next-generation routers.

Miss Ericsson do Brasil, telephone set production, São Paulo.

Facilitating convergence. 2: access

At the user's fingertips ...

1999 saw the introduction of several new models of mobile telephones, the first of which was the T28, a completely new technical platform using three volts instead of four and with many new features, including a new chipset and radio subsystem.

A series of three different phones employing WAP, Wireless Application Protocol, was also introduced.

The MC 218 is a separate hand-held computer for wireless communication using the EPOC operating system developed by Symbian. (Symbian is the joint venture set up by Ericsson, Nokia, Motorola, Psion and other parties. In 1999, it was joined by Matsushita).

Bluetooth is a small radio frequency chip first developed by Ericsson and manufactured by Ericsson Components. Bluetooth is the subject of a consortium including Ericsson, IBM, Nokia and Toshiba, formed specifically to support the technology. The special interest group established now includes some 2000 companies, which makes Bluetooth a de facto global standard for short-distance radio communication between various devices. Ericsson's first application, introduced in 1999, was a cordless headset.

Cordless headset incorporating Bluetooth.

MC 218 terminal equiped with EPOC operating system and WAP browser. Works with Ericsson telephones via infra-red, cable or Bluetooth.

Microsoft President Steve Ballmer and Ericsson President Kurt Hellström have agreed to cooperate. December 1999.

Late in 1999 Ericsson formed a partnership with Microsoft in the form of a joint venture company in Stockholm, to bring out telephones including mobile Internet solutions based on Microsoft's Mobile Explorer.

The concept of 'The networked home' is rapidly gaining attention. A partnership to develop the concept into reality was formed in 1999 between Ericsson and Electrolux, the Swedish maker of refrigerators and a range of household appliances.

Broadband access

Here, Ericsson's efforts are concentrated on the development of products within three areas: ADSL, LMDS and IP over cable-TV networks.

ADSL (Asymmetrical Digital Subscriber Line) provides increased capacity in existing copper wire networks, suitable for video-on-demand, high-speed Internet access and similar services.

LMDS (Local Multipoint Distribution Services) is a technology for high-speed radio networks based on microwave transmission for connection to voice and Internet services, primarily for small and medium-sized businesses and apartment buildings. In other words, LMDS is an example of employing radio technology for broadband access to the fixed network. The main product is MiniLink Bas.

For IP over cable-TV, Ericsson introduced PipeRider in 1999, which is a cable-TV modem used to provide voice and Internet access for the home.

PipeRider

427

Preparations for broadband.
Laying fibre optic cable along
the railway, Sweden.

The enterprise market

For this segment, product development mirrors the trends in the fixed and mobile networks and is focused on solutions for IP applications and mobile Internet – supporting the move to wireless business networks.

At the core of the product offering are the two business switches, MD 110 for large installations and BusinessPhone for the smaller enterprises.

The acquisition of the US company TouchWave (re-named Ericsson WebCom), added the WebSwitch 2000 to the portfolio. WebSwitch 2000 handles analogue and IP-based telephony.

IT consulting has become an important operation in the enterprise market. During 1999 a new business unit, Ericsson Business Consulting, made a vigorous start, with some 2,700 people working as consultants in business solutions, IT and telecom, and WAP applications.

In business solutions for the mobile Internet, Ericsson is concentrating on the banking and finance, transport, travel, media and entertainment segments.

Support for convergence

Ericsson Microelectronics

The components, cable and defence operations of Ericsson are often referred to, a little slightingly one might think, as 'other operations'. That does not reflect the truly strategic importance of what is going on in Ericsson Microelectronics AB (formerly Ericsson Components AB), Ericsson Cables AB and Ericsson Microwave AB. The story of the development of the defence business, with today's focus on the MiniLink microwave systems, and the cable business has been covered earlier: what follows here is a summary of the components activities today.

Ericsson Microelectronics' first line of business is the development and manufacture of microelectronic chips. In modern telecommunications, system and product hardware is to a very large extent implemented 'in silicon' (and certain other substrates such as gallium arsenide). System design 'moved into silicon' with the arrival of integrated circuits and system designers had to learn chip design. Thus started the very close cooperation between the development engineers and the chip designers at Ericsson Components/Microelectronics.

Ericsson Microelectronics AB, ECA, is run as a business standing on its own two feet. This means, among other things, that microelectronic chips developed by the company are supplied not only to the different Ericsson operations but also on the open market – though of course a newly developed chip will not be sold externally until after a given time lapse. The Ericsson Group uses ECA on a competitive basis – there is no product area within the Group for which Ericsson Components is the sole source.

ECA's development work is supported by a Submicron Wafer Fabrication facility, one outcome of the strategically crucial cooperation agreement with Texas Instruments. The facility allows the company to contribute at any stage in the development and manufacture of a chip. On the other hand, volume production is normally outsourced, mostly to the Far East.

In the '80s, it became vital for Ericsson's AXE program to establish itself at the leading edge in the design and manufacture of SLICs, Subscriber Line Interface Circuits. Competition was increasing and as there is one SLIC for each subscriber line connection in an AXE exchange, it became a key objective to reduce the cost of the SLIC. ECA succeeded, and is now the recognised world leader in SLIC manufacture, supplying not only Ericsson's different switching systems but also several competitors.

Development focus today is on different types of access solutions for wire and fibre connections, such as ADSL and ISDN, including an ATM chip for ADSL that handles video, data and voice traffic simultaneously. Also important are Wavelength Division Multiplexing, WDM, chips for

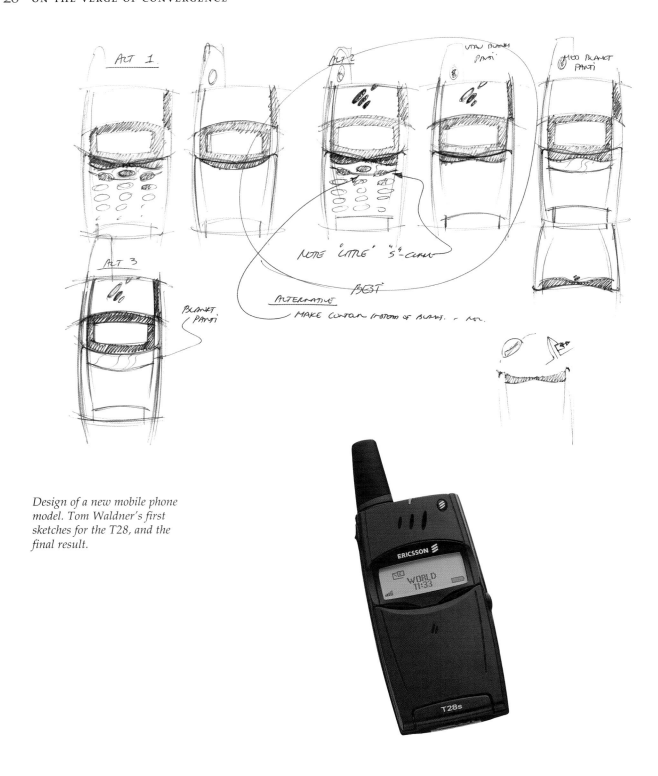

Design of a new mobile phone model. Tom Waldner's first sketches for the T28, and the final result.

optical fibre cable transmission systems (for which, incidentally, the largest customer today is Lucent Technologies). By the mid '90s Ericsson Microelectronics had also become a leading source for RF circuits to go into mobile telephones and base stations. In 1999 a partnership agreement was reached with Chartered Semiconductor for joint development and production of integrated circuits for next-generation radio.

The chip for Bluetooth was developed by Ericsson Microelectronics and is now in volume production.

Yet another product line is a full range of board-mounted power modules of which Ericsson is at present the world's largest supplier.

The second line of business for Ericsson Components used to be Energy Systems, comprising power supply systems for exchanges, PBX and computer installations, base stations and so on. The business also included climate control and energy control equipment for telecommunications installations. In late 1999 the Energy Systems operations were sold to Emerson Electric Co. in the US and Ericsson Components was re-named Ericsson Microelectronics.

Today, the second business of Ericsson Microelectronics is the Supply House, which sells and distributes the company's products internally and externally. The Supply House also acts as a distributor for a number of non-Ericsson component manufacturers. The original RIFA subsidiaries in several countries have been discontinued, and Ericsson Microelectronics now works through the various local Ericsson companies. The Supply House pioneered selling via the Internet, and the Electronics Catalogue which used to be widely distributed is now found on the net and no longer published as a paper product. The latest generation of this catalogue has introduced credit card payments over the Internet.

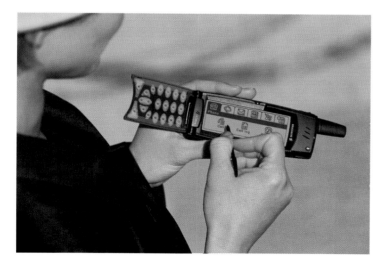

The R380. It incorporates a WAP browser, has a touch screen, takes voice notes and serves as a speaker phone.

The R320 – a small WAP mobile phone with large screen and in-built infra-red modem.

ERIEYE airborne surveillance radar system. Here mounted on a SAAB 340 turboprop aircraft.

Ericsson Microwave Systems

The two main product areas of Ericsson Microwave Systems are microwave communications and defence systems.

Over the past few years Ericsson's MiniLink has dominated the market for microwave links, with over 60,000 units produced during 1999. Point-to-multipoint systems have been developed and today play a key role, especially in building mobile infrastructure. A further new product, introduced in 1999, is MiniLink Bas for broadband access. Ericsson Microwave also develops and produces base stations for WCDMA, the third generation mobile networks. In 1999 the first order for these base stations came from NTT-DoCoMo in Japan.

The defence systems operations focus on sensors and information technology. Such control and communications systems are an area of top priority for military organisations in many countries.

The Erieye airborne surveillance radar continues to sell on the international market and development of a next generation, based on AESA technology, has been commissioned by the Swedish Armed Forces.

During 1999 the ARTHUR artillery localisation radar was sold to four countries, and the South African order for JAS 28 aircraft includes substantial subsystems from Ericsson Microwave Systems and the associated Ericsson SAAB Avionics.

The dream gets real

So ... the Internet is gearing up to carry voice (Voice over IP), and WCDMA is designed to handle mobile voice and data (wireless IP). And in the fixed networks, increasingly, new solutions for IP and ATM are coming into place to create our new machine. At last, convergence is happening, and the signs of convergence are everywhere.

There is also convergence to an almost reckless degree in the structure of the market: joint ventures, mergers and consortia and takeovers mean that this week's customer is next week's subsidiary, this month's competitor is next month's collaborator. Left to itself, the second law of thermodynamics would produce an almost random distribution of functions among the thousands of businesses involved: no doubt commercial considerations will ensure a comparatively orderly outcome from this rather feverish period in the industry.

Perhaps in many ways most interesting of all, we are now seeing the convergence of computing and telecommunications – that Siren song which brought to grief Ericsson (with EIS) and other industry majors who, like the great auk, forgot how to fly before they learned how to walk. Or in other words, saw the logic of a course of action before the technology – or, indeed, the market – was there to accomplish it.

Of course, convergence will still leave us with a pluralist world, a world in which there will be more than one way of arriving at the result we want at any one time. We shall have what is regarded as the great consumer blessing: choice.

The commissionaire, New Delhi.

433

CHAPTER 21

Next ...

C onvergence – of technology, services, and markets – is defining a totally new environment for Ericsson. The company has a name for it: *The New Telecoms World*.

In April 1998 Lars Ramqvist took over as Chairman of the Board, and Sven-Christer Nilsson assumed the position of President and CEO of Telefonaktiebolaget LM Ericsson. One of his first tasks, based on in-depth analysis that had been undertaken during the preceding years, was to implement a new strategy for Ericsson's business in The New Telecoms World, including a change of the organisation of the company.

Evolving the organisation

To reflect the changes in the market, the organisation of Ericsson which was introduced in 1983 was re-defined in 1990, altered in 1992, refocused in 1995, revised in 1997 and finally replaced in 1999.

In various ways, the organisational change of 1990 shows Ericsson on the move towards becoming a more clearly market-orientated organisation. The business areas were defined in clearly market-orientated terms. The local companies were strengthened. The major local companies in particular took on increased responsibility for sales (including exports), product development and manufacturing, with full responsibility for operating results.

Further organisational change was instituted in 1992, when network construction operations were transferred into Business Communications.

OPPOSITE:
The end of the millennium,
Ericsson headquarters,
Midsommarkransen, Stockholm.

Sven-Christer Nilsson.

The refocusing of 1995 began with the realisation that the market for large broadband switches, AXE-N, would not develop as envisaged, and the ATM-based switching system development was discontinued. The SDH Flexnode development, a large cross-connect system based on the Synchronous Digital Hierachy, was also stopped. To round out the product line, a strategic cooperation agreement was set up with the Italian Marconi company, generating a new product line of SDH cross-connect systems.

The trend in the industry, from telecommunications to infocommunications, was reflected in a further change in the organisation of the company, on 1 January 1997. Public Telecom and Business Communications were merged into a new, single Business Area, Infocom Systems, bringing together all Ericsson's fixed-network equipment. Mobile telephones were broken out as a separate new Business Area headed by the Ericsson Mobile Communications company.

Organising for today's business and tomorrow's

A new organisational structure to correspond to the demands of the New Telecoms World was introduced on 1 January, 1999.

The key objectives of the new structure were:

- to speed up product development and supply so as to offer new products and complete solutions fast;

- to work closely with key customers, and to be able to supply new customers with new solutions;

- a 'flatter' organisation with shortened lines of command; and

- an organisation with plenty of room to grow the competence of the employees.

In brief, the outlines of this new organisation were as follows.

Three *Business Segments* were created:

- *Business Segment Network Operators and Service Providers*
  To develop and market systems solutions, large wired exchanges, data and telecom networks and mobile telephone systems, and offer services to public network operators worldwide. In 1999, this segment accounted for 69 per cent of Ericsson's total net sales.

Long-distance operator in a small community in Ethiopia. Only 10 per cent of the world's population possesses a telephone. Over half the world's population has never even made a telephone call.

- *Business Segment Consumer Products*
  Production and sales through distributors of mobile telephones and terminals to private consumers. The Consumer Products segment's sales in 1999 corresponded to 21 per cent of Ericsson's total.

- *Business Segment Enterprise Systems*
  To provide complete telecom and datacom solutions and a range of services for enterprise customers. Enterprise Solutions' share of Ericsson's total sales in 1999 was 8 per cent.

Within each Business Segment there were a number of Business Units and Product Units.

The market-orientation of the new Business Segments was obvious. Each Segment brought together prospects and customers with common network needs, with which the appropriate part of Ericsson could become intimately familiar, and for which solutions could be developed.

Swedish adventurer Göran Kropp in the Himalayas.

These customers and their needs and solutions also tend to cluster by geography, and the second part of the organisation recognised this area of commonality as well: the company's market organisation was structured into new *Market Areas*, as follows:

- *Market Area Western Europe*, headquartered in London;

- *Market Area Eastern Europe, the Middle East and Africa*, headquartered in London;

- *Market Area North America*, headquartered in Richardson, Texas;

- *Market Area Asia Pacific*, with offices in Hong Kong;

- *Market Area Latin America*, headquartered in Miami.

Defence and Microwave Systems, Cables, and Components, each of which has its own rather separate set of preoccupations, are run as three separate companies. In 1999 these companies accounted for about 7 per cent of total sales (including internal).

Corporate functions include Finance, Technology, Supply and Information Technology, Marketing and Strategic Business Development, Human Resources and Organisation, and Corporate Communications.

Organisations are always imperfect. People are always human. But for people with intelligence and goodwill, this organisation used the lessons of the last restless decade, provided a structure with a lot of flexibility, and was unmistakably market-, customer- and prospect-facing.

So ... the last of the red-hot reorganisations? Of course not! Management consultants often describe the natural state for a successful company as one of continuous reorganisation because successful companies create, reflect and respond to their markets, and markets are nothing if not volatile.

The key is speed. The management text books are littered with the bones of companies which saw the right thing to do and took too long to do it. Fast implementation of a reorganisation allows time to reap the benefits before the next wave of change makes new and different demands. In the '90s, Ericsson has learned to live with change. Now it has to learn to live with change fast.

The Ericsson R190, a dual mode phone for GSM and satellite networks. Early in 2000 it was tested in the new ACS, Asian Cellular Satellite, network.

Analysing the past – defining the future

How is Ericsson placed for meeting the challenge? How is the company positioned for doing business in The New Telecoms World?

Let us start by going back for an overall view of the history of the LM Ericsson company, to understand how change has occurred over time. The major phases of 125 years of operation and the forces that defined them may be summarised as follows:

In its first 25 years, the company developed from a small workshop to a business with sales in a wide range of markets, and manufacturing both in Sweden and in some countries outside Sweden. It served, above all, the growing needs of the emerging telephone operators.

Though they included World War I, the following 30 years saw steady growth, increased competition on the home market, the gaining of telephone operating concessions and the establishment of LM Ericsson factories in several more countries. It also saw the birth of LM Ericsson's first automatic exchange system – with Televerket as its godfather.

After the Kreuger crash of 1932, a period of reconstruction followed, during a world economic depression. It meant the retreat from many of the telephone concessions, retirement from several markets and the introduction of various new products to compensate for a decline in the telephone business. It also included the severe disruption by World War II.

In the post-war era, the modern LM Ericsson company began to emerge. It was driven by the timely introduction of new switching technology, the crossbar systems (again with Televerket as godfather), at a time when telephone penetration was once more on the rise, and automatic long-distance and international services were rapidly being extended. The pattern of the telecoms manufacturing industry was changing: several competitors withdrew from the international market, leaving fewer, but larger and stronger, main players.

From the 1960s onwards, LM Ericsson was among the top international suppliers, but not yet in the top echelon.

The telephone administration monopolies were the dominant customers and ruled supreme. Many markets were closed to LM Ericsson. Often, political considerations rather than product excellence and price decided the outcome of successful business.

But, notwithstanding political ties and traditional relationships, by the 1970s telecommunications had become a largely technology-driven business. Stored program control and digital switching and transmission offered manufacturers incentives to develop superior products and gain market shares. With AXE, Ericsson was eminently successful (and once more, Televerket was in at the birth with Ellemtel).

Lebanon, business as usual ...

The mobile systems business emerged in the mid 1980s, and again Ericsson successfully exploited its ability to develop new technology. During the 1990s, the digital mobile systems at last brought the company to a leading position in a world that was dramatically restructured by worldwide liberalisation and de-regulation. Ericsson faced a global market and global competition.

Why the success?

First of all, LM Ericsson had developed a real-life understanding of the strategic value of *product development* – the strength and willingness to invest increasing amounts of money in R&D.

Second, the company built up the special know-how and technology to develop *large systems*, to manage development projects involving thousands of people in many countries, and running over several years.

Third, the company steadily expanded and strengthened its *market presence* worldwide, which meant that it had a growing installed base and existing customers to whom it could market its large systems.

The fourth strength was the company's *manufacturing facilities* – LM

Ericsson was, basically, an international network of telecommunications equipment factories. This ensured capability to build equipment, and was also a key political element in gaining new markets and maintaining market presence.

And the fifth element of strength was, of course, *the Ericsson people.* Professional, loyal and with a collective outlook defined by long and strong LM Ericsson traditions.

LM Ericsson had its culture, rigid but rewarding: its soul was that of a manufacturer, its operations to a large extent centred around its factories. The technology drive of the business from around 1950 brought out new generations of telecoms engineers and internationally-focused marketers to make the most of these facilities.

During the 1980s Ericsson had a sound base, and, adept at exploiting its market presence, was able to take the lead in digital switching and in the first generation of mobile telephone systems. With mobile systems for the new digital world standards, the company finally claimed its place among the half dozen leading telecommunications companies of the world.

Cambodia, recovery aided by telecoms.

But by the mid '90s, the whole traditional reference framework had dissolved, and in a few years it had become evident that the tactics that served the company so well for over a hundred years were less and less relevant.

A new market has emerged, with new rules and tactics. It is a global market, and furthermore, a market that no longer depends on large systems. It is a market looking for networks and networking, driven to a very high degree by the spread of the Internet and mobility. And as a consequence of new technology and new political thinking, telecoms has become an industry in which manufacturing, the building of the system hardware, has lost most of its strategic importance.

The traditional competitors are still there, and they too are meeting new conditions. But, as a typical outcome of the new era in telecommunications, new business opportunities have created a community of new companies as competitors – fast-moving, market-orientated, technology-based and hungry. Many of them are focused on networking: software, Internet access, routers, and so on.

How is Ericsson reacting to this tremendous set of challenges?

Notwithstanding its rapid expansion, company traditions have been strong and the large-systems philosophy lived on in parts of the organisation. In the late '80s a new major development programme, AXE-N, was begun – and it took several years before reality caught up and the project was stopped.

At the same time, in another new area, mobile telephones, new skills in consumer electronics production and consumer marketing had to be acquired. The company showed that it could acquire them, even though some knocks had to be taken and tough lessons had to be learned.

Now, the company is coming through its metamorphosis. Much manufacturing is being outsourced, many factories have been sold or closed. R&D spending continues at a high level, but with a different focus: smaller systems with networking ability; software technology; network-integration and the creation of new applications and services.

The toughest challenge has been to change the mindsets of Ericsson's people – to develop an understanding of the changes in today's business process; to develop the competence to create new business situations, not just new technology; to build an ability to create situations in which Ericsson itself can determine the direction of its own business.

It's happening. Ericsson continues to develop technology and new products, as it must, at a high rate; but above all it is building the competence to develop *business*, to create business platforms. The company must have the competence to *use* technology in its business, instead of *making* technology its business. Today, technology is the lubricant of Ericsson's business.

Excellence in product development must continue high, but with projects on a somewhat different scale. Development programmes will be intense, but limited in time.

The modern start-up companies demonstrate the potential for creating new products around a business idea. Ericsson has introduced a 'small company within the company' mode of working – dedicated project organisations set up for specific development (or other) programmes, highly independent and providing individual incentives. And, most important, each 'small company' works close to, or together with, one or more key customers. Ericsson is learning to understand and to be part of its customers' development – and to help customers create their own business opportunities.

The biggest job in corporate management: changing the company culture

In the '80s and early '90s, the concept of 'change' became one of the most overworked clichés in management speak. 'Embracing change', 'welcoming change', 'living with change', 'adapting to change' – the subject appeared with boring predictability in every management conference, every meeting between management and staff, every consultant's report.

That shouldn't surprise anybody. The rate of change in business, as in every other area of life, *has* increased dramatically. And change is hard to understand and cope with. We've already seen how in 1983 Ericsson recreated itself to deal with change. And in that 1983 structure, mobile telephones aren't even mentioned! 15 years later, mobile telephones are Ericsson's second largest business ...

Such a shift is bigger than that from operator-manned to automatic exchanges, bigger than the shift from analogue to digital systems. The shift from selling business systems to selling consumer electronics means a more or less complete change-out at every level below the company's ultimate core values. The people who willed the business, like Åke Lundqvist, may have had the traditional systems background; but the people who made it, like Flemming Örneholm, had to have consumer marketing experience. And very few consumer marketers would see opportunities in a systems house like Ericsson. Mostly, Ericsson had to learn all on its own. It was slow and painful, but it happened – and Ericsson managed itself successfully through one of the most difficult transformations any company can undertake.

It's worth pointing out that as time went by, and it became clear that the mobile phones were not only a big business but by far the most visible business, the pain went in two directions. For the Ericsson people involved,

The importance of being first

For Kurt Hellström the operational word is speed. As he puts it, 'in the market today we have to be *first* with new technology and new products. If we also are the *best* – so much the better, but being first is key. The third requirement is that we must be *cost-effective* in all our processes, from development through manufacture to distribution'.

Kurt Hellström

there was the great difficulty of remaking their business lives. For the Ericsson people not involved with mobiles, there was the chagrin when all the glamour became attached to these upstart products. The traditional Ericsson values of long, patient, persevering development of systems with a lifetime of years, even decades – values of which most people were fiercely proud – suddenly seemed almost irrelevant in this new, frivolous fashion business.

Today, both sides happily co-exist, and respect each other's professionalism. In order to cope with more change!

Management of change has indeed been and continues to be the challenge. And, as will occur in any dynamic industrial organisation, *change of management* may also at times become necessary. It came as a surprise in July 1999 when the Board of Directors announced that the President and CEO, Sven-Christer Nilsson, had been asked to step down. The main reason was that the Board was not satisfied with the rate of change. The company had not moved fast enough to show that it had become the fleet-footed, nimble and hungry organisation that it desired to be.

Dr Lars Ramqvist continues as Chairman of the Board, but will also take on, through the year 2000, the responsibilities of CEO, and Kurt Hellström has been named President of Telefonaktiebolaget LM Ericsson.

And what about the 'world's largest man-made machine'?

The worldwide machine is still there, but it is no longer correct to describe it as a machine, or even a large system. As new pieces are linked in, as additional uses and services are introduced, the man-made machine is changing character. It is truly becoming a network, a network incorporating all the various services and capabilities we know – telephony, data, Internet, mobile services, satellite communication, multimedia, video ... System integration, which for so long was the outstanding capability of Ericsson, is being replaced by network integration. A true challenge.

Where do we go from here?

Today, Ericsson is one of the world's great companies.

How the company reached that position is the subject of the previous pages of this book, and a few things must surely strike anybody who reads this story.

The first is that *success has never, ever, come easily to Ericsson*.

Ericsson has always had to fight for its prosperity. The big successes that there have been – its first decade or so of growth, its electromechanical switch, crossbar, AXE, mobile systems and mobile terminals – have mostly had uncertain beginnings, have often encountered quite stiff opposition within Ericsson itself and sometimes adverse conditions in the markets, and have not always been able to rely on adequate financial or management support.

Somehow, it has often been the persistence of individuals that has pulled the projects through, and the professionalism of the company has eventually turned them into blazing successes.

That situation eased to a large degree in the '90s (though even in the '90s the mobile terminals had a somewhat uncertain start). Ericsson has become much more market- and customer-orientated, which means that the right projects have a much better chance to get the support and resources they deserve. And that's reflected in the growth over the last decade.

What is being done now, as we enter the new millennium – by restructuring, by streamlining, by flattening management, by fostering small companies within the big one, by clearing the lines of communication to and from the customers – is to make it as easy as possible to be successful. There's no real glory in doing things the hard way.

The second thing that emerges very forcefully is *how effectively Ericsson can react to change*. And not just react to it, but actually help to create it. Over and over again, by its work in developing new standards, by partnering, by competitive demonstrations of its preferred technologies and by acquisitions, Ericsson has affected and continues to affect the course of world telecoms.

An English poet, Hilaire Belloc, described the stereotypical Scandinavian:

His legs are long, his mind is slow,
His hair is lank, and made of tow.

And indeed there is a sort of recurring myth about Ericsson that it is slow and reluctant when confronted by change. We believe this chronicle shows that quite the opposite is true.

And, although the story we have told has – for obvious reasons – its centre of gravity in Sweden, and in Stockholm, we could ask ourselves:

how Swedish is Ericsson today? It is a company registered in Sweden with dominant ownership in Swedish institutions, but with a large percentage of its shares owned by non-Swedish individuals and institutions.

Change came with deregulation and liberalisation and the largely politically-driven creation of the global market. Ericsson flourished in response to these challenges, grew – and matured.

100 years ago LM Ericsson employed about 1,000 people. Today there are over 100,000, fewer than 45,000 of whom are in Sweden. Many of the factories in different countries have gone and the company depends instead on its many research and development centres, all over the world, along with a growing cadre of marketing and sales people.

Ericsson has applied flair, skill and endless hard work to tackling these changes, and the outcome is a community which is large, successful, and truly global. Its headquarters may still be in Stockholm, but on any given day Ericsson's CEO and his executive committee may be in London, New York, Tokyo – anywhere in the world's telecommunications market-place.

The next generation: Jennifer keeping in touch.

Chronology

1846   5 May. Lars Magnus Ericsson born.

1853   Sweden introduces electric telegraph. Kongliga Electriska Telegraf-Werket, later Televerket, founded. Food shortages, bread riots.

1864   Televerket employs first women telegraph operators.

1866   Lars Magnus Ericsson apprenticed to A. H. Öller workshop in Stockholm.

1872   Lars Magnus Ericsson begins studies abroad.

1875   Lars Magnus Ericsson returns, and …

1876   leaves Öller. 1 April, Lars Magnus Ericsson, together with Carl Johan Andersson, opens telegraph repair workshop in Drottninggatan 15. Stockholm; total staff: 3. Alexander Graham Bell patents his new invention, the telephone, but not in Sweden. The workshop moves to Jakobsbergsgatan.

1877   Bell telephones on sale in Sweden. Move to Lästmakargatan.

1878   Lars Magnus Ericsson sells improved version of Bell telephone. 22 pairs sold. Marries Hilda Simonsson.

1879   Total staff 10, including owners. 74 telephones sold. Fire telegraph manufacture started. Trade union movement begins.

1880   Bell Telephone Co. operating switchboard and subscriber network in Stockholm. LM Ericsson moves to Biblioteksgatan, and sells first switchboard. Ivar Kreuger born.

1881   First major contracts (Gävle, Bergen) for LM Ericsson. Telegrafverket opens own telephone network in Stockholm.

1882   Total staff: 50. Working week: 65 hours.

1883   H. T. Cedergren founds Stockholms Allmänna Telefonaktiebolag, SAT. Cedergren and Ericsson jointly patent 'automatic exchange'. First SAT order for LM Ericsson.

1884   LM Ericsson moves to Thulegatan 5.

1885   First handset produced.

1887   SAT exchange at Malmskillnadsgatan opened, the largest in the world.

1888   Swedish parliament approves Telegrafverket proposal for first nation-wide network: Rikstelefon. Ericsson patents carbon granule microphone. Max Sieverts Tråd och Kabelfabrik established. SAT purchases the share majority of Stockholm Bell Co.

1890   Number of employees 153.

1891   Strowger principle patented. Strowger Automatic Telephone Co. founded. Telegrafverket starts manufacture of telephones and switchboards.

1892   First desk telephone introduced.

1893   Over 11,000 telephones produced during year.

1896   27 April. LM Ericsson converted to joint stock company, Aktiebolaget LM Ericsson & Co. Share capital: SEK 1 m. SAT sets up AB Telefonfabriken.

1897   LM Ericsson's first foreign manufacturing operation established in St Petersburg.

1898   LM Ericsson Shop Union founded. Ericsson opens UK sales office.

1899   Construction of new factory begun in St Petersburg.

1900   Sales pass SEK 4 m; 50,000 telephones produced per year. About 1,000 employees. Lars Magnus Ericsson resigns as MD, succeeded by Axel Boström. Ericsson active in Sweden, Nordic countries, UK, US, Germany, Netherlands, Russia, Spain, Egypt, Ethiopia, South Africa, China, Asia/Oceania.

1901   New St Petersburg factory opens. Ericsson considers relocation of headquarters to Russia. LM Ericsson takes over SAT's AB Telefonfabriken. Lars Magnus Ericsson resigns as Chairman. First experimental European automatic exchange built by Strowger in Berlin.

1902   US sales office established in New York. Office employees granted a fortnight annual holiday.

OPPOSITE: *Valencia, Spain, 1923.*

1903   Lars Magnus Ericsson retired from board of LM Ericsson. Joint LME/SAT Swedish patent for central-battery system. British LM Ericsson Manufacturing Co. Ltd (half-owned) established at Beeston, UK.

1905   Union between Sweden and Norway dissolved. LM Ericsson, with SAT and Marcus Wallenberg, acquires first operating concession: Empresa de Teléfonos Ericsson S.A., Mexeric, in Mexico. Strowger receives US Patent 638249.

1906   Strowger Automatic Telephone Co. becomes Automatic Electric Co., Autelco. LME establishes sanatorium for employees suffering from tuberculosis.

1907   US company, LM Ericsson Telephone Manufacturing Co. established in Buffalo. Over 82,000 telephones produced. Telephone service started up in Mexico City.

1908   LME enters collaboration agreement with Deckert & Homolka to manufacture in Budapest. Carl Johan Andersson retires.

1909   First Siemens automatic exchanges, built under licence from Autelco, in service in Germany. Axel Boström dies, Hemming Johansson appointed MD. H. T. Cedergren dies.

1910   Gottlieb Piltz succeeds Cedergren as MD of SAT.

1911   Société des Téléphones Ericsson S.A., STE, set up to manufacture in France. Beeston UK factory becomes wholly-owned. British Post Office established as UK PTT.

1912   LM Ericsson becomes owner of manufacturing facilities in Budapest and Vienna.

1913   Ivar Kreuger sets up Swedish Match Company. First crossbar switch patented in the US.

1914   Start of World War I. Ericsson receives contract to manufacture electricity meters.

1915   Railway switchpoint and signalling department established.

1917   Russian revolutions. USA acquires Virgin Islands for $ 30 m: Sosthenes Behn becomes US citizen.

1918   Merger of LM Ericsson and Stockholms Allmänna Telefon AB, SAT, to form Allmänna Telefon AB LM Ericsson. SAT concession in Russia, Svensk-Dansk-Ryska Telefon, and LME Russia both nationalised. World War I ends. A/B LM Ericsson i Finland formed.

1919   LME's Polish operating concession returned to merged companies. Ericsson part-owner of Svenska Radio Aktiebolaget, SRA.

1920   US: LM Ericsson Telephone Manufacturing Co. closed. Ericsson a partner in Argentina's Compañía Entrerriana de Teléfonos S.A.

1921   Telverket standardises on LM Ericsson's 500-point automatic switch system.

1922   Joint company, Polska Aksynja Spólka Telefoniczna, PAST, formed with Polish government; receives 25-year Warsaw concession. K. F. Wincrantz becomes Joint President, together with Gottlieb Piltz, of Allmänna Telefonaktiebolaget LM Ericsson. LM Ericsson halves its share value. First 'punched-card' workers' time control systems delivered.

1923   First LM Ericsson 500-point switches in service. ITT beats Ericsson to Spanish concession. Ericsson Manufacturing Co. in US sold.

1925   Compensation claims for St Petersburg factory and SAT Moscow concession abandoned. ITT buys International Western Electric Co., sets up International Standard Electric, acquires Mexicana. Ericsson a partner in Italy's Societá Esercizi Telefonici, SET, with concession for south; and in Fabbrica Apparechi Telefonici e Materiale Elettrico, FATME, with factory in Rome. K. F. Wincrantz becomes sole President, sets up AB Ängsvik with Ivar Kreuger, buys Cedergren shares to add to his control of voting of Allmänna Telefon AB LM Ericsson.

1926   Allmänna Telefon AB LM Ericsson becomes Telefon AB LM Ericsson. 50-year long-distance concession granted to Mexeric. Televerket instals first crossbar switch in Sundsvall. Lars Magnus Ericsson dies.

1928   Ericsson acquires Sieverts Kabelverk, and major interest in A/S Elektrisk Bureau, Oslo. Mexico City concession for Mexeric renewed.

1929   ITT takes over Compañía Unión Telefónica del Rio de la Plata in Argentina. LME joins Herlitzka counter-consortium. Wall Street crash. New railway systems company, LM Ericsson Signalaktiebolag established.

Mexico, 16.9.1929.

1930   In Germany, ITT forms Standard Electric and acquires Lorenz from Philips. Opens discussions with Ivar Kreuger. Wins Romanian concession. Ivar Kreuger discovered to own majority voting rights in Ericsson. K. F. Wincrantz steps down as MD, sells shares, loses voting rights, and position on Board. Johan Grönberg becomes MD. Ericsson buys land for expansion at Midsommarkransen, Stockholm.

1931   Ivar Kreuger sells voting majority in LME to ITT. Ericsson introduces the bakelite phone, and acquires rights to the Centralograph machine-status-recorder.

1932   ITT examines Ericsson's assets and withdraws from agreement to buy Ericsson. Ivar Kreuger shoots himself. Unravelling begins. Staff salaries and bonuses cut.

1933   A change of Ericsson's Articles of Association is approved by the King in Council. Marcus Wallenberg Jr becomes Vice Chairman of LM Ericsson and Hans Theobald Holm Managing Director. Industrial Salaried Employees' Association (SIF) formed.

1935   Ericsson assembling Televerket crossbar exchanges.

Publicity in the 20s, Austria.

1936   Rationalisation of competing Ericsson/ITT interests in Mexico and Argentina achieved in principle. Ericsson in Sweden starts cash register manufacture.

1937   Share capital reduced by 30 per cent.

1938   Ericsson starts electron tubes manufacture at AB Svenska Elektronrör, SER. Building of new head offices and factory starts at Midsommarkransen.

1939   Status quo agreement with ITT in Mexico. World War II begins. Factory employs c. 3,500. SRA introduces Radiola home radio receivers.

1940   LME begins move to new offices and factory at Midsommarkransen. Ericsson substantially involved in manufacture of ammunition and machine guns. Reduces holding in UK company to under 50 per cent to avoid seizure for 'trading with the enemy.' LME forms Panama Corporación Teleric as safe haven for its assets in Latin American companies. LME involved in manufacture of exchanges incorporating Televerket's crossbar switches.

1941   Shareholder dividends reinstated. Factory employs c. 2,800.

1942   Factory employs c. 3,500. Echo radar tests by SRA. Helge Ericsson becomes MD of LM Ericsson.

1944 FATME factory seriously damaged. SRA delivers first police mobile radio systems. Foundation of Ericsson long-service gold medal scheme.

1945 Development under way on Ericsson crossbar systems. 5-month Swedish general engineering strike. Ulvsunda factory opens.

1946 Katrineholm factory opens. Ericsson establishes foundation for research into television. Instrument and meter departments combined in new company, LM Ericsson Mätinstrument AB. AT&T sets up first commercial mobile telephone network (St Louis).

1947 Mexeric's operations transferred to Teléfonos de México S.A. with 10-year supply agreement. Gröndal factory opens. Karlskrona factory opens. AT&T brings out cellular mobile telephone concept.

1948 Labour-Management councils instituted. Söderhamn factory opens. First order for metropolitan crossbar (Helsinki).

1949 First Danish orders for Ericsson crossbar local exchanges. Ericsson sells out in UK. Radio tower added at Midsommarkransen. Radar manufacture begins.

1950 First Ericsson crossbar metropolitan exchanges in service in Finland. Mextelco's operations transferred to Teléfonos de México S.A. with new supply agreements. First coaxial cable installation, in Sweden. Televerket sets up first mobile telephone system in Sweden. World's first automatic international call placed through trial LME exchange. Sven Ture Åberg takes over as MD of LM Ericsson.

1951 Ericsson acquires majority interest in North Electric Manufacturing Company in Ohio; sells last remaining shares in British ETL.

1952 Ericsson crossbar trunk exchange in service in Rotterdam.

1954 First crossbar orders from Australia. New Brazil factory completed outside São Paulo. EMAX, TDM-based trial electronic exchange completed. TV set manufacture begins at SRA.

1955 First Brazil crossbar order. Mölndal factory opens. LM Ericsson Mätinstrument AB in Sweden becomes ERMI.

1956 Ericsson launches Ericofon. Swedish television begins to broadcast regularly. Joint Televerket-Ericsson Electronics Council (Elektroniknämnden) established. 6,000,000th telephone manufactured.

1958 Ericsson claims compensation from Germany for war losses in Poland. LME and ITT transfer their Teléfonos de México holdings into Mexican hands.

1959 Contract for 412L electronic exchange for US Air Force received through Northern Electric. Private line market liberalised in US. LME crossbar is system choice for Australia's automatic system.

1960 ITT agrees sale of Ericsson shares back to Swedish institutions. Toowoomba crossbar exchange delivered in Australia. Ericsson buys Trimax Transformers Pty Ltd at Melbourne.

Pay phone in the Stocholm archipelago, 1960s.

Adding value to a fashion photo, 1950s.

1961   Land acquired at Broadmeadows outside Melbourne. First airborne radar delivered in Sweden. Code switch introduced.

1962   LM Ericsson-Trimax Pty becomes LM Ericsson Pty Ltd. First code switch installation at Stockholm. New Dialog phone introduced.

1963   Broadmeadows factory opens in Australia. First PCM transmission trial in Sweden. SRA radio and TV business sold. Sven Ture Åberg resigns as MD, succeeded by Björn Lundvall.

1964   Semiconductor-based airborne radar systems delivered in Sweden. Televerket sets up mobile-telephony study group.

1965   Ericsson acquires Teleindustria de México and majority interest in Latinoamericana de Cables S. A. MTB mobile telephony in operation in Sweden.

1966   Compensation for war losses received from Germany. Östersund factory, the 23rd in Sweden outside Stockholm area, opened. North Electric Co sold.

1967   Prototype laser distance-measuring and range-finder systems delivered to the Swedish Navy and Finland. Televerket mobile telephony study group recommends full national cellular mobile telephone service.

1968   First computer controlled, SPC, exchange, AKE 12, installed at Tumba, Sweden.

1969   First Ericsson keyset phones. ERMI electricity meter company sold. The APO awards Pitt Street, Sydney, contract to ITT for Metaconta. Nordic Telecommunications Conference sets up pan-Nordic NMT Group to define mobile telephone system.

1970   Computer-controlled airborne doppler radar systems with digital signal processor delivered in Sweden. Advanced satellite systems supplied to ESRO. Ellemtel established. NMT Group recommendations submitted. Tellus building opened.

1971   First Ericsson picture phones. UAC 1610 computer goes into production. Ellemtel receives requirement specification for all-new SPC switch. Specialized Common Carrier principle established in US. World's first SPC STD exchange (AKE 13) installed in Rotterdam.

1972   Teleindustria de México moves to Tlalnepantla. Decision to pursue AX exchange development at Ellemtel.

1973   Name 'AXE' adopted. World oil crisis begins. Turku orders analogue AXE exchange. New factory established at Kumla. Group sales exceed SEK 5,000 m.

1974   AXE customer presentations begin. International crossbar exchange opened in London.

1975   France chooses AXE as second system.

1976   Södertälje exchange trials start. 100-year anniversary celebrations. 60 MHz coax cable transmission system for 10,800 channels introduced.

A phone 'bubble', Sweden, 1970s.

1977   1 March: Södertälje AXE exchange cut over. Turku analogue exchange delivered. AXE system choice in Australia. Saudi Arabia AXE contract announced. AXE orders received from Finland, Kuwait, Sweden, Yugoslavia and Denmark. Successful field trial of NMT. Tenders for supply of NMT systems invited. SRA acquires SONAB base-station and terminal manufacturing divisions. Dr Marcus Wallenberg resigns as Chairman of the board and is succeeded by Björn Lundvall. Björn Svedberg becomes new President and CEO.

1978   First digital AXE exchange installed at Turku. AOM centralised network management system and ASB electronic PBX introduced.

1979   Mrs Thatcher elected as prime minister in UK. Electronic systems production exceeds electromechanical. First global advertising agency appointed.

1980   Ericsson buys Datasaab. Anaconda-Ericsson joint venture established in US.

1981   First AXE cut over in Mexico. Ericsson Information Systems (EIS) set up. Ericsson buys Facit. 1 September: first NMT system inaugurated, in Saudi Arabia. 1 October: Nordic NMT system inaugurated. SRA takes responsibility for all mobile systems, becomes ERA. Kumla factory makes first NMT mobile stations.

1982   Judge Green rules to break up AT&T in US. 44 countries have chosen AXE. Over 2.3 million lines installed; 4.1 million lines on order. Loss in Norway to ITT. CMS 8800 mobile system introduced to US market. Ericsson prominent in operators' bids for first 30 US cellular markets. In Europe, CEPT sets up standardisation Groupe Spéciale Mobile (GSM) for digital second-generation mobile system. First fully digital AXE exchange opened in Tampere, Finland.

1983   MD 110 PBX introduced. First US mobile system contract (Buffalo). 1 January: Ericsson reorganised into Business Areas. New Ericsson logotype introduced. Ericsson Mobile Telephone laboratory opens in Lund.

Saudi Arabia.

From Rojan factory, Thailand.

1984 'Divestiture' of AT&T in US. Richardson, Dallas, facility established to adapt AXE for US. Buffalo cellular system cut over. BT requests tenders for UK second fixed network switching system supply.

1985 1 January: Ericsson infrastructure in Vodafone cellular network cut over in UK. AXE becomes second system choice (System Y) in UK. Ericsson Inc becomes wholly owned US subsidiary. Dutch PTT chooses AXE.

1986 First Ericsson implementation of Intelligent Network. ITT leaves telecoms market: sells interests to Alcatel. AXE receives Phase A approval in US. Share of world market for mobile cellular systems reaches 40 per cent.

1987 First US orders and cutovers for AXE. China signs its largest telecoms contract to date, for AXE. 200,000 lines of AXE installed in China. Technical cooperation agreement with Texas Instruments. GSM MoU commits Europe to GSM. MET is formed in partnership with Matra in France. Mobile Telephones becomes separate business unit within Ericsson Radio Systems. First Ericsson hand-held mobile telephone produced, for NMT 900.

1988 EIS discontinued, Data Systems and Office Equipment divisions sold.to Nokia. Ericsson has 30 per cent of US cellular systems market. First GSM system order, from Vodafone, UK. Ericsson invited by NTT to participate in design of Japanese digital mobile system, PDC. 37,000 mobiles produced at Kumla.

1989 Joint venture with General Electric of US to handle mobile telephones world-wide (Ericsson GE Mobile Communications). Production in Lynchburg; R&D at RTP. First DECT 900 cordless telephone. Corporate values defined: professionalism, respect and perseverance. Deregulation of telecoms operating monopolies gains momentum.

1990 Björn Svedberg becomes chairman of the board and Lars Ramqvist is named President and CEO. GSM system order from Mannesmann, Germany. World's largest personal paging system, delivered by Ericsson, is cut into service in Taiwan with 650,000 subscribers.

1991 Total mobile telephone production: 225,000 (over half from Lynchburg). Ericsson has c. 3 per cent of world market for mobiles. First GSM phones in service. ISO 9000 quality standard introduced in the Group.

1992 EHPT joint venture with Hewlett Packard set up. GSM launched. MATRA-Ericsson GSM partnership dissolved. 200,000 phones produced at Kumla. GE reduces its share in Ericsson GE Mobile Communications. AXE now chosen by 101 countries. Building starts at Kista of production plant for 'submicroelectronic' components.

1993 First PCN network: One-to-One, UK. Ericsson supplies first D-AMPS, now TDMA, second-generation mobile system in US. Ericsson GE Mobile Communications moves HQ to Sweden; renamed Ericsson Mobile Communications. 12 m lines of AXE installed in year, but Radio Communications Business Area becomes largest in Ericsson.

1994 First LME operations in Russia since 1917: Ericsson Corporatia AO. Ericsson acquires the Teli AB group of companies from Telia. First digital PDC mobile system in service in Japan.

A call for help.
Bucharest, 1997.

1995 World's first GSM 1900 mobile system in service in the US. AXE total lines installed exceed 105 million lines in 110 countries. Mobile systems installed in 74 countries and serving 34 million subscribers. A total of 8.5 million lines of MD 110 have been sold. Ericsson acquires 49 per cent of Nicola Tesla. Telia half of Ellemtel acquired and company renamed Ericsson Utvecklings AB. New submicroelectronics plant in production.

1996 Mobile systems account for 40 per cent of world market, serving a total of 54 million subscribers. Mobile telephones about 15 per cent market share. AXE sold to 117 countries. First ERIEYE surveillance radar system sold outside Sweden.

1997 Mobile and IP communications increase dramatically. Further restructuring is announced. Major R&D investments (16 per cent of total sales in 1997) begin to pay off. First test systems for WCDMA, third generation mobile, in Japan.

1998 Lars Ramqvist becomes Chairman of the Board and Sven-Christer Nilsson President and CEO. Large contract with British Telecom for upgrading of wireline AXE network to handle packet data services. New organisation announced in September – 11,000 jobs (out of a total of 104,000) to disappear. AXD 301 ATM switch introduced. Ericsson acquires Advanced Computer Communications, ACC, and an interest in Mariposa, ATM access router

manufacturer. Ericsson enters wireless LAN market. WCDMA standard, adopted by ETSI and proposed to the ITU as a world standard. Wireless Application Protocol, WAP, introduced together with Motorola, Nokia and Unwired Planet. Ericsson CyberLab set up in New York City. Bluetooth consortium formed. Symbian JV for development of EPOC operating system established with Nokia, Motorola, Panasonic and Psion.

1999 Ericsson takes c. 50 per cent of the orders for GPRS. Agreements to exploit WAP set up with i a VISA International and Sonera SmartTrust. IT Business Consulting set up, with 2,700 employees in 36 countries. Strategic breakthrough orders received from British Telecom, Diginet in Latin Americe, KPN in the Netherlands and Telefónica for updating fixed networks with Engine platform. Acquisition of Qualcomm infrastructure division. Other acquisitions include Torrent and Touchwave. Strategic cooperation established with Microsoft and Juniper. First mobile terminal with EPOC operating system introduced. Sales of mobile telephones pick up dramatically during last quarter of year. 70 per cent of total sales refer to mobile systems. World's first WAP terminals introduced. In July, Sven-Christer Nilsson steps down as President and CEO. Lars Ramqvist returns as CEO and Kurt Hellström takes over as President.

Indexes

Index of persons mentioned in the text

Names beginning with the Swedish letters Å, Ä and Ö are listed under A and O respectively.

Baku, Russia, c 1910.

Companies, of the Ericsson Group and others

Tables

Glossary

Abbreviations, acronyms and other abominations.

The secret words of telecommunications and some things defined:

Access	In a telecoms network, fixed or mobile, the access network is the portion that connects the subscriber to (normally) a local exchange or mobile exchange.
Access systems	Different types of equipment for subscriber access by copper or optical fibre cable, multiplexers, concentrators or wireless.
ADSL	Asymmetrical Digital Subscriber Line. For high-speed data transmission towards the subscriber (for instance a video) and lower speed from sub. For copper cable access networks.
AGF	Ericsson's first automatic telephone switching system, using the 500-point selector.
AGM	Annual General Meeting
AKE	Ericsson's computer-controlled switching systems using the code switch.
AKF	Ericsson's code switch-based electromechanical switching systems.
Algorithm	In a computer program: a series of instructions or procedural steps for the solving of a specific problem.
AMPS	Advanced Mobile Phone System, the original American analogue standard specification developed by Bell Labs.
Analogue	An analogue signal is a continuous waveform representing voice, tones, etc.
ARE	Ericsson's crossbar system with computer control.
ARF	Crossbar systems for local exchanges.
ARK	Crossbar system for rural exchanges.
ARM	Crossbar systems for transit and tandem exchanges.
ASP	Application Service Positioning. A technology that, for a fixed fee, facilitates downloading of software of the Internet instead of purchasing the program over the counter.
ATM	Asynchronous Transfer Mode. A technology for broadband transmission of digital signals, such as packet data. ATM switches handle ATM connections.
AXD 301	The Ericsson ATM switch.
AXE	Ericsson's digital switching system, also used in mobile networks. Today, a communications platform.
Beewip (BWIP)	Broadband Wireless IP, an Ericsson 3 Mbps access solution for the 3.5 GHz band.
BHCA	Busy Hour Call Attempts, a measure of telephone call intensity, defines call-handling capacity of a switching system.

Bluetooth	A radio technology built around a new chip developed by Ericsson and other companies for short-distance radio communication between telephones, computers and a range of other devices.
Broadband	The term defines data transmission, over wireline or radio, at a speed higher than 2 Megabits per second. Wideband denotes the range from about 200 kbps up to 2 Mbps.
CCIR	Comité Consultatif International des Radiocommunications, the radio standards setting committee of the ITU.
CCITT	Comité Consultatif International Télégraphique et Téléphonique, the telecommunications standards setting committee of the ITU.
CDMA	Code Division Multiple Access, a cellular telephone technology. See also IS 95.
CeBIT	The major European trade fair for the telecoms and data industries, held each Spring in Hannover, Germany.
Cell	The area covered by the radio signals from a base station.
Cellular system	A mobile telephone network built on the cellular concept. All mobile networks are cellular today.
Centrex	PBX functionality provided at the local exchange, thus eliminating the installation of a switchboard on the company´s premises. Mostly used in the US.
CEO	Chief Executive Officer, also Managing Director.
CEPT	Conference of European Postal and Telecommunications administrations.
Cordless	A telephone in which the handset is connected to the set via radio. Also, in offices for instance, increasingly used instead of regular, wired, phones.
CP 400	A crossbar switching system developed during the 1950s by the French Ericsson company, STE.
CT1, CT2	First- and second-generation cordless telephone standards.
Customers	In public networks they used to be called subscribers.
D-AMPS	Digital Advanced Mobile Phone System, the American standard for digital mobile telephony. Now known as TDMA. See also TDMA and IS-136.
DCS 1800	A GSM variant used for Personal Communications (PCN).
DECT	Digital European Cordless Telecommunications standard developed by ETSI, 1800 MHz.
Digital	Digital transmission means that an analogue signal, such as voice, has been sampled and encoded in binary form and is transmitted as a stream of 1s and 0s.
Edge	A technology for providing both GSM and TDMA systems with capability to handle third-generation mobile telephony. Transmission of data of up to 384 kilobits per second.
ENGINE	Ericsson's solution for the migration of fixed circuit-switched networks into a new generation of circuit-switched and IP/ATM-based packet-switched traffic.

e-commerce	Shopping, money transaction, etc. over the Internet.
e-mail	The modern postal service.
EPOC	An operating system for mobile terminals, developed by Symbian, a joint venture company formed by Ericsson, Nokia, Motorola and Psion.
Erlang	The commonly-used measure for telephone traffic. Erlang means the number of minutes per busy hour that a circuit is used. If a subscriber uses his phone for 12 minutes during the busy hour he is generating 0.20 Erlangs. A K Erlang was a Danish mathematician working with the Copenhagen Telephone Company in the early years of the last century.
ETSI	European Telecommunications Standards Institute.
Exchange	Telephone exchanges are the nodes in a telephone network. In an exchange are found the switching system, transmission equipment, cable terminations and, sometimes, test equipment. Subscriber lines (the access network) are connected to local exchanges, while there are also tandem and transit exchanges, international exchanges and rural exchanges. And in increasing numbers there are mobile telephone exchanges for handling the switching and intelligence of mobile networks. In the US a local exchange is usually referred to as a central office.
FCC	Federal Communications Commission, the US telecommunications regulating authority.
GPRS	General Packet Radio Service. A packet-linked technology that allows high speed (115 kbit per second) wireless Internet and other data services
GSM	Global System for Mobile communication, the European digital mobile standard at 900 MHz, originally developed for Europe by ETSI but now in use in most parts of the world. DCS 1800 is the GSM standard at 1800 MHz.
HSCSD	High Speed Circuit Switched Data. A technology for higher data transmission speeds (up to 57 kbits per second) in primarily GSM networks.
IMT-2000	International Mobile Telecommunications, the standard adopted by the ITU for the third generation of mobile telephony, introduced in the year 2000. IMT-2000 is a family of five different specifications for the radio interface in this new generation.
Intelligent Network	In a telecommunications network, a node (data base) which is accessed by high speed data signalling and provides value-added functions such as number translation and virtual private network services.
Internet	An informally created global communications network.
IP	Internet Protocol. IP defines how information travels between systems across the Internet.
IPR	Intellectual Property Rights.
IR	Infrared.

ISDN	Integrated Services Digital Network. A standard integrating voice and data on the same access line.
ISP	Internet Service Provider – a company that specialises in offering end-users access to the Internet.
IS-95	In the US, a digital mobile telephony standard based on CDMA technology.
IS-136	A digital mobile telephony standard based on TDMA.
IT	Information Technology.
ITU (UIT)	International Telecommunications Union, a United Nations agency, in Geneva.
LAN	Local Area Network – a common data network within, for example, an office.
LMDS	Local Multipoint Distribution System. An American point-to-multipoint standard used for wireless broadband access for offices and apartment buildings.
MD	Managing Director. What they call a President in the US.
MD110	The Ericsson private branch exchange, PBX.
MiniLink	Ericsson's family of digital radio links.
Mobile Phone	An ever smaller communications device. Also referred to as a cellular phone.
Mobitex	Ericsson's dedicated network for wireless data communication.
Modem	Modulator-Demodulator, an adapter for transmitting data over an analogue line, or connecting a PC.
MTA, MTB, MTD	The early Swedish (non-cellular) mobile telephone networks.
NMT	Nordic Mobile Telephone network, the analogue standard developed by the Nordic Telephone administrations.
ONP	Open Network Provision, the basis for European Union telecommunications legislation, which promotes the harmonisation of network access, tariffs and regulatory conditions in EU member states to achieve fair and equal reciprocal access to other operators' networks.
PABX	Private Automatic Branch eXchange, a switchboard serving a company, organisation, etc. Mostly we just say PBX.
Packet	In this book packet switching and packet transmission refer to the handling of 'packetised' data.
Paging	Single-direction radio service for alerting subscribers and leaving messages.
PCM	Pulse Code Modulation. The predominant method for converting an analogue signal to digital.
PCN	Personal Communications Network (Europe).
PCS	Personal Communications Services (US). PCN and PCS are mobile services provided over mobile networks operating in the 1.8 GHz – 2.3 GHz range. Are seen as a potential competitor to the fixed networks.
PDC	Personal Digital Cellular, the first digital Japanese standard.
Perkele	Management by … Claimed as the Nokia way.

PSTN	Public Switched Telephone Network.
PTT	Post, Telegraph & Telephone, commonly refers to the traditional (government) administrations responsible for building and running the country's postal and telecoms services. Becoming extinct.
RLL	Radio in the Local Loop. Also WLL, Wireless Local Loop. Products for providing, for example, radio access in fixed networks and in PBX networks.
Router	A data switching system that handles connections between different networks. A router identifies the addresses of data passing through the switch, determines which route the transmission should take and assembles data in 'packets' which are sent to their respective destinations.
SDH	Synchronous Digital Hierarchy, a standard for digital transmission within transport networks.
SEK	The Swedish krona, plural kronor. With about SEK 8.50 you could buy 1 Euro (in 1999).
SLIC	Subscriber Line Interface Circuit. A key component in a switching system, which handles the functions of the subscriber line.
SMS	Short Message Service.
SPC	Stored Program Control, the technology of computer control of telephone switches – and other systems.
Subscriber	…or customer on your network.
TACS	Total Access Communication System. A mobile analogue telephony standard originally used in the UK. Evolved into E-TACS.
TDMA	Time Division Multiple Access. A technology for digital transmission of radio signals between, for example, a mobile phone and a base station.
Telefax	Facsimile service over the public telephone networks.
Telex	A service for communication between teletypewriters over telex networks. The service rapidly declined after the introduction of telefax in the 1970s.
3GPP	Third Generation Partnership Project, a global cooperative project for coordinating WCDMA issues, with standardisation organisations in Europe, Japan, South Korea and the US as founders.
UMTS	Universal Mobile Telecommunications System. In Europe, the name for the third-generation mobile telephone standard, defined by ETSI.
VoIP	Voice over IP. A technology for transmitting telephone calls over the Internet using packet-linked routes. Sometimes referred to as IP telephony.

WAP A free, unlicensed protocol for wireless communication that supports the creation of advanced telecoms services and access to Internet pages from a mobile telephone. WAP is a de facto standard supported by a large number of suppliers. In late 1999, WAP was also understood to mean 'Where Are the Phones?'.

WCDMA Wideband Code Division Multiple Access. A technology for wideband digital radio communications for Internet, multimedia, video and other capacity-demanding applications. WCDMA was strongly promoted and developed by Ericsson and other organisations, and has been selected for the third-generation mobile telephone systems in Europe, Japan and the US. It is the principal alternative being discussed for other parts of the world, notably Asia.

WDM Wavelength Division Multiplex. A technology using optical signals on different wavelengths to increase the capacity of optical fibre transmission.

Wideband See broadband.

W-LAN Wireless Local Area Network. A wireless version of LAN, providing access to the LAN even, when the user is not in the office.

WLL See RLL.

WOS Wireless Office Systems. In an office system (PABX) a technology that allows the user to have calls transferred to a mobile telephone.

Bibliography

For the story of LM Ericsson during its first one hundred years we have drawn heavily on the three-volume history published in 1976 to mark the centenary of the company:

LM Ericsson 100 years. Stockholm 1976. Volumes I – III.

Vol. I. Arthur Attman, Jan Kuuse & Ulf Olsson,
The pioneering years, struggle for concessions, crisis. 1876–1932.

Vol. II. Arthur Attman & Ulf Olsson,
Rescue, reconstruction, worldwide enterprise. 1932–1976.

Vol. III. Christian Jacobæus and collaborators,
Evolution of the technology. 1876–1976.

The following is a selective list of books and sundry publications from which we have learned a lot:

Aris, Stephen, *Arnold Weinstock and the making of GEC.* Aurum Press: London 1998.

Baglehole, K. C., *A century of service – A brief history of Cable & Wireless, 1868–1968.* London 1986.

Bringing information to people. Celebrating the wireless decade. Published by CTIA (Cellular Telecommunications Industry Association): Washington 1993. (A most informative booklet, also noticeable for managing to present the evolution of cellular telephony in the USA without mentioning Ericsson.)

Electronic switching: Central office systems of the world. Amos E. Joel Jr, editor. The Institute of Electrical and Electronics Engineers: New York 1976.

From semaphore to satellite. Published on the occasion of the centenary of the International Telecommunication Union, ITU: Geneva 1965.

Great discoveries: Telecommunications – A pictorial history of telecommunications. Published by the ITU. Romain Pages Editions: Geneva 1991.

A history of engineering & science in the Bell System. The early years (1875–1925). M. D. Fagan, editor. Bell Telephone Laboratories: Holmdel, NJ 1975.

International telecommunication standards organizations. Andrew McPherson, editor. Artech House, USA 1990.

Mabon Prescott C., *Mission communications. The story of Bell Laboratories.* Murray Hill: New Jersey 1975.

Morris, Robert C., *Between the lines.* Just Write Publishing Ltd: London 1994.

Noam, Eli, *Telecommunications in Europe.* Oxford University Press:
New York and Oxford 1992.

Ring up Britain. The early years of the telephone in the United Kingdom.
Neil Johannessen, editor. British Telecommunications plc: London 1991.

Robertson, J. H., *The story of the telephone. A history of the telecommunications
industry of Britain.* Pitman & Sons: London 1947.

Sampson, Anthony, *Sovereign state – The secret history of ITT.*
Stein & Day: New York 1973.

Sobel, Robert, *ITT: The management of opportunity.*
Truman Talley Books – Times Books: New York 1982.

The battle which made Nokia into a super-power. Timo Paukko, Riikka
Venäläinen, Anssi Miettinen & Tuomo Pietiläinen. Selection of articles
in the June 1999 monthly magazine of Helsingin Sanomat, Helsinki.
(Translated from Finnish.)

Thord-Gray, Ivar, *Gringo rebel, Mexico 1913–1914.*
University of Miami: Coral Gables 1960.
(Swedish edition, *Gringo bland rebeller.* Bonniers: Stockholm 1961.)

150 years of Siemens: The company from 1847 to 1997. Siemens AG: Munich 1997.

The writers have also, unblushingly, used their own earlier books:

Meurling, John & Jeans, Richard, *The mobile phone book.*
Communications Week International: London 1994.

Meurling, John & Jeans, Richard, *A switch in time.*
Ericsson Telecom AB: Stockholm 1995.

Meurling, John & Jeans, Richard, *The ugly duckling.*
Ericsson Mobile Communications AB: Stockholm 1997.

IN SWEDISH

Andersson, Karl-Olof, *Vårt dramatiska sekel. 3 volymer.* Brevskolan 1993.

Boëthius, Maria-Pia, *Sfär-Fäderna: Kreuger, Wallenberg & Co.*
Stockholm: Ordfront 1998.

Bruun, Staffan & Wallén, Mosse, *Boken om Nokia.*
Bokförlaget Fischer & Co: Stockholm 1999.

Bäckström, Knut, *Arbetarrörelsen i Sverige.* Del 1 och 2.
Rabén & Sjögren: Stockholm 1971.

Den konstruerade världen – Tekniska system i historiskt perspektiv.
Pär Blomkvist & Arne Kaijser (ed.) Brutus Östlinds Bokförlag:
Stockholm 1998. We are especially indebted to two essays: Jane
Summerton's *Stora tekniska system* and Lars Illshammar's *Från
supervapen till supermarket* for the early history of the internet.

Från bondeuppror till storstrejk, dokument om folkets kamp 1720–1920.
Editors: Jan af Geijerstam, Lars Frendel & Johan Söderberg,
Ordfront 1987.

Historia kring Stockholm. Henrik Ahnlund, ed., Wahlström & Widstrand:
Stockholm 1985.

Högberg, Staffan, *Stockholms historia. Del 2.* Bonnier Fakta: Stockholm 1981.

Jangfeldt, Bengt, *Svenska vägar till S:t Petersburg.* Wahlström & Widstrand:
Stockholm 1998.

Johansson, Hemming, *Hemming Johansson berättar några telefonminnen.*
LM Ericsson: Stockholm 1949.

Johansson, Hemming, *Telefonaktiebolaget L.M. Ericsson.*

Band I: *Från 1876 till 1918.* Stockholm 1953.

Band II: 1918–1932. Unpublished manuscript.

Kretsbilder, en kavalkad genom Ericsson Components, första 50 år. Ed. Bengt
Callmer et al., Ericsson Components AB: Stockholm 1992.

Kristensson, Kaj; Nyström, Hans; Nyström, Örjan, *Från mörkret stiga vi mot
ljuset. Arbetarrörelsens historia i Sverige.* Proletärkultur: Göteborg 1980.

Malmgren, Einar, *Bilder ur svensk telehistoria.* Televerket 1972.

Norrman, Lennart, *Hur L. M. Ericsson skapade Teléfonos de México.*
Stockholm 1993.

Palm, Göran, *Ett år på LM.* Författarförlaget: Göteborg 1972.

Palm, Göran, *Bokslut från LM.* Författarförlaget: Göteborg 1974.

Sund, Bill, *Hundra år på LM. LM Ericsson's verkstadsklubb, 1898–1998.*
Sigma Förlag: Stockholm 1998.

Den svenska historien. Band 9: Industri och folkrörelser 1866–1920. Sten Carlsson
et al., Albert Bonniers Förlag: Stockholm 1968.

*Svenska Telegraf Verket, 1853–1903. Minnesskrift enligt nådigt bemyndigande
utgifven av Kungl. Telegrafstyrelsen.* Stockholm 1903.

Tahvanainen, K. V., *Telegrafboken, Den elektriska telegrafen i Sverige 1853–1996.*
Telemuseum: Stockholm 1997.

Tahvanainen, K. V., *140 år i ledningen, Televerket 1853–1993.*
Televerket: Stockholm 1993.

Tahvanainen, K. V., *Stockholm 33 00 00, Norra Vasa telefonstation 1924–1985.*
Televerket: Stockholm 1986.

Thunholm, Lars–Erik, *Ivar Kreuger.* T. Fischer & Co: Stockholm 1995.

Trahn, Christian & Kjellnäs, Per, *AB Transvertex 1951–1984.* Stockholm 1984.

af Trolle, Ulf, *Bröderna Kreuger.* Svenska Dagbladet: Stockholm 1989.

Vedin, Bengt-Arne, *Teknisk revolt.* Atlantis: Stockholm 1992.

Photographs and drawings

A majority of the photographs included in the book are the property of Ericsson and in the custody of The Society of Historical Business Archives in Stockholm. SHBAS is a non-profit organisation for the preservation and presentation of documentation of Swedish companies, including, among others, the historical records of Ericsson. Research: Göran Graveleij and Kajsa Larsson.

For most of the older pictures the originators are not known.

The following photographers are acknowledged:
Toivo Steen 199, 313, 322, 334, 401; Lars Åström/Världsbilden 206, 259, 320, 351, 352, 353, 354, 366, 368, 382 right, 385, 392, 400, 404, 405, 424, 425, 432, 434, 457; Anders Anjou 212, 332; Studio Nilsson & Lundberg 387.

Other sources:
LM Verkstadsklubben 24. Swedish Telecommunications Museum 27 below, 31, 32, 34, 51, 52, 152, 204, 219 below, 221 centre, 225 left, 453, 455, 476; Björn Tång 8, 13, 459; Carl-Erik Viphammar 26 left, 76; Nisse Cronestrand 43, 46-47, 51, 52. Archives of the Bonnier Publishing Group 14. Neil Goldstein 37, 56, 230, 231, 249, 285. Harold Mohlström 67. Mrs Karin Forslund has kindly lent us the photo of her father on page 89. IMS 119, 183. The Royal Library National Library of Sweden 121. Jesper Wikström 126. The International Historical Press Photo Collection 155 right. The Military Archives, Sweden 169. VLT/Åke Larsson 173. Jean Hermanson/Mira 246. Nino Monastra/Mira 248. Ulf Berglund 371. Jan Halaska/Tiofoto 403. Max Goldstein 413. David Isaksson 437. Göran Kropp 438. Peter Meurling 447. Sten Didrik Bellander/Tiofoto 454. Ericsson Microwave Systems AB 253, 254, 255, 432. Ericsson Microelectronics AB 331, 333. Ericsson Radio Systems AB 164-165, 233 above, 336, 340, 359, 380, 383 above right. Ericsson Mobile Communications AB 376-377, 391, 416, 430; Robert Brenner 379, 382, 383 above left, below 384, above 391. Jonas Ekström/Pressens Bild 390. Thord Andersson 417. Contact, editorial board of the corporate magazine 176, 189, 132, 202, 208, 212, 228, 235, 418 below; Leif Hansson 356. Nils Sundström 406, 418 below, 421. Victor Lenson Brott 373. Tommy Landberg 383 above right. Peter Nordahl 427. Peder Majiet 436. Nils Backman 456, 458.

Bobo Hermanson did the line drawings.

Endpapers

Decalcomania

Hardware, in particular the telephone sets, supplied by Ericsson to its telephone operator customers often carried decals – transfers or stickers – of their coats of arms or company badges. These early brand icons, which were produced by Ericsson and attached before the products were delivered, were often elaborate and beautiful. They deserve study as a branch of commercial art of the highest quality, and together make up a miniature history of Ericsson's early progress through the markets of the world.

Acknowledgements

In preparing this book we have had conversations with a number of people at Ericsson – some now retired, others very much on the active list. Among them we wish to mention:

Dr Björn Svedberg, former President and former Chairman of the Board.
Dr Lars Ramqvist, President and CEO 1990–1998, Chairman 1998– .
Kurt Hellström, President.
Jan Uddenfeldt, Executive VP and CTO.

And also – Torbjörn Nilsson, Mats Nilsson, Gunnar Sandegren, Bengt Svensson, Ingvar Bevenius, Hans Flinck, Rolf Eriksson, Haijo Pietersma, Jorma Mobrin, Tord Andersson, Olle Höstbeck, Carl-Henrik Ström, Harold Mohlström, Bert Nilsson, Lars-Olof Norén, Jörgen Nilsson, Leif Wockatz, Nael Salah, Hector Pérez.

We also wish to thank Bertil Bjurel, former Director General of Televerket, for sharing with us some of his memories of a long and active career in the telephone business.

Major parts of the Ericsson company archives are today in the care of 'Föreningen Stockholms Företagsminnen', whose director, Alexander Huseby, and staff have been most helpful. Krister Hillerud has assisted in searching out documents, catalogues and other material, Kajsa Larsson has prepared and catalogued a very large number of photos and other illustrations and Göran Graveleij has shown a magic ability to locate negatives of long forgotten photographs. At the archives at Ericsson headquarters, Inge Sävström has been of great assistance.

Carl-Henrik Ström has read the full manuscript and made numerous helpful comments and corrections, and added personal recollections. Jan Uddenfeldt has also read the draft and been particularly helpful in sorting out the key issues of technology and standards development over the last twenty years. Björn Svedberg and Lars Ramqvist have also read the draft and made helpful suggestions. Gösta Lindström and Olle Höstbeck have assisted in ensuring that facts and figures recorded in this chronicle are correct and relevant. Harold Mohlström has shared with us numerous recollections of his, and his father's life in Mexico. The writers take full responsibility for any faulty facts, misrepresentation of history or omissions that may have crept in.

Johan W. Fischerström has for three years acted as liaison channel with the company and been the enthusiastic, if idiosyncratic, project administrator. Different, but equally valuable support, has been provided by Lars 'Limpan' Lindström, who has the miraculous ability to make a sulky computer cooperate, and to restore hundreds of pages of manuscript when a single keystroke appears to have deleted the text forever. His ceaseless flow of jokes – unprintable, alas! – helped us through some of the gloomier days.

The senior of the two writers is a strong believer in carefully administered nepotism. Hence, the design and lay-out of the book have been undertaken by his daughter Kate, whom we thank for many hours of professional and dedicated work, along with her husband, Bobo Hermanson, who has made the line drawings.

TEXT John Meurling and Richard Jeans

COVER AND GRAPHIC DESIGN Kate Meurling

PROJECT ADMINISTRATOR ERICSSON Johan W. Fischerström

PICTURE RESEARCH John Meurling and Irene Berggren

COVER PHOTO Max Plunger

PROJECT LEADER AND PRODUCTION Majbritt Hagdahl, Bokform

TYPE FACE Palatino and News Gothic

PAPER G-Print, wood-free, coated, 130 gsm

PREPRESS Respons, Örebro, Sweden

PRINTING Almqvist & Wiksell Tryckeri, Uppsala, Sweden

PROJECT MANAGEMENT AND ADMINISTRATION Informationsförlaget

Informationsförlaget Heimdahls AB
Box 6884, 113 86 Stockholm, Sweden
Telephone 08-34 09 15, Telefax 08-31 39 03
red@informationsforlaget.se
www.informationsforlaget.se

ARTHUR NILSSON & Co.
HONG-KONG.

寶 香 洋 全 代 電 話
行 臣 瑞 典 權 理

POLSKA AKCYJNA SPÓŁKA TELEFONICZNA

CONSEJO MUNICIPAL
AMBATO
1929

A.B.
L.M. ERICSSON & Co.
TRADE MARK
STOCKHOLM

COMPANIA NACIONAL
DE TELEFONOS DEL PERU.

CUERPO DE TELEGRAFOS

CCTT

COMPAÑIA CONSTRUCTORA DE TELEFONOS Y TELEGRAFOS

KESKI-SUOMEN
PUHELIN OSAKEYHTIÖ

RIKSTELEFON

DO WELL DOUBT NOT

ТЕЛЕФОННЫЙ
АВТОМАТЪ
AUTOMAT
TELEFONICZNY

CAPE GOVERNMENT RAILWAYS

SPES BONA

ELECTRICAL SIGNALLING DEPT